J. Secada

HUMAN HISTOLOGY

A TEXTBOOK IN OUTLINE FORM

LESLIE BRAINERD AREY,
Ph.D., Sc.D., LL.D.

Robert Laughlin Rea Professor of Anatomy, Emeritus
Northwestern University

SECOND EDITION

398 ILLUSTRATIONS ON 22 PLATES—IN COLOR

W. B. SAUNDERS COMPANY

PHILADELPHIA AND LONDON

Human Histology

Reprinted November, 1963, September, 1964 and January, 1966

Preface to the Second Edition

HUMAN HISTOLOGY was produced originally as an innovation in textbook design that featured a distinctive outline-format. Through it information was so arranged under heads and subheads that the skeleton framework of an orderly, progressive organization was obvious. In keeping with the outline form went a staccato text, mostly of single-line sentences. This permitted the grouping and progressive indenting of subordinate material so that, even in details, the complete organizational skeleton showed through, and information of primary and secondary importance became apparent. A liberal use of italicized terms and phrases was employed, to catch the eye and add emphasis. *Functional Correlations*, in relation to known structure, were introduced as a consistent feature, as were the *Regenerative Abilities* of each tissue and organ. A practical summary for each tissue (*Appearance in Sections*) and each organ (*Diagnostic Features*) offered aid in interpretation and diagnosis.

The endorsement of the first edition in the United States and other countries, as also a granted request for translation into the Spanish language, was a sufficient earnest of its usefulness to warrant the preparation of a second, revised edition. In doing this, opportunity was afforded to replace many statements and descriptions by the newer information that has made the advances of the last six years so epochal. Such advances involve the cell, all tissues and most organs. Changed, fundamental concepts within these areas in the last decade transcend by far all other basic advances of the past century in this science.

A new feature of the present edition is the incorporation of 398 drawings, most of them done in two colors and all assembled into 22 plates. These have been prepared by the author with an attempt to obtain an adequate coverage in illustrative content and to achieve teaching values consonant with the limitations of the media employed. Valuable aid in producing intermediate stages of most of the finished drawings was rendered by Miss Jean McConnell. The continued support and cooperation of the W. B. Saunders Company, through Mr. John L. Dusseau and his staff, is acknowledged gratefully.

Chicago, Illinois   L. B. AREY

Contents

PART III. SPECIAL HISTOLOGY (ORGANOLOGY)

Illustrative Plates

Chapter I. INTRODUCTORY TOPICS

Histology treats of the minute structure of living organisms.
>Only the most superficial features of tissues and organs are discernible by the naked eye.
>Hence the details are 'microscopic' (as opposed to gross, or 'macroscopic' features).

There is an *animal histology* and a *plant histology*, but they differ widely in structural style.
>Each records the separate paths taken in adapting to quite different living conditions.

Among animals *comparative histology* covers the animal groups from lowest to highest forms.
>The building units (cells and tissues) are much alike in all animals.
>But the kinds of organs differ widely from one major group to another.
>Each has adapted to the demands of its particular environment.

Vertebrate histology reveals a fairly common plan of organs among its several subgroups.
>Yet considerable variation still exists in the structure of individual organs.

Mammalian histology finds a high degree of structural uniformity among its representatives.
>Yet striking specializations occur in some animal types.
>Example: scent glands; dermal plates of armadillos; stomach of ruminants.

Human histology limits itself to the one species that interests the greatest number of people.
>In so doing, the countless minor variations among mammals are disregarded.

I. THE POSITION OF HISTOLOGY AMONG SCIENCES DEALING WITH STRUCTURE

Morphology is the study of the form and structure, in the broadest sense, of living organisms.
>It is considered under two divisions:
>>*Embryology* deals with the development of form and structure before maturity is achieved.
>>*Anatomy* deals with the form, positions and relations of mature organs and parts.

Anatomy has two aspects: normal and abnormal.
>*Abnormal anatomy* is commonly called pathological anatomy, or *pathology*.
>*Normal anatomy* is subdivided into: *gross anatomy;* and *microscopic anatomy*.
>>The latter is subdivided into: *organology* (organs); *histology* (tissues); and *cytology* (cells).
>>Note that 'histology' is also used loosely to include all microscopic categories.
>>'Textbooks of Histology' treat of cells and organs as well as tissues.

II. THE HISTORICAL BACKGROUND

Early microscopists (Malpighi; Leeuwenhoek; Swammerdam) saw various structural features,
>but did not recognize or interpret properly their fundamental cellular composition.

Hooke (1665) gave the name *cell* to the walled compartments of dead cork tissue.

Brown (1831) discovered the nucleus.
>But the idea of the cell in this period was still very imperfect.

The '*cell theory*' was asserted by Schleiden (1838) and Schwann (1839).

They taught that animals and plants were composed of cells as units.

Virchow (1863) emphasized the body as a 'cell state,' with specialized categories of cells.

Tissues and organs were described relatively early, as concerns their general features.

In 1841 Henle published the first thorough account of human histology.

Cytology lagged, incidental to the progress of embryological knowledge.

It dates from the discovery of fertilization of the egg by O. Hertwig (1875).

Hence cytology is the infant anatomical science.

It has also waited on adequate technical methods for revealing cellular composition.

These optical, staining and histochemical methods are still being developed.

Much still remains unknown, especially in the fields of microstructure and microchemistry.

III. THE IMPORTANCE OF HISTOLOGY

The base rock of scientific medicine is the understanding of *normal physiology*.

But cells and tissues are the unit materials that underlie such functioning.

All physiology (including physiological chemistry and pharmacology) is a study of how cells, singly or in combination, work and react.

Structure and function are reciprocals, hence the study of histology is fundamental.

Function cannot be inconsistent with the mechanism that does the work.

Ideally one should be able to deduce function from structure.

Actually ignorance of the details of cellular composition is profound.

This is especially true of histochemical relations.

Hence such correlated forecasting is realized but partially.

Pathology deals with cells that exhibit deranged functions.

This condition, disease, is accompanied by alterations of cell structure.

But nothing new, either in structure or in function, enters during disease.

Normal functional processes are then merely exaggerated or decreased.

This tends to be reflected in the altered appearance of cells.

By contrast, in health there is harmonious balance, known as normality.

The problem of cure, therefore, is to restore cells to their normal states.

A necessary basis of understanding is a sound knowledge of the normal.

IV. THE METHODS FOR EXAMINING TISSUES

A. MICROSCOPE-TYPES AS TOOLS:

Several kinds of microscopes are available for revealing structural details.

1. Bright-field.

This type is the ordinary, compound microscope.

Its useful power of magnification ceases at about 1200 diameters.

Even more important than more magnification is the ability to resolve detail better.

That is, the capacity of separating, clearly, points located close together.

The resolving capacity under ordinary conditions is about 0.2 micron (0.0002 mm.).

Objects lying less than that distance apart merge.

Particles less than that diameter are not recognizable.

2. Phase Contrast.

This type employs a system by means of which contrast is created.

Objects, ordinarily transparent, become visible through contrast differences.

Its application lies chiefly in the study of living cells and unstained tissues.

3. Polarizing.

This type interposes two Nicol prisms (or Polaroid sheets) in the light path.

The prisms, when rotated, detect the presence of double refraction in objects.

This demonstrates the orientation of particles too small to be seen.

It permits deductions concerning organization not demonstrable otherwise.

4. Fluorescence.

Specimens are examined when fluorescing under invisible, ultraviolet radiation.

Many objects then emit visible light of different colors and qualities.

This permits the localization of large molecules within cells.

5. Dark-field.

This type employs strong, oblique light that does not enter the objective.

A vacant field of view then shows merely as a dark background.

Objects present in the field reflect some light into the objective.

Thus it is possible to demonstrate the presence of particles far below the limits of bright-light resolution.

The effect is similar to invisible dust particles that are 'seen' in a strong beam of light in a darkened room.

Also small transparent objects can be seen that would be invisible in a glare.

6. Invisible Radiation.

Images can be formed by rays other than visible light.

In this instance the image is photographed on a suitably sensitized film.

A. ULTRAVIOLET RAYS.

Illumination in the ultraviolet wave length, and quartz lenses, improve resolution.

This (0.1 micron) is double that obtainable by visible light.

B. ELECTRON RAYS.

Beams of electrons replace light, and electromagnetic or electrostatic fields replace lenses in the relatively recent invention of the electron microscope.

The final image is visualized on a fluorescent screen and photographed.

Resolving power has been pushed to 0.001 micron (0.000001 mm.).

The photographed image may be as much as 50,000 times the original size.

This image can be profitably enlarged still further.

C. X-RAYS.

Differential absorption by a section produces a focussed, photographable image.

The negative permits the dry weight of cytological structures to be determined.

Also, chemical analyses of extremely minute objects can be deduced.

B. OBSERVATION OF LIVING TISSUE:

1. Direct Observation.

A. Some *intact animals* offer favorable materials.

Examples: protozoa; tail of tadpole; wing of bat.

B. *Quartz-rod illumination* transmits cold light into the interior of organs.

This medium traps light, conducts it and avoids the coagulation of protoplasm.

C. *Glass windows* have been inserted into an animal's ear and left indefinitely.

Tissue regeneration, vascular activities, etc., can then be followed.

D. Delicate *microdissection needles* can isolate, cut, tear or stretch cells and parts.

The needles are activated by a precision, supertype of mechanical stage.

Capillary tubes can replace needles and inject or suck the cell contents.

E. *Tissues may be cultured* in plasma and grown indefinitely for study.

F. *Motion-picture records* aid in the analysis of cellular activities.

Lapsed-time films demonstrate slower motions at a speeded-up rate.

Mitosis, phagocytosis, ameboid motion, etc., can be shown to advantage.

Slow-motion films permit fast action to be analyzed.

Beating cilia, rupturing ovarian follicles, etc., can be followed.

2. Staining of Unfixed Tissues.

A. VITAL STAINING.

Some dyes are neither toxic to living cells nor destroyed by them.

These exist as colloidal particles, rather than as true solutions.

Examples of such vital dyes: trypan blue; India ink; Thorotrast.

Such pigmented substances are injected into the body as dilute suspensions.

They are then removed from the blood stream by phagocytic cells.

These scavenger cells ingest particles and store them in concentrated form.

This colors the phagocytic cells and renders them conspicuous.

B. SUPRAVITAL STAINING.

Other dyes, though toxic, are taken up by dying cells.

These cells are stained usually after their removal from the body.

Such moribund cells may survive for hours.

Examples: mitochondria, stained by Janus green; nerve fibers, stained by methylene blue; connective-tissue elements (white or elastic fibers; fat or mast cells; leucocytes), stained by suitable dyes.

C. PREPARATION OF DEAD TISSUE:

1. Fixation.

The primary objective is to preserve protoplasm with the least alteration.

In killing, which produces 'setting' (*i.e.*, gelation) of protoplasm, the fixative should accomplish several objectives:

Penetrate quickly, preventing postmortem changes (autolytic; bacterial).

Preserve the living conditions as faithfully as possible.

Render the protoplasm insoluble and harden it.

Increase the affinity of protoplasm for future stains.

Faulty preservation produces artificial changes, called *artefacts*.

The ability to recognize such induced and unnatural states is indispensable to the proper interpretation of microscopical preparations.

Chemical solutions are most commonly employed as fixing agents.

Typical reagents are: alcohol; formalin; mercuric bichloride; potassium bichromate; acids (acetic; formic; osmic; picric).

But no single fixative possesses all the desirable qualities just listed.

Hence resort is made to mixtures designed for specific tissues and purposes.

Such mixtures are: Zenker's fluid; Bouin's fluid; Mueller's fluid; etc.

The freezing-drying technique introduces less alterations than chemicals do.

Tissue is frozen in isopentane, chilled to $-170°$ C., and dehydrated in a vacuum.

2. Embedding.

The tissue is dehydrated and hardened in alcohol.

Next it is 'cleared' (*i.e.*, made translucent) in a reagent, such as xylol (or ether).
These fluids are soluble both in alcohol and in melted paraffin (or celloidin).
This permits paraffin (or celloidin) to infiltrate the tissues.
Finally the specimen is encased in a block of solid paraffin (or celloidin).

3. Sectioning.
Extremely thin slices of the impregnated and blocked tissue are cut.
The thickness is usually between 3 and 10 microns (0.003–0.010 mm.).
Sections are then affixed to a slide and the paraffin dissolved away.

4. Staining.
Staining in contrasting colors brings out the structural details still further.
The coloring ability of most dyes resides in either their acid or basic radical.
If in the anion, the dye is called acid; if in the cation, it is called basic.
In general, cellular components are either acid or basic in nature.
Those that are acid (*e.g.*, nuclear chromatin) stain with basic dyes.
Such components are said to be *basophilic*.
Those that are basic (*e.g.*, various kinds of cytoplasm) stain with acid dyes.
Such constituents are said to be *acidophilic*.
These reactions make selective, differential staining possible.
Some constituents may attract both dyes (or stain by their interaction product).
The granules of neutrophilic leucocytes exemplify this behavior.

5. Mounting.
Stained sections are placed on a slide in a gummy medium that eventually hardens.
This has the same refractive index as glass.
The preparation is covered with a thin wafer of glass.

D. MISCELLANEOUS TECHNIQUES:
1. Teased and spread bits of tissue are examined fresh or after supravital staining.

2. Maceration softens binding material and thus isolates cells, tubules, lobules, etc.

3. Microincineration of tissue slices leaves ash that retains fine structural details.
Some minerals can then be identified within cells in exact locations.

4. Centrifuging gives information on the relative weights of cell constituents.
It shows the displaceability of parts, consistent with continued life.
It can isolate cell components for purposes of investigation.

5. Autoradiography demonstrates the presence of tracer isotopes, segregated in a tissue.
A photographic emulsion is affected when placed in contact with a section of the radioactive tissue.
Development shows the location and preferential concentration of the radioactive substance administered.
This throws light on the metabolic activity of local regions, cells and even cell components.

6. Microchemical testing by qualitative analytical methods on local areas is possible.
A large number of organic and inorganic constituents, and numerous enzymes, can be
identified and localized by suitable tests.

7. Interference.
Microspectroscopic information is obtainable by several methods.
Visible light, ultraviolet light and x-rays are used.
Absorption spectra identify and show the distribution of specific substances.
The dry mass of cell components can be measured with exactitude.

8. X-ray diffraction employs a crystal-grating of molecular dimensions.
Its application is limited to crystalline, laminar and linear structures.
An enormously magnified diffraction pattern is recorded photographically.
The presence, spacing and orientation of molecules can be deduced.
It permits certain chemical analyses of objects to be made.
These may be only a few cubic microns in size.

Part I. Cytology

Chapter II. PROTOPLASM

"*Protoplasm* is the material basis of life" (Thomas Huxley).

It is the living, essential substance of which all animals and plants are made.

Protoplasm occurs in living organisms as unit masses called *cells*.

A cell is a mass of protoplasm, named *cytoplasm*, containing a central kernel of specialized protoplasm named the *nucleus*.

I. PROPERTIES

In order to study protoplasm intimately, it must be killed by fixation.

Good fixation entails the precipitation and coagulation of proteins; hence changes enter.

1. Physical Characteristics.

Protoplasm is semifluid, viscid, ductile, and more or less transparent.

It is an aggregate of crystalloids and colloids.

More precisely, it is an aqueous solution holding complex colloids in suspension.

It is also a reversible sol-gel system.

It is predominantly fluid, but capable of becoming more viscous.

At death, or on fixation, an irreversible gelation occurs.

2. Chemical Constitution.

Analysis shows the presence of C, O, H, N as major constituents.

Also S, P, Ca, Na, Cl, Mg, K, Fe, etc. are present in smaller amounts.

These combine into proteins, carbohydrates, lipids and salts, which are associated in a watery medium.

Considerable progress has been made in demonstrating the presence of specific chemical substances and their exact locations within tissues.

The proteins are of types known as simple, conjugated and derived proteins.

Protoplasm is largely a mosaic of reactive polypeptide chains.

Enzymes are important proteins, since they function as biological catalysts.

Some are located in particular structures (mitochondria; lysosomes).

Others seem to be distributed uniformly through the cytoplasm.

7

Water comprises 75 per cent of the slightly alkaline protoplasm.

Could protoplasm be synthesized, and life created artificially?

> Mechanists say: "Yes, if proper stereo-isomeric relations could be established among the chemical components."

> Vitalists say: "No, there will always be lacking an additional vital principle that is essential to life and unique to it."

II. STRUCTURE

Living protoplasm is a colorless, colloidal jelly in which granules, threads and fluid droplets are sometimes demonstrable even without the use of phase-contrast microscopy.

Many of these demonstrable objects are nonliving products of cell activity.

Fixed protoplasm tends to vary in appearance, depending on the reagents used.

> Acid fixatives favor precipitation into granules or fibrils.

> Neutral fixatives favor a more homogeneous coagulation.

> A net-like *spongioplasm* and more homogeneous *hyaloplasm* are commonly obtained.

> > This change from the living state is clearly artefactual.

Living protoplasm, at best, shows only as a granular gel under the light microscope.

> Yet even a clear, apparently structureless protoplasm consists of both gelled and fluid protein-components, demonstrable with the electron microscope.

> The fibrillar proteins of cytoplasm constitute important structural features.

> > Nevertheless, fibrillar proteins disperse at times and later return to a fibrillar state.

> > They are responsible for the reversible sol-gel behavior of cytoplasm.

III. VITAL ACTIVITIES

Protoplasmic components are stereo-isomerically associated and combined in such a manner that the resulting complex acquires the characteristics of life.

Four general categories of visible activity are recognizable in living protoplasm.

A. MOTILITY (AND MOBILITY):

1. Protoplasmic Streaming.

> Internal streaming of cytoplasm is a generalized type of mobility.

> This is well illustrated in the rotatory movements within some plant cells.

> Less rapid and more irregular shiftings occur in various animal cells.

> > These are best appreciated when viewed in lapsed-time motion pictures.

2. Ameboid Movement.

> This is a type of progression achieved by flowing or rolling over a substrate.

> The cytoplasm extends a pseudopodial process and then flows into it.

> > Example: ameba; leucocytes; macrophage.

> Local activity of the peripheral cytoplasm accomplishes *phagocytosis*.

> > This response may or may not be associated with ameboid movement.

> > The cell membrane cups about a particle and encloses it.

> > The enclosed portion of the membrane then breaks down.

> > > In this way the particle becomes intracellular.

> > Phagocytosed material includes: bacteria; red corpuscles; dye particles; soot.

> A comparable process ingests fluid droplets.

> > This activity has been named *pinocytosis*.

3. Ciliary and Flagellate Lashing.

Cilia are hair-like protoplasmic processes that vibrate in rhythmic sequence.
> They are numerous and relatively short, acting like oars or lashes.
> Example: mobile ciliate protozoans; stationary epithelial sheets.

Flagella are longer and often stouter; they are few to a cell, or even single.
> Example: flagellate protozoans; spermatozoa.

4. Contractility.

Shortening and thickening characterize this type of protoplasmic activity.
Most common and distinctive is a shortening limited to one axis.
> This is illustrated in some protozoans and coelenterates.
> It reaches its highest expression in true muscle fibers.

B. IRRITABILITY:

Protoplasm has the capacity to receive stimuli and set up an impulse.
> An impulse is a wave of excitation passing through protoplasm.
> The ability to transmit an impulse constitutes the property of *conductivity*.

Various kinds of stimuli are able to educe such excitation.
> Example: mechanical; thermal; chemical; photic; electric.

All cells are irritable, but the quality is best developed in nerve cells.

C. METABOLISM:

Included are all the transformations of energy and matter accomplished by protoplasm.
It presents two phases—one constructive, the other destructive.

1. Anabolism.

During digestion, food is split into simpler stuffs (*e.g.*, glucose; glycerine; fatty acids;
> amino acids).

Some substances are stored as such (*e.g.*, glucose; fat).
Other substances are built into complex products (*e.g.*, secretions; cellular enzymes).
> Even protoplasm itself is synthesized.

Synthesis and reduction are involved; energy is stored.

2. Catabolism.

Energy is released by breaking down and burning up materials.
> In this process cellular enzymes serve as biologic catalysts.
> Hydrolysis and oxidation of stored products are the chief processes involved.
> Protoplasm itself is largely spared from catabolic destruction.

The end-products are unutilizable wastes; these are eliminated from the body.
> *Excretion* is a sifting out from the circulation of such residual waste products.
>> Also excess materials (*e.g.*, water; salts; glucose; hormones) are removed.

One type of growth results from protoplasmic synthesis in excess of maintenance.
> This method of growth is a distinctive feature of living organisms.
> By contrast, nonliving things (*e.g.*, crystals) grow by accretion.

D. REPRODUCTION:

Protoplasm is able to perpetuate itself through a process of growth and division.
> Every cell arises from the halving of pre-existing cells.

Cell division is a necessary consequence of continued growth that is brought about by the
> unrestrained synthesis of protoplasm.

In a growing cell the ratio of surface area to volume becomes progressively smaller.
Soon the surface is inadequate to take care of (feed, etc.) the interior.
A proper surface-volume relation is re-established by halving the mass.
The characteristic sizes of cells are determined by genetic factors.
Another significant factor is the maintenance of the nucleo-plasmic ratio.
This ratio is the optimal relation between nuclear and cytoplasmic mass.
If varied beyond normal limits, cell physiology becomes altered.
An understanding of cell division depends upon a knowledge of cell structure.
For this reason the detailed descriptions will be given later (p. 19).

IV. THE CORRELATION OF ACTIVITIES

Motility and irritability are primarily functions of the cytoplasm.
Metabolism and reproduction are primarily functions controlled by the nucleus.
These statements are corroborated when a large protozoan is cut into two parts.
A part consisting wholly of cytoplasm moves and responds to stimuli.
But after a time it dies, incapable of anabolism, growth or reproduction.
A part containing the nucleus regenerates, metabolizes and reproduces.

Chapter III. THE CELL

Studies of cell structure, and the correlations of these features with cell function, comprise the
subject of *cytology.*
The *cell* is the structural and functional unit of the body.
It is a minute (and usually definitely circumscribed) mass of protoplasm, containing a
central kernel named the *nucleus.*
All animal cells also contain a division center, or *centriole.*
There is a delicate *plasma membrane* at the peripheral boundary.
Various other 'cell organs' (*organoids,* or organelles) are present also.
In short, the cell is not a simple thing, but is extremely complex.
Functionally the cell is characterized by the ability to assimilate, grow, reproduce and re-
spond to external stimuli.

I. SOME CELL GENERALITIES

1. Shape.
The primary, fundamental shape of isolated cells is spherical.
Example: contracted leucocyte; egg cell; fat cell.
Specialization alters the shape of some cells profoundly.
Example: nerve cell (including its processes); muscle cell.
Contact with a surface promotes flattening of a cell.
Mutual pressure produces a faceted surface, as in a mass of soap bubbles.
Such cells tend to be 14-sided, thus offering minimal surface area.
A section, cut through a 14-sided solid, shows usually six sides.
In practice, this is the commonest shape seen in sections of massed cells.
Sections of compact fat illustrate this fact well.
Modified shapes accompany specialized activities and stresses.
Example: discoid; columnar; pyramidal; spindle; stellate.
An unstable, changeable shape is characteristic of some cells.
Example: ameba; leucocyte; macrophage.

2. Polarity.
The constituent parts of a cell often exhibit a definite spatial arrangement.
This is with respect both to each other and to the cell as a whole.
When the cell is elongate, the nucleus becomes ovoid to cigar-shaped.
The nucleus then lies in the long axis of the cell.
The location of the nucleus may be correlated with the position and orientation of
various other cell components.
In some cells the nucleus takes its position nearer the base.
Certain cell-components then lie still nearer the base.
Other cell-components locate above the nucleus, nearer the top.
Rod-like mitochondria orient in the long dimension of the cell.
Such regularity illustrates how a cell may possess structural *polarity.*

11

3. Size.

Only rarely are cells visible to the naked eye; they are then 'macroscopic.'
Example: most eggs (but mammalian eggs are barely visible).
Some cells are greatly elongate; they then become extremely slender.
Example: a muscle cell may be inches long; a neuron may be a yard long.
Superorganization sometimes leads to giant cells.
A *syncytium* is brought about by cell fusion.
Example: superficial layer of chorionic villi.
A *multinucleate cell* is produced by repeated nuclear division within a single cell.
Example: skeletal muscle fiber.
Cell size varies somewhat among the several vertebrate groups.
Amphibia have the largest cells; mammals have rather small cells.
There is no correlation between the size of an animal and the size of its cells.
The cells of an elephant are scarcely larger than those of a mouse.
The unit of microscopical measurement is the *micron*, whose symbol is μ (Greek mu).
It is 0.001 mm. or 1/25,000 in.
The human red blood corpuscle is often used as a visual measuring stick.
Its diameter in stained sections is about 5 microns.
It may be found in any section.
The average diameter of mammalian cells is 10 to 30 μ.
Yet some are very small; certain brain cells measure only 4 μ.

4. Numbers.

The size of an animal is determined by the number of its cells rather than by their size.
Colonial protozoa may consist of a cluster containing but few cells.
Rotifers have less than 1000 cells.
The total number in a mouse, man or whale is prodigious.
In the human brain the total number of nerve cells is said to be 12,000,000,000.
The red blood corpuscles of an average-sized man total 25,000,000,000,000.

II. THE CYTOPLASM

The *cytoplasm* is a specific kind of protoplasm.
It includes all of the protoplasm of a cell, except that of the nucleus.

A. PLASMA MEMBRANE:

The cytoplasmic boundary is a condensed peripheral film, the *plasma membrane*.
It is very thin, about 0.008 μ; it is only a few molecules thick, yet resistant and elastic.
The light microscope indicates its position merely as a limiting line.
The electron microscope resolves a middle layer, bounded by denser layers.
It also reveals extensive infoldings of the membrane in some cells.
The membrane is a lipid film, with attached (*i.e.*, adsorbed) protein molecules.
It is a semipermeable living membrane, essential to cell life.
It determines what exchanges occur by osmosis, and what by vital control.
If broken locally, cytoplasm may extrude; but repair tends to follow.
Too great an injury, mechanical or chemical, leads to cell death.
Microdissection proves the membrane to be quite elastic.
It is also tougher than cytoplasm proper.
In addition to the plasma membrane there may be an outer reinforcement.
It is a product of cell metabolism (*i.e.*, nonliving *metaplasm*).

Example: the supporting, cellulose *cell wall* of plants; the clear zone that envelops mammalian eggs; the 'capsule' bordering cartilage cells.

B. CYTOPLASM PROPER:

The extreme periphery of some cells is specialized as an *ectoplasm*, whereas the more internal protoplasm is called *endoplasm*.

Example: ameboid cells; some eggs.

Body cells, in general, do not show this distinction clearly.

Ectoplasm is a clear zone; it is gelled and more refractive.

Endoplasm, by contrast, is more fluid and granular.

It contains various constituents, some living and others not.

Living, specialized components are *organoids*, or *organelles*.

Nonliving components are designated as *inclusions*.

Mature cytoplasm is commonly acidophilic; it, therefore, stains with eosin (an acid stain).

Cytoplasm, however, may be basophilic or neutrophilic.

Basophily is associated with the presence of ribonucleic acid.

Such cytoplasm, or cytoplasmic region, stains with hematoxylin (a basic stain).

C. ORGANOIDS:

These are definite, specialized masses of the living cytoplasm.

They are permanent constituents of a cell and act like 'cell organs.'

They apparently perpetuate themselves during cell division.

1. Endoplasmic Reticulum.

The cytoplasm contains systems of closely spaced, interconnecting membranes.

Their form and relations are revealed only by the electron microscope.

They take the form of tubules, vesicles or flattened sacs.

Sometimes the external surfaces bear granules (*ribosomes*) rich in ribonucleic acid.

These particles are causally related to the synthesis of proteins.

A grosser, allied material has long been known as *chromidial* (or *chromophil*) *substance*.

It occurs as plainly seen masses that stain heavily with basic dyes.

Diffusely distributed are the granular *Nissl bodies* of nerve cells.

Localized is the 'fibrillar' *ergastoplasm*, at the base of serous gland cells.

2. Mitochondria.

These elements are present in all cells; each may contain many hundreds of them.

The dark-field and phase-contrast techniques demonstrate them in living cells.

A dye, Janus green, stains them supravitally.

Mitochondria range in shape from granules to long filaments.

Their shape varies in different cell-types, and it can be altered.

Yet in many cells they maintain well a characteristic form and arrangement.

Mitochondria consist of a matrix contained within a double-layered sheath.

The inner layer makes extensive, thin infoldings into the matrix.

This produces numerous transverse partial partitions (*cristae*).

Mitochondria tend to dissolve during the course of routine slide-making.

But special methods preserve and stain them selectively.

Oxidative and other enzymes are localized in mitochondria.

These are responsible for various essential life processes.

Included are cell respiration and the Krebs cycle which produces energy.

3. Cell Center (Centrosome).

This body tends to occupy a central position within the cell.

It is often displaced by the nucleus or by synthesized cytoplasmic products.

It is inconspicuous in resting cells, but becomes prominent during mitosis.

The most constant feature of the complex is a deeply staining granule, the *centriole*.

Commonly two centrioles are present; they constitute a *diplosome*.

The electron microscope shows the centriole to be a cylindrical structure.

Its wall contains nine sets of rodlets and basal corpuscles, as in cilia.

During mitosis a globular *centrosphere* and radiating *astral rays* become prominent.

Both astral rays and centriole have been seen in living cells.

The total mass can be pushed about by the micro-needle.

The complex as a whole is a dynamic center, important during cell division.

Yet higher (flowering) plants lack cell centers.

4. Golgi Apparatus.

This organoid is a highly controversial structure.

It is commonly demonstrated as a network of stained fibrils.

Hence it has also been called the *internal reticular apparatus*.

The electron microscope shows the region to contain a set of smooth-surfaced double membranes (flattened sacs), tiny vesicles and large vacuoles.

The Golgi complex is often localized above the nucleus and about the centrosome.

But it may be scattered or dispersed widely in the cytoplasm.

It can also be displaced bodily by centrifuging.

The complex probably occurs in all living cells.

Phase microscopy can demonstrate it in living cells as a system of clear canals.

Osmic acid or silver treatment demonstrates the 'network' clearly.

The Golgi complex contains lipids chiefly, but also proteins.

Because of its fatty nature, fixatives used must omit fat solvents.

Functionally it is associated with secretory activity.

It increases and decreases in size during the glandular cycle.

The earliest and smallest secretory granules seen, occur about the complex.

Perhaps it acts as a condensation center.

Here secretory material, formed elsewhere, becomes 'granules.'

The primary synthesis occurs on the ribosomes of endoplasmic reticulum.

5. Fibrils.

Some cells contain specific *fibrils* wholly unrelated to mitochondria.

Each of these threads is a bundle of smaller *filaments*, or *protofibrils*.

There are three categories of such fibrils, all visible with a light microscope.

A. TONOFIBRILS.

These are fine fibrils that probably give stability to some epithelial cells.

They arise by the clumping of submicroscopic protein filaments.

They do not continue into adjoining cells, as was formerly believed.

During cell division they disappear, but later reappear.

B. NEUROFIBRILS.

These are delicate threads that have been demonstrated in living neurons.

They are also shown well by supravital methylene blue and by silver stains.

Their function is not clear: supporting? metabolic?

A role in impulse conduction is not sustained by modern research.

c. MYOFIBRILS.

These are demonstrable in living fibers, but are not conspicuous.

They are plainly seen in teased or stained muscle-fibers.

Such fibrils are held responsible for muscular contraction.

6. Lysosomes.

These are small elements, bounded by a membrane and containing hydrolytic enzymes.

D. INCLUSIONS:

Both metabolic products and ingested substances are occupants of the cytoplasm.

1. Secretory Granules.

They are characteristic features of glandular activity, particularly in epithelium.

Their identification as precursors of secretion products is well established.

Their history is cyclic, paralleling that of the gland cell.

In life they are globules, whereas on fixation they coagulate into granules.

Some globules give rise to enzymes; others to mucus, etc.

Their association with the Golgi apparatus was discussed in a previous paragraph.

2. Nutritive Substances.

A. PROTEINS.

Cytoplasm is largely protein, but how much protein is also 'free' as an inclusion is problematical.

At least, much of it can be catabolized when nutrition is deficient.

On fixation, proteins precipitate as granules.

B. CARBOHYDRATES.

The carbohydrate reserves of the body are almost exclusively glycogen.

The richest sites of storage are in cells of the liver and skeletal muscles.

In life glycogen probably occurs in solution as fluid droplets.

Fixation precipitates it in the form of granules.

C. FAT.

This reserve occurs most prominently as globules within specialized cells.

There may be separate globules or a single fat pool in each cell.

Such fat-stores dissolve out of fixed tissues unless rendered insoluble.

Some of the fat is invisible and is spoken of as 'masked' or 'bound.'

It is either very finely dispersed or is combined with proteins.

D. YOLK.

Lipo-proteins may be present in the form of yolk spheres.

They are characteristic of eggs, and hence of the yolk sac of many embryos.

Cells of the gut of some vertebrates contain yolk for a while.

3. Pigment Granules.

Pigment is synthesized by various cells of the body (*e.g.*, *melanoblasts*, etc.).

The chief types are *melanin*, *hemoglobin* and *lipochromes*.

They are light-absorptive, oxygen-binding, and wear-and-tear products.

Some cells take up and store pigment, but do not make any.

Such cells are *chromatophores* (*e.g.*, pigment cells of chorioid of eye).

Of the pigments stored, some come from plants eaten as food.

4. Bodies of Unknown Significance.

Crystals sometimes occur, apparently protein in nature.

Example: interstitial cells of the testis.

Specific granules (colorless) occur in some cells and stain distinctively.

5. Vacuoles.

True vacuoles, containing fluid, occur in protozoa and plants.

These are spheroidal cavities bounded by a membrane, similar to the plasma membrane at the periphery of the cytoplasm.

Fluid, drunk in by active macrophages, occupies temporary cavities within cytoplasm.

So-called vacuoles of higher animals are usually storage cavities.

Examples: fat droplets; glycogen droplets; secretion precursors.

When the contents are lost or dissolved, a vacant space may become apparent.

Such 'vacuoles' are still different from artefacts produced by faulty fixation and by degenerative and postmortem changes.

6. Foreign Substances.

Extraneous material may come to lie within the cytoplasm.

These have been taken up by phagocytosis and similar ingestive activities.

Example: bacteria; cellular debris; carbon-particles; dust.

E. FUNCTIONAL CORRELATIONS:

The cytoplasm contains the specializations that carry out the work of the cell.

This range covers all of the functions discussed previously as 'vital activities' (p. 8).

Of course, the nucleus plays a direct or indirect role in some of these actions (p. 18).

But the factory and its machinery are cytoplasm.

III. THE NUCLEUS

Near the center of the cell is a prominent body, known as the nucleus.

The Latin word *nucleus* or Greek word *karyon* signifies 'the kernel of a nut.'

Hence nucleo- and karyo- are used in combined words referring to the nucleus.

A. NUMBER:

Usually there is but one nucleus to a cell.

Sometimes two occur; such cells are *binucleate*.

Example: some cells of the liver; some cells of the bladder- and stomach-lining.

More rarely several to many nuclei occur; such cells are *multinucleate*.

Example: skeletal muscle fibers; giant cells of bone; some ganglion cells.

(In some protozoa nuclear material is scattered as granules throughout the cytoplasm.)

B. SHAPE:

Usually the nucleus is globular to ovoid, somewhat in conformity with cell shape.

Cytoplasmic inclusions may temporarily flatten or otherwise distort the nucleus.

Other shapes occur in special cell types.

Example: elongate (smooth muscle); crescentic (monocyte); lobate (neutrophil).

C. GENERAL CHARACTERISTICS:

Descriptions are usually based on the appearance of the so-called resting cell.

This term refers to the relatively stable period between cell divisions.

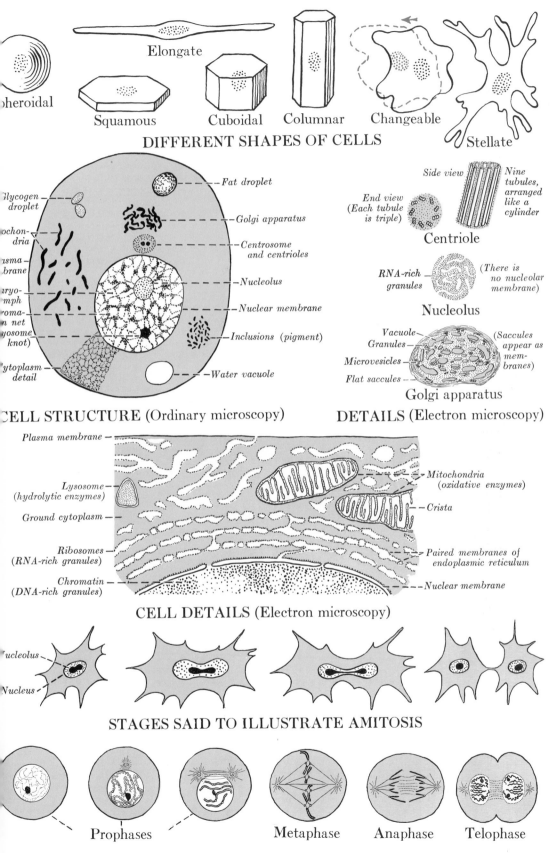

Elongate

pheroidal
Squamous   Cuboidal   Columnar   Changeable
Stellate

DIFFERENT SHAPES OF CELLS

Fat droplet

Glycogen droplet

ochon-dria

asma brane

aryo-mph
oma-n net
yosome knot)

ytoplasm detail

Golgi apparatus

Centrosome and centrioles

Nucleolus

Nuclear membrane

Inclusions (pigment)

Water vacuole

CELL STRUCTURE (Ordinary microscopy)

Side view   Nine tubules, arranged like a cylinder
End view (Each tubule is triple)

Centriole

RNA-rich granules   (There is no nucleolar membrane)

Nucleolus

Vacuole
Granules   (Saccules appear as mem-branes)
Microvesicles
Flat saccules

Golgi apparatus

DETAILS (Electron microscopy)

Plasma membrane

Lysosome (hydrolytic enzymes)

Ground cytoplasm

Ribosomes (RNA-rich granules)

Chromatin (DNA-rich granules)

Mitochondria (oxidative enzymes)

Crista

Paired membranes of endoplasmic reticulum

Nuclear membrane

CELL DETAILS (Electron microscopy)

ucleolus

Nucleus

STAGES SAID TO ILLUSTRATE AMITOSIS

Prophases   Metaphase   Anaphase   Telophase

STAGES OF MITOSIS IN ANIMAL CELLS

At this time (the *interphase*) the ordinary functions of a cell are performed.
A living nucleus is usually more of a gel and more refractile than the cytoplasm.
The micro-needle can move the nucleus about in the cytoplasm.
The nucleus has a higher specific gravity than the cytoplasm.
It is plastic under pressure, but on release regains its shape.
It is often more viscous than cytoplasm and gels quickly when cut.
The nuclear protoplasm, as a whole, is named *nucleoplasm* or *karyoplasm*.
A generalized nucleoplasmic ground-substance is called *karyolymph*.
Interspersed with the karyolymph are globular *nucleoli* and a mesh of *chromatin*.
If the chromatin meshwork is well spaced, the nucleus is said to be *vesicular*.
If the nucleus is shrunken and the chromatin condensed, it is said to be *pycnotic*.
The nucleus is bounded by a thin *nuclear membrane*.

D. DETECTED STRUCTURE:

When viewed with the ordinary microscope, the living nucleus appears homogeneous, except
for the presence of a much smaller nucleolus within it.
But phase contrast or ultraviolet light may demonstrate the chromatin meshwork.
The nuclear protoplasm (*nucleoplasm*) specializes into four distinctive parts.

1. Nuclear Membrane.

This is a plainly seen, and sharply demarcated, limiting membrane.
It is considerably thicker than the plasma membrane about the cytoplasm.
The electron microscope demonstrates two layers, perforated at intervals.
The outer layer, at least, is continuous with the endoplasmic reticulum.
Microdissection proves it to be often tough and definitely elastic.
When punctured, the nuclear contents may run out, leaving a wrinkled 'bag.'

2. Nuclear Sap (or Karyolymph).

This is a feebly-staining nucleoplasm, without any obvious structure.
It is a clear ground-substance that is more viscous than cytoplasm.

3. Chromatin.

This substance was so named because of its strong colorability with dyes.
Its ordinary affinity is for basic dyes, such as hematoxylin.
Chromatin commonly appears in the form of twisted threads or an actual meshwork.
Larger, angular masses often occur at intersections of this *chromatin net*.
These masses are called *karyosomes* (also chromatin knots or false nucleoli).
Paler-staining threads link up the larger masses.
These so-called *linin fibers* are perhaps protein precipitation products.
The chromatin pattern and its coarseness vary considerably with different fixatives.
The threads and meshwork represent a relatively diffuse condition of *chromosomes*.
These, however, retain their essential individuality during the interphase.
Karyosomes are portions of chromosomes least altered in the interphase.
(The structure of chromosomes will be described under mitosis (p. 19.)
One (or both?) of the sex chromosomes remains compact in body cells of the female.
It can be recognized in 'resting' nuclei as a prominent, stained mass.
This mass (or its absence in the male) is useful in diagnosing doubtful sex.

4. Nucleolus.

This 'little nucleus' is a conspicuous feature of most interphasic nuclei.

It is small, yet prominent, and there may be more than one.

It disappears from sight during the active period of mitosis.

It has a rounded, smooth contour (in contrast to karyosomes), but no membrane.

Some electron micrographs show tangled strands in a ground substance.

Basophilic stainability sometimes shifts to an acidophilic response.

This depends on the relative proportions of nucleic acid and protein present.

In life the nucleolus is highly refractile and sharply defined.

It appears like a semifluid drop of protoplasm.

It is displaceable and is one of the heaviest constituents of the nucleus.

(The behavior of the nucleolus during mitosis will be considered on pp. 19, 20.)

5. Chemical Composition.

The most important components are the *nucleoproteins*.

These consist of nucleic acids combined with complex proteins.

Nucleic acids are complex structures that include a pentose sugar.

The exact type of sugar subdivides the nucleic acids into two main groups.

Deoxyribonucleic acid (abbreviated to DNA) occurs only in chromosomes.

Ribonucleic acid (abbreviated to RNA) is abundant in nucleoli.

Responses to dyes depend on the dominance of nucleic acid or protein.

Chromatin is strongly basophilic because of its high content of DNA.

The nucleolus is likewise commonly basophilic because of its ribonucleic acid.

But it may become acidophilic when its protein-content dominates.

E. FUNCTIONAL CORRELATIONS:

The nucleus controls constructive metabolism.

It is necessary to life, growth and differentiation.

Hence the nucleus must exert some control over the cytoplasm.

The nucleus is also essential to reproduction and heredity-transmission.

The mechanism of heredity is identified with the presence of *genes*.

These are distributed along the chromatin-strands in definite order and position.

Continuous interchanges of substances occur between nucleus and cytoplasm.

This makes possible the maintenance of an equilibrium between the various functional activities of a cell.

The nucleolus, rich in ribonucleic acid, disappears from view during cell division.

Its RNA perhaps also serves as the intermediary ('messenger RNA'), conveying genic (DNA) 'instructions' to the RNA of ribosomes engaged in protein synthesis.

RNA is also present in the cytoplasm, and especially so in certain cells.

Such cells are those that are elaborating proteins, growing and dividing.

IV. CELL DIVISION

Two methods of cell division are recognized: *amitosis* and *mitosis*.

A. AMITOSIS:

The term *amitosis* (no thread) refers to the incidental role played by chromatin.

'Direct cell division' is another designation of the process.

The method is one in which nucleolus, nucleus and cytoplasm constrict and separate.

It is an inexact halving of a cell.

The incidence of amitosis is controversial; many alleged cases are spurious.

Living cells have been observed to stretch, but never to separate completely.

Binucleate cells are not proof of an uncompleted direct division.

It is said that some transitory, specialized or moribund cells do utilize amitosis.

But this method never occurs in young, unspecialized cells or in germ cells.

B. MITOSIS:

All cells pass through interphasic and mitotic periods at some time in their course.

The *interphase* designates the stage between successive *mitoses*.

During this period the cell performs its ordinary biochemical functions.

Mitosis is also called *karyokinesis* and 'indirect cell division.'

In this method chromatin threads (*chromosomes*) play a most important role.

Mitosis is the ordinary method of division, easily verified in all tissues.

Germ cells have to utilize it to insure a precise distribution of genes.

In this way the body acquires cells accustomed to the mitotic method of division.

For descriptive convenience, four stages (phases) in the cycle are recognized.

These are wholly arbitrary subdivisions of a continuous cyclic process.

1. Prophase.

A. CHANGES WITHIN THE NUCLEUS.

In the *interphase*, chromatin takes the form of threads that seem to connect.

This meshwork gives the impression of a lack of organization.

Actually, permanent *chromosomes* are present within the meshwork as entities.

Though definitely organized, they exist in a loosely diffuse state.

Yet the characteristic sequence and spacing of genes remains unchanged.

The *prophase* begins when these chromosome-threads shorten and thicken.

Such shortening may reduce their length by 95 per cent.

The individuality of separate chromosomes thereby becomes plain.

The number in man is 46 (each parent having contributed 23).

Each chromosome consists of two coiled filaments, parallel and touching.

The coiling becomes so tight that a solid cylinder seems to result.

Before the prophase each chromosome duplicates itself (twin chromosomes).

This double state temporarily increases the human total to 92.

Also the amount of deoxyribonucleic acid (DNA) is doubled.

The nucleolus and nuclear membrane disappear from sight.

B. CHANGES WITHIN THE CYTOPLASM.

The cell tends to become spherical.

The pair of *centrioles* (diplosome) divides into two daughter sets of centrioles.

About each set appears a so-called *aster* (*i.e.,* star).

This is a system of achromatic radiations called *astral rays.*

The two centriole-aster complexes migrate toward opposite poles of the cell.

Higher (flowering) plants lack centrioles and asters.

A bundle of delicate filaments, the *spindle*, arises between the asters.

2. Metaphase.

This stage is characterized by chromosomes moving to the equatorial plane of the cell.

Here they arrange themselves in a radial manner and each shows as a pair of rods.

This grouping is midway along the spindle, and at its periphery.

The arrangement (like the spokes of a wheel) is called the *equatorial plate.*

A spindle fiber attaches to each daughter chromosome at a special constricted region.

3. Anaphase.

The paired daughter chromosomes next begin to move apart.

In this way separate daughter-chromosomes become apparent.

The human number in each set again totals 46.

Migration of both chromosome sets, toward opposite poles, continues.

Between the retreating sets *interzonal fibers* appear.

Possibly these act as a pushing body, moving the sets apart.

4. Telophase.

A. NUCLEAR RECONSTRUCTION.

Prophasic processes occur in reverse.

Chromosomes lose their condensed state and become diffuse.

The spiral threads partly unwind.

Their investing protoplasm becomes invisible.

The nuclear membrane and nucleolus reappear.

The nucleolus arises at a particular region of a special chromosome.

B. CYTOPLASMIC DIVISION.

In animals the cytoplasm constricts in the equatorial region.

Following a figure-8 stage, two daughter cells become separate.

In plants, with rigid-cell walls, a *cell-plate* appears midway along the spindle.

Mitochondria and Golgi apparatus distribute to the daughter cells.

It is not proved that the distribution of these organoids is equal.

The centriole-aster-spindle complex ceases its activities.

Each daughter cell thereby acquires a centriole.

Duration of a Mitotic Cycle.

The total period varies with animal types, different organs of the same individual, physiological state and age.

The following are examples of timing in living cells, as observed in tissue cultures:

Mitotic stage	Embryonic mesenchyme	Fibroblasts
Prophase	10–15 minutes	30–60 minutes
Metaphase	2– 3 "	2–10 "
Anaphase	3– 4 "	2– 3 "
Telophase	7–15 "	3–12 "
Interphase	37–97 "	30–120 "

V. CELL AGING AND DEGENERATION

The term *cytomorphosis* denotes the series of successive changes undergone normally by a cell during its total life-span.

Although the changes are continuous, four stages may be recognized.

1. Embryonal Stage.

Cell division is active; nuclei are large; cytoplasm is relatively scanty and lacks visible signs of differentiation.

Example: embryonic cells; reserve mesenchyme of adult; germinal layer of epidermis.

2. Stage of Specialization and Maturity.

   Maximal *differentiation* in form, structure and function occurs.

   These changes involve chiefly the cytoplasm and its elaborated products.

   Also there is interstitial substance laid down between cells.

   Occasionally cells *dedifferentiate* and return to their former, less specialized state.

   Example: cartilage into mesenchyme; cardiac muscle (in tissue-culture).

   Under proper conditions such reverted cells can apparently redifferentiate.

   But probably they merely repeat the previous course of specialization.

3. Stage of Regression.

   Alterations appear in the character of both the nucleus and cytoplasm.

   The cell undergoes degenerative changes that characterize *senescence*.

   The ordinary and distinctive functions of a cell wane and finally fail.

4. Stage of Death and Removal.

   Cell death ensues when the vital processes of protoplasm cease.

   As an accompaniment, the protoplasm becomes irreversibly coagulated.

   A microscopic sign of death is the diffuse vital staining of nucleus and cytoplasm.

   Cells are ultimately lost by shedding, dissolution or phagocytosis.

The course leading to cell death by degenerative processes is called *necrobiosis*.

   When ordinarily timed, it is a normal and inevitable phase in the life of a cell.

   But such retrograde phenomena are different from postmortem changes.

   In the latter, *autolysis* (due to intracellular enzymes) is the causative agent.

There are several types of necrobiotic processes leading to cell death, or *necrosis:*

   1. CYTOLYSIS.

   Protoplasmic viscosity decreases; cells liquefy, swell and burst.

   2. COAGULATION.

   Protoplasmic viscosity increases, and irreversible gelation occurs.

   3. PYCNOSIS.

   The nucleus contracts; chromatin condenses to one or more heavily staining clumps.

   4. KARYOLYSIS.

   The nucleus and its chromatin lose their stainability and disappear, as if dissolved.

   (The loss of colorability by cell constituents, in general, is *chromatolysis*.)

   5. KARYORRHEXIS.

   The nucleus fragments and scatters.

Some cells have a transitory life, while others last part or all of the human life span.

   Example: leucocytes, 9 days; epidermal cell, 3 weeks; fetal cortex of suprarenal, 10 months;

   thymus, 15 years plus; muscle and nerve, much or all of the life span.

Aging of tissues and organs, with discernible changes, is a normal feature of the life span.

It enters at different times and proceeds at different speeds.

   Some organs run their course and regress before birth.

   Example: yolk sac; mesonephros.

   Others become obsolete and start their degenerative course at birth.

   Example: superseded, fetal blood vessels; fetal cortex of suprarenal gland.

   Most organs, though impaired, continue to function even into old age.

An appreciation of the importance of understanding the aging process is recent.

   Out of it has emerged the science of *gerontology* (or, including treatment, *geriatrics*).

Part II.   General Histology

FOREWORD ON THE ORIGIN AND NATURE OF TISSUES

The study of tissues is *histology* in the strict sense of that term.
But *Histology*, as commonly used, includes the consideration of cells and organs as well.
Hence the term *General Histology* can be employed to denote tissue structure alone.
This term then contrasts with *Special Histology*, which is a synonym of *Organology*.
These terms denote the subscience dealing with the arrangement of tissues in organs.
Special Histology also examines adaptations of tissues for specific organ-purposes.

Tissues and organs are understood best in the light of their development.
These topics belong to the science of *Embryology*.
Accordingly, only a few basic facts concerning the origin of tissues will be mentioned.
A ripe egg, when fertilized by a sperm cell, divides repeatedly into smaller cells.
These *cleavage cells* segregate into three superimposed *germ layers*.
From its position each layer receives a descriptive name, as follows:
Ectoderm (externally); *mesoderm* (middle position); *entoderm* (internally).
The germ layers produce a tubular embryo by processes of folding, budding, etc.
They also differentiate into the *tissues* that characterize the developing organs and parts.
This process of tissue specialization is called *histogenesis*.
Histogenesis produces four chief groups of tissues:
1. *Epithelia* arise from all three germ layers.
2. *Supporting tissues* arise from mesoderm.
3. *Muscular tissues* arise from mesoderm.
4. *Nervous tissues* arise from ectoderm.

A tissue is a group of similar cells (together with their cell products), specialized in a common direction and set apart for the performance of a common function.
Also, the cells of any particular kind of local tissue have the same embryonic origin.
Tissues are the practical building materials that fashion the various organs.
A sound understanding of tissues is more fundamentally useful than is organ structure.
This is because organ activities, normal and abnormal, are those of their tissues.

23

There are four major types of tissues; these are structurally and functionally distinct.

1. Epithelium.

These are sheet-like coverings, with one surface free and the other attached.

2. Supporting tissues.

These perform connecting, binding and supporting functions.

3. Muscle.

These cells respond to stimulation by producing oriented, contractile movements.

4. Nerve.

This tissue is irritable; it conducts waves of excitation as nerve impulses.

Two others, 'vascular tissue' and 'lymphoid tissue,' are really organs (pp. 121, 137).

It is only because they are so widespread and occur so frequently as components of other organs that they are often, loosely, termed tissues.

The role of fluids in the composition and functioning of the body is important.

Water comprises 70 per cent of the body weight of man.

Obviously some tissues (blood; muscle) contain much more water than others (fat; bone).

Protoplasm is 75 per cent water.

Part of the water is free, but much is bound to other components of the protoplasm.

As a whole, the intracellular fluid constitutes 50 per cent of body weight.

In addition, every living cell is bathed with fluid on at least one surface.

These extracellular fluids are: blood; lymph; cerebrospinal fluid; tissue fluid.

Of supreme importance is the relation existing between cells and the extracellular fluid residing in the tissue spaces.

This interstitial fluid constitutes 15 per cent of body weight.

In it are the raw anabolic materials and the end-products of catabolism.

Firmer substances than watery fluids may be deposited upon a cell surface.

Or they may be deposited as an interstitial substance that embeds cells.

This nonliving, formed material is named *ground substance* or *matrix*.

Chapter IV. EPITHELIUM

An *epithelium* is a layer of contiguous cells that covers an external or internal surface.
Typically one of its surfaces is free, facing against either air or fluid.
This exposed surface may be an expansive sheet or a tiny, microscopic tubule.
The other surface almost always rests upon a vascularized connective-tissue bed.
A small amount of intercellular, formed substance occurs between cells.
Directly beneath an epithelium, and attached to it, is the *basement membrane.*
This thin sheet of noncellular material serves to bind down the epithelium.
Epithelia frequently send ingrowths into the underlying connective tissue.
Most of these are actual diverticula (*i.e.*, blind tubes) that specialize as glands.
In a few instances they become detached, solid cords.
These may never acquire a cavity (*e.g.*, parathyroid; suprarenal cortex).
Contrariwise, the solid mass of the primordial thyroid gland cavitates secondarily.
The free surface of the epithelial sheets is frequently increased by folds (*e.g.*, stomach), finger-like
elevations (*e.g.*, intestinal villi) and inpocketings (*e.g.*, glands).
Beginners sometimes misinterpret certain conditions encountered in sections.
An epithelium that is folded or collapsed, so that free surfaces are brought into contact,
will seem to lack an obvious free surface.
Artificial clefts or shrinkage spaces, usually occurring in connective tissue, may give the
appearance of a cavity bordered by flat or stretched cells.
Solid 'islands' of epithelium are often seen, surrounded by connective tissue.
These are almost always glancing slices of epithelial folds, glands, etc.

I. OCCURRENCE AND TYPES

A. OCCURRENCE:
In general, epithelium occurs wherever free surfaces exist in relation to an organism.
The free surface may be expansive.
Example: skin; gut lining; body-cavity lining.
The free surface may be limited, and the bounded cavity small to tiny.
Example: small blood vessels; ducts and tubules of glands; liver cords.
A few special free surfaces are not lined by typical epithelium.
Example: joint cavities; bursae; cavity of brain and spinal cord.

B. CLASSIFICATION:
The basis of classification is cell layering and cell shape.
The three main groups are named in accordance with the presence of one layer, or of several to many layers:
1. *Simple epithelium:* one layer thick.
2. *Pseudostratified epithelium:* one layer thick, but apparently two or three layers.
3. *Stratified epithelium:* several to many layers are superposed.
Pseudostratified epithelium has no subgroups of consequence.

25

Simple and stratified epithelia have three important subgroups each.

In simple epithelium these minor groups are classified on the basis of cell shape.

    1. Simple squamous epithelium; the cells are flat plates.

    2. Simple cuboidal epithelium; the cells have about the same height and width.

    3. Simple columnar epithelium; the cells are taller than they are wide.

In stratified epithelium the minor groups are classified on the basis of the shape of the superficial cells at the free surface.

    1. Stratified squamous epithelium; the superficial cells are flattened.

    2. Stratified cuboidal epithelium; the superficial cells are roughly cubical.

    3. Stratified columnar epithelium; the superficial cells are elongated prisms.

Special names are employed, for convenience, for two epithelia of wide occurrence.

    Actually these are merely simple epithelia, characteristic of definite locations.

    Endothelium is the simple squamous lining of blood vessels and lymphatics.

    Mesothelium is the simple squamous lining of the several body cavities.

Mesenchymal epithelium is another special name frequently used.

    It denotes the simple layer of squamous cells that lines certain spaces.

        Such spaces arise as clefts in the embryonic mesenchyme.

    These spaces are: subdural and subarachnoid spaces; perilymphatic spaces of the ear; anterior chamber of the eyeball.

    This type is indistinguishable structurally from mesothelium.

False epithelium is a name sometimes given to the membrane that encloses the cavities of joints and bursae.

    It is a layer made of white fibers and scattered, flattened fibroblasts.

        Hence it is not epithelium, but connective tissue.

Epithelioid is an adjective applied to layers of cells that imitate epithelium.

    Example: connective-tissue osteoblasts and odontoblasts, arranged as sheets in developing bone; ependymal cells lining the central canal of the spinal cord.

II. GENERAL CHARACTERISTICS OF THE EPITHELIAL TYPES

A. SIMPLE EPITHELIUM:

1. Squamous.

It was formerly called 'pavement epithelium' because of its thin, covering nature.

The cells are scales or plates, definitely broader than they are thick.

    A. OCCURRENCE.

        Body cavities (mesothelium).

        Cardio-vascular and lymphatic systems (endothelium).

        Smallest ducts of many glands.

        Terminal respiratory ducts and air sacs.

        Membranous labyrinth (except sensory areas); tympanic cavity.

        Kidney tubules (in part).

        Mesenchymal epithelium (see above).

    B. ARRANGEMENT.

        The component cells are flat plates, joined to make a simple sheet.

            A pan-full of fried eggs is a fairly faithful model of this arrangement.

        The cell body is often expansive in comparison to its nuclear extent.

            Centrally the cells are thicker because the nucleus bulges there.

            Cell borders are often serrated and interlocking.

c. APPEARANCE IN SURFACE VIEW.

    The cell outline is usually hexagonal; the whole sheet is a mosaic.

       There is a geometrical reason for this, since six circles can be circumscribed
about a central circle; pressure makes hexagons.

    Mesothelial cells are polygons with all diameters approximately equal.

    Endothelial cells are typically elongated polygons, commonly diamond-shaped.

d. APPEARANCE IN VERTICAL SECTION.

    ('Vertical section' is in a plane perpendicular to the surface and base.)

    Cell boundaries are frequently indeterminable with ordinary stains.

    Cells cut through the nucleus appear as slender spindles.

       Nuclei usually are relatively far apart.

       They cause the thin epithelial disk to bulge locally.

    Cells, cut so as to miss the nucleus, vary in thickness and length.

       This depends on the distance of the section from the nucleus.

2. Cuboidal.

    The cells are short prisms; they have a top, bottom and, usually, six sides.

       Since a vertical section gives a square outline, this type became named 'cuboidal.'

       The name 'cubical' is also used, but the shape is rarely an exact square.

    Actually, all intermediates occur between squamous and columnar types.

       Hence there is the problem of naming borderline types.

       'Low cuboidal' and 'low columnar' are the terms then used by most histologists.

A. OCCURRENCE.

    Many glands; portions of their ducts.

    Pigmented epithelium of retina; epithelioid covering of chorioid plexus.

    Germinal layer of ovary.

B. ARRANGEMENT; APPEARANCE IN SECTIONS.

    The cells are arranged like regular mosaic blocks in a pavement.

    In surface view or horizontal section the cell outline tends to be hexagonal.

       Cell diameters are less than in the squamous type.

    In vertical section the pattern is that of a row of approximate squares.

       Nuclei are practically centered, and hence are evenly spaced.

3. Columnar.

    The component cells are distinctly taller than they are wide.

A. OCCURRENCE.

    Stomach and intestine.

    Many glands; portions of the ducts of some glands; gall bladder.

    Uterine tube and uterus.

    Bronchioles.

B. ARRANGEMENT; APPEARANCE IN SECTIONS.

    The cells are prisms, set on end and closely packed.

       The arrangement resembles the grouping of the 'cells' of a honeycomb.

    In surface view the cell outline is most commonly hexagonal.

    In horizontal section the pattern is like that in surface view.

       Nuclei may or may not show, depending on the level of the section.

    In vertical section the pattern is that of a row of rectangles.

       The nuclei lie at one general level.

          Usually this is below the middle of the cell.

Sometimes, however, crowding displaces nuclei into a staggered row.

The nuclei may even occur at two levels.

The cells are frequently pyramidal in shape.

This is due to folds or curves in the epithelium.

Example: tubules; thick-walled sacs; alveoli of glands.

Note that all three types of epithelium appear much alike in surface view or horizontal section; that is, they are arranged in an hexagonal mosaic.

It is the vertical section that identifies the three types by shapes.

4. Specialized Types of Epithelium.

Simple epithelium (usually columnar) frequently undergoes specializations.

There are four lines of such distinctive specialization.

A. GLANDULAR.

Details of these types are given in the chapter dealing with glands (pp. 162–167)

1. UNICELLULAR.

Generalized secretory cells (example: stomach lining).

Goblet cells (example: in intestinal lining).

The cell is swollen with an ovoid mass of premucin droplets.

The nucleus is pressed downward and flattened by this accumulation.

2. MULTICELLULAR.

Invaginations produce tubules, thick **pear**-shaped dilatations (alveoli or acini) or actual sacs.

Cells assume a pyramidal shape, with their broader ends as bases.

B. CILIATED.

The cells bear tiny protoplasmic lashes, or cilia (p. 32).

Example: nasal cavity; bronchi; uterine tube; uterus.

C. PIGMENTED.

The cells contain colored pigment granules (p. 15).

Example: pigment epithelium of retina.

D. NEURO-EPITHELIUM.

Some columnar cells are specialized for sensory reception.

Example: receptive cells of smell, taste, and hearing (pp. 304, 305, 319).

B. PSEUDOSTRATIFIED EPITHELIUM:

This type was formerly confused with stratified columnar epithelium.

Actually there is a deceptive appearance of stratification.

However, maceration separates the cells and shows the true relations.

It is then seen that there is a closer resemblance to simple epithelium.

That is, cells vary in height but all rest on the basement membrane.

1. Occurrence.

Larger ducts of glands opening onto a stratified epithelial surface.

Nasal cavity; trachea; bronchi.

Much of male urethra; some of female urethra.

Most of male sexual duct.

2. Arrangement.

In a fully specialized epithelium, three cell types occur:

(*a*) *Basal cells;* (*b*) *fusiform cells;* (*c*) *columnar cells.*

All these cells rest on a basement membrane.

Their upper ends extend to varying heights in the order just listed.

The columnar cells alone reach the free surface.

They are commonly ciliated, and often some are goblet mucous cells.

Nuclei of the three cell types lie at fairly distinct levels.

Most regular in this regard are the nuclei of the basal cells.

The majority of nuclei lie well below the middle level of the total layer.

Apparently the three cell types do not represent progressive growth stages.

In some regions fusiform cells are lacking.

Such an epithelium consists of columnar and basal cells.

3. Appearance in Sections.

Cell boundaries of the basal cells are usually quite easy to see.

Columnar cells are often reasonably distinct as they approach the surface.

It is the middle level that is crowded and confused.

Hence fusiform cells are difficult to demonstrate as entities.

Sometimes a middle stratum of nuclei furnishes a practical aid.

These belong to fusiform cells and to some columnar cells.

Also the total number of nuclei in the middle level is often greater than might be expected were a third cell type not present as fusiform cells.

The basal halves of columnar cells and fusiform cells are crowded (hence slender) as they extend toward the basement membrane.

They are easiest to trace when cells are shrunken and somewhat separated.

Simple columnar epithelium sometimes deceptively resembles pseudostratification.

Its nuclei may be crowded (somewhat alternatingly) into different levels.

Its cells, cut slantingly, may seem to lie in more than one layer.

C. STRATIFIED EPITHELIUM:

This type contains truly superposed cells.

The subtypes are named according to the shape of the surface cells alone.

1. Stratified Squamous.

A. OCCURRENCE.

Wherever there is exposure to friction, mechanical insult or drying.

Skin; conjunctiva (in part); cornea; external acoustic meatus.

Mouth; esophagus; anus.

Urethra (near outlet); vagina.

B. LIMITS OF STRATIFICATION.

The layering may vary from a few layers to dozens or scores of layers.

Example: corneal epithelium, few; epidermis, many.

C. ARRANGEMENT.

This type is usually draped over connective-tissue papillae.

It is this condition that gave epithelium its name—'upon nipples.'

The deepest cells are soft, delicate and are arranged in one layer.

Their shape is cuboidal to low columnar.

The intermediate cells are polygonal in outline, and larger.

Intercellular bridges of cytoplasm seem to bind them together.

These give the cell border a prickly or spiny appearance.

The more superficial layers are progressively flattened by pressure.

At the surface, flattening reaches a maximum and cells become dead scales.

Dry epithelia undergo cornification; moist epithelia show little or none.

'Dry' cells contain keratin granules, and the nucleus has disappeared.

This type of epithelium shows well the stages of cytomorphosis.

D. APPEARANCE IN SECTIONS.

The layering and the gradual flattening (and spreading) of cells are diagnostic.

In cornified epithelium the upper layers may separate or shred irregularly.

Boundaries of the caked cells are often obscure.

2. Stratified Cuboidal.

A. OCCURRENCE.

Testis tubules; vesicular (Graafian) follicles of ovary.

Ducts of sweat glands; sebaceous glands.

Intermediate zones of some regions, such as the urethra and conjunctiva.

Urinary tract from kidney to urethra (so-called transitional epithelium).

B. ARRANGEMENT; APPEARANCE IN SECTIONS.

Typically there is a superposition of polyhedral cells, with the superficial cell taking a more cuboidal shape.

Mostly this type occurs in special situations, but best known is the epithelium c the urinary tract commonly called *transitional epithelium.*

This example is, by far, the most widespread in its distribution.

C. TRANSITIONAL EPITHELIUM.

The name is inappropriate and without real meaning.

It is a plastic epithelium, whose appearance varies with stretching.

It is not indented by papillae; there is no basement membrane.

In a relaxed epithelium the cells are about six layers deep.

The basal cells are small, polyhedral elements.

The middle layers of cells are larger, often club- or pear-shaped.

The surface cells are bloated and cuboidal, with bulging tops.

The lower surface of a superficial cell bears several indentations.

Into these pits fit the clubbed ends of the cells next below.

On stretching, the epithelium becomes markedly thinner.

Cells flatten out and apparently slip by one another.

This is aided by the lack of intercellular bridges.

The layering may become reduced to two or three cells.

The sheet is then more like a stratified squamous type.

3. Stratified Columnar.

A. OCCURRENCE.

Pharynx (in part); larynx (in part).

Urethra (in part).

Excretory ducts of salivary and mammary glands (in part).

(In general, where columnar or pseudostratified epithelium meets stratifie squamous epithelium.)

B. ARRANGEMENT; APPEARANCE IN SECTIONS.

The surface cells are columnar and sometimes ciliated.

The deeper cells are irregular polyhedrons.

The occurrence of this type in mammals is limited and localized.

In sections it cannot be distinguished surely from pseudostratified epithelium.

(Also simple columnar epithelium cut slantingly has an appearance resemblin either stratified columnar or cuboidal.)

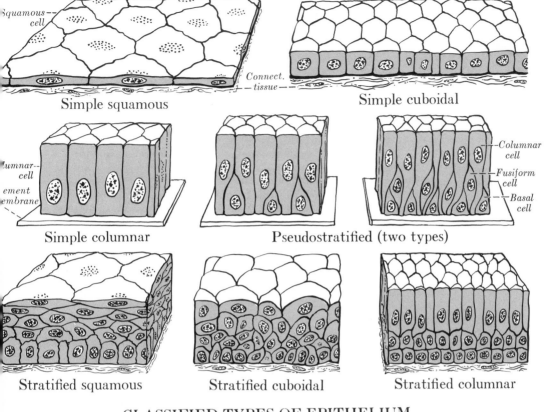

CLASSIFIED TYPES OF EPITHELIUM

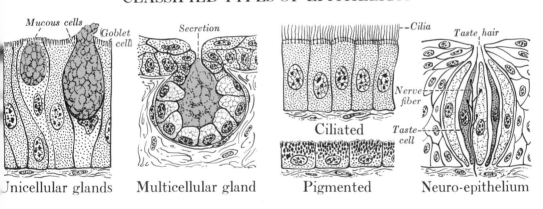

TYPES OF SPECIALIZED EPITHELIUM

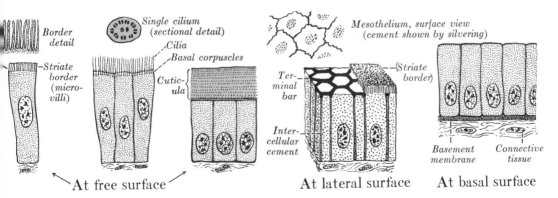

DIFFERENTIATIONS AT CELL SURFACES

III. THE GENERAL CHARACTERISTICS
OF EPITHELIAL CELLS

In large measure, epithelial cells can be considered as rather typical cells.
Only their general features will be treated in the present topic.

A. NUCLEUS:
This conforms to the shape of its particular cell.
In squamous cells it is a flattened disk.
In cuboidal cells it is spheroidal.
In columnar cells it is ovoid to elongate.

B. CYTOPLASM:
It is usually much like that of a generalized cell, as already described (pp. 12–16).
The usual organoids are represented: tonofibrils are common, and prominent in some cells.
Secretion precursors and storage products are sometimes encountered.

C. POLARITY:
Epithelial cells are organized differently at their free and attached ends.
Such differences are inherent in a sheet-like arrangement of cells.
They are most clearly seen in simple epithelia.
There is a proximal, attached surface, and a distal, free surface.
The *proximal surface* is usually less specialized.
It is the receptive side through which nutriment comes from nearby vessels.
The *distal surface* is more highly specialized.
It is directly subject to external influences.
Here specialized borders and cilia are elaborated.
The position above the nucleus of metabolic products (*e.g.*, secretion precursors), centriole
and Golgi apparatus is an expression of cellular polarity.
Some gland cells are further polarized by the presence of chromidia below the nucleus.
In columnar cells, the nucleus tends to take a more basal position.
Rod-shaped mitochondria orient in the long dimension of the cell.
In some cells they are filamentous in form (near top) and granular (near base).

IV. DIFFERENTIATIONS AT THE SURFACES OF CELLS

Epithelial cells have different kinds of functional surfaces.
These are best illustrated in simple epithelium where there are three such surfaces.
1. Free surface: either exposed to air or bathed by fluids.
2. Lateral surface: in contact with other cells of the same kind.
3. Basal surface (or attached surface): resting on a connective-tissue substrate.
In stratified epithelia no cell can possess more than two of these surface-relations.
Basal cells have *2* and *3*, as listed above; intermediate cells, *2*; exposed cells, *1* and *2*.

A. FREE SURFACE:
1. **Cytoplasmic Specializations.**
Several different kinds of elaborations have been developed by cells where exposed.
A. CONDENSED BORDER.
A superficial condensation blends into ordinary cytoplasm beneath.
It becomes visible by taking a deeper stain than the general cytoplasm.
Example: some simple squamous epithelia; exposed cells of transitional epithelium.

B. NONMOTILE PROCESSES.

Protoplasmic processes that project from the free surface of cells.

Some are easily visible; others are resolved only by electron microscopy.

They are related to absorption, secretion and sensory reception.

Nothing is known as to any structural difference between them.

1. PROCESSES RELATED TO ABSORPTION.

In general, these short, delicate processes have been named *microvilli*.

Those occurring on intestinal epithelium are known as a *striate border*.

With the light microscope it shows only as delicate vertical striae.

The electron microscope reveals myriads of vertical, parallel rodlets.

These are closely packed and of uniform length.

Those occurring on kidney tubules are designated as a *brush border*.

It contains coarser, longer filaments, not uniform in length.

Between these microvilli is an amorphous substance.

Its appearance varies with the functional condition of the cells.

A similar border occurs on placental trophoblast.

2. PROCESSES RELATED TO SECRETION.

Delicate, short microvilli occur in glands of the stomach and uterus.

They are demonstrable only with the electron microscope.

Long, hair-like processes occur in the male sex duct.

Cytoplasm keeps these clumped together, like a wet brush.

Droplets of secretion can be observed oozing at the tip.

They have often been called nonmotile cilia or *stereocilia*.

3. SENSORY HAIRS.

Certain sensory epithelial cells have hair-like receptor-processes.

Such occur in relation to smell, taste, hearing and equilibration.

C. MOTILE PROCESSES (CILIA).

These are lashing protoplasmic processes that vary in length and fineness.

Such '*cilia*' (*i.e.*, eyelashes) may number up to 100 or more to a cell.

If there are but one to several long ones, each is a *flagellum* (*i.e.*, whip).

1. OCCURRENCE.

Respiratory tract; uterine tube; uterus; efferent ductules of testis.

2. STRUCTURE.

A cilium is a slender thread of cytoplasm.

It contains two axial *fibrils* and nine double ones arranged about them.

These are demonstrable only with the electron microscope.

Cilia arise from a row of granules just beneath the plasma membrane.

These are called *basal corpuscles*; some are centriolar in origin.

The flagellum of a sperm cell arises from a double centriole (*diplosome*)

In some cases ciliary rootlets continue far into the cell body.

3. MOVEMENT.

In mammals cilia beat toward outlets of the body.

The stroke consists of a vigorous lash and a slower recovery.

A cilium beats and then the next one in front, and so on.

Thus a wave is propagated and fluids are moved onward.

The transport of mucus is as fast as 0.5 mm. per second.

Recurring rhythms produce wave after wave of motion.

Thus a ciliated epithelial sheet, in surface view, resembles a wind-swept field of grain.

Ciliary activity is independent of nervous control.

The mechanisms of the stroke and co-ordination are not surely known

2. Secreted Plates.

These are more or less solid formed-substances, secreted by the cytoplasm.

They lie on an epithelial surface and can be detached from it; they are *cuticulae*.

Commonly they become impregnated with a hard substance of some kind.

Example: clam shell (lime); beetle shell (chitin).

Even mammals have some representatives of this specialization.

Example: enamel of tooth; lens capsule; tectorial membrane of ear.

B. LATERAL SURFACE:

'Lateral', as used, means any cell surface not at the top or base of an epithelium.

Along those surfaces provision is made to enhance cell coherence.

Between cells there is a minute space into which fluids and leucocytes can penetrate.

1. Intercellular Bridges.

These interconnections occur wherever there is special need for cellular cohesion.

They are conspicuous in the lower layers of the epidermis.

Cytoplasmic bridges seem to cross the spaces between these cells.

They carry *tonofibrils*, which are elements that resist stretching.

Actually midway of the 'bridge' there is a bridge corpuscle, the *desmosome*.

It is a local thickening, formed by opposing plasma membranes.

On this corpuscle the tonofibrils of adjoining cells insert.

When cells are forcibly separated, a break occurs at the desmosome.

The cell outline is then spiny; hence the name, *prickle cells*.

Other types of epithelia lack obvious intercellular spaces.

Yet they exhibit desmosomes on their plane, facing surfaces.

The original idea of true cytoplasmic continuity between cells is false.

2. Intercellular Cement.

Epithelial cells are held together by some method of cohesion.

It is customary to attribute this adhesion largely to a plastic cementing substance.

Such permits cells to change shape, and wandering cells to invade between them.

It provides avenues of communication with fluid of the connective-tissue spaces.

Yet the demonstration of an actual intercellular cement is difficult.

Ordinary dyes do not stain it; the electron microscope usually fails to show it.

Cell boundaries may blacken (*i.e.*, reduce) silver nitrate on exposure to sunlight.

Example: mesothelium; endothelium. Is this a reaction induced by cement?

Cement sometimes does take a special stain, suggesting a mucoid nature.

3. Terminal Bars.

A ring-like band is seen in many simple cuboidal and columnar epithelia.

This lies just beneath the free surface, closing off the intercellular space.

The sealing effect is proved when fluid collects pathologically between cells.

It then distends the space, but does not escape upward.

These *terminal bars* have long been described as condensed cement.

The electron microscope, however, shows them as thickenings of plasma membranes.

Hence a bar is a double structure, formed jointly by adjacent cells.

It is essentially like an elongated desmosome.

The encircling band stains especially well with iron hematoxylin.

In vertical section it appears either as dots between cells (if cut through), or as a rod paralleling the top of a cell (if not cut at all).

In horizontal section the 'rings' make a polygonal pattern, like chick netting.
The same appearance is obtained in a surface view.

4. Interlocking Membranes.

Some epithelial cells have their facing surfaces thrown into ridges and grooves.
These corrugations fit together in an interlocking manner.
Example: deeper cells of lingual epithelium; convoluted tubules of kidney
Mechanical resistance to shearing forces is an obvious 'explanation' for this.
But highly complicated foldings imply another and deeper significance.

C. BASAL SURFACE:

There are extensive infoldings of the basal plasma membrane into some cells.
They occur in cells notable for water transport (*e.g.*, kidney tubules).
Epithelia typically lie upon a bed of connective tissue and attach to it.
There are several ways in which the two become firmly united:
1. The epithelium may send processes into the connective tissue beneath.
2. The connective tissue may send projections up into the epithelium.
3. Usually there is a relatively smooth *basement membrane* beneath the epithelium.
   To this layer, attachment is made by the epithelium.

Basement Membrane, or Membrana Propria.

Epithelium, of itself, has little tensile strength.
On the other hand, intercellular bridges and cement, terminal bars and inter
locked cell surfaces resist forces that would tear cells apart.
Similarly, anchorage to a stronger support prevents both dislocation and disruption.
An underlying *basement membrane* is the usual medium employed.
This membrane, in turn, is bound to the connective tissue beneath it.
The basement membrane is refractory to ordinary stains.
Hence it is commonly not seen unless it is unusually thick.
The actual thickness varies greatly in different locations.
In the cornea and trachea it is very thick, and is conspicuous without staining.
In the skin, intestine and kidney it is thin and escapes notice.
But special staining demonstrates it readily.
In some locations it is uncertain or lacking.
Example: bladder; thyroid of young persons.
The membrane is composed primarily of a structureless, hyaline ground substance.
Reticular fibers beneath it (and in it?) constitute a second component.
Reticulin stains, but especially the PAS technique, demonstrate it well.
The latter has an affinity for the ground substance, a mucopolysaccharide.
The method of attachment of epithelium to the membrane differs.
In some instances there seems to be a simple cementing.
In others, tooth-like projections bury themselves in the membrane.
The membrane acts as a support and barrier; it is permeable to metabolites.

V. THE RELATIONS OF EXTRANEOUS ELEMENTS TO EPITHELIUM

1. Blood Vessels.

These tubules do not penetrate into the epithelium proper.
Exceptions are the cochlear epithelium and the egg follicle.

Hence fluids escape from the vessels, join the fluids of the tissue spaces, cross the basement membrane, and seep along the spaces between epithelial cells.
This is the pathway used for epithelial nutrition, respiration and excretion.
The vascular supply to thick, stratified epithelium is made easier by the presence of finger-like, connective-tissue papillae.
These indent the epithelial sheet and may carry blood capillaries far 'into' it.
Yet the capillaries still remain outside the basement membrane.
In other words, the epithelium is draped over these vascular papillae.

Nerve Fibers.
Fine fibers pierce the basement membrane and pass between epithelial cells.
Possibly some fine twigs actually penetrate into the interior of some cells.

Wandering Cells.
Migratory cells may invade epithelia and wander or lodge in the spaces between cells.
Example: lymphocytes in intestine; pigmented cell-processes in epidermis.

VI. EPITHELIAL REPLACEMENT AND REPAIR

Epithelia are subject to wear and replacement, but at different rates.
Epidermal and intestinal cells are shed continuously.
It is claimed that intestinal cells live only 36 hours.
Cells of respiratory passages, protected cavities and glands are replaced infrequently.
Hence some cells of a layer must retain the capacity of cell division.
In a stratified epithelium these are the deeper cells.
Daughter cells get pushed gradually to the surface by those formed later.
In a simple epithelium the newly-divided cells naturally lie side by side.
In certain epithelia, such as glands, the proliferative regions are restricted.
Daughter cells may then gradually shift far from their site of origin.
Epithelia also are capable of repairing losses produced by trauma, disease, etc.
Although their cells are normally immobile, those near the injury become activated.
Their gliding movements alone can cover defects of fair size.
Mitosis is a secondary phenomenon in point of time.
It may add new cells to the denuded region.
It also restores cell losses to adjacent regions that furnished the migratory cells.

VII. THE FUNCTIONS OF EPITHELIUM

Protection.
The effects of mechanical insult or noxious substances are minimized.
Epidermis, mouth and vagina furnish examples of protection against mechanical trauma.
The bladder lining furnishes protection against the hypertonic excretory-wastes in urine.
The total body is enveloped in a casing of cornified dead cells.
In this way the body is protected against drying and bacterial invasion.

Secretion.
Cells synthesize products and pass them out of the body or into the blood.
This sequence characterizes all glandular activity, both exocrine and endocrine.

3. Excretion

Certain cells filter from the blood the wastes that were produced elsewhere.

Urine, sweat and carbon dioxide illustrate such excreted filtrates.

4. Absorption.

Cells are permeable to certain substances in solution.

Lungs pass oxygen; intestines absorb nutriment; kidneys recapture sugar from raw urine.

5. Lubrication.

Mechanical chafing of part on part is avoided.

Secreted mucus is a principal agent used as a lubricant (*e.g.*, rectal mucus).

The mesothelial lining and serous fluid of the body cavities prevent undue friction.

That is, viscera play smoothly against each other and the body wall.

6. Sensory Reception.

Some cells of an epithelium specialize as intermediaries in nervous transmission.

Certain cells of taste buds, olfactory epithelium and the organ of hearing perform this function; they even develop bristle-like, receptive processes.

7. Reproduction.

Certain cells are set aside for the sole purpose of species-perpetuation.

These cells are produced in the ovary and testis, which are glands that 'secrete' cells.

Chapter V. THE CONNECTIVE TISSUES

Connective tissue, cartilage and bone share in performing certain mechanical functions.
> They connect and anchor parts, and give support to the body and its organs.
> Hence this larger group is sometimes given an inclusive name, the *supporting tissues.*
All of the supporting tissues are notable for the presence of nonliving *formed substance.*
> This material, located between the cells, varies in amount and firmness.
> > Yet its abundance is the feature that characterizes the group as a whole.
> In many ways, at least, it is the most important part of these tissues.
All of the supporting tissues have *cells* interspersed in the intercellular substance.
> > There are different kinds of cells; in some tissues they are relatively sparse.
In all of the supporting tissues, *fibers* occur as a constituent of the formed substance.
> They lie in an amorphous *ground substance,* semifluid to solid in consistency.
> Fibers and ground substance, together, are often designated as *matrix.*
The origin of fibers in connective tissue, cartilage and bone is disputed.
> The controversy hinges on whether to interpret them as transformed cytoplasm or as an
> > organized, nonliving ground substance.
> The dominant view is that cells secrete ground substance, out of which fibers arise through
> > some influence (enzymic?) exerted by the cells.
Sometimes 'connective tissues' has been used as synonymous with 'supporting tissues.'
> In a better, narrow sense the former applies to the obviously fibrous, binding tissues.
> This excludes essentially rigid, supporting tissues, such as cartilage and bone.

I. EMBRYONAL TISSUES

Two subtypes are usually recognized, but they are only the early and late phases of a tem-
> porary tissue occurring normally in prenatal development.
These are important also because they reappear in wound healing and as tumorous new growths.

A. MESENCHYME:
> **1. Occurrence.**
> > It is the typical, unspecialized packing-tissue of the early weeks of embryonic life.
> > Subsequently it disappears as such when its cells enter into tissue differentiation.

> **2. Structure.**
> > Mesenchyme is a spongy and delicate tissue, filling-in between layers and parts.
> > It consists of cells and intercellular ground substance.
> > A. MESENCHYMAL CELLS.
> > > Their shape ranges from stellate (star-shape) to fusiform (spindle-shape).
> > > Cytoplasm is scanty, but the nucleus is relatively large and pale.
> > > Cells appear to join by their processes, forming a syncytium.
> > > > Some claim there is merely intimate contact, not fusion.
> > B. GROUND SUBSTANCE.
> > > In the earliest stages of development this is simply a coagulable fluid.

37

Later it becomes a mucoid jelly that contains fine, scanty fibrils.
This condition passes imperceptibly into the type called *mucous tissue*.
Young mesenchyme is a generalized tissue whose further differentiation produce
the supporting tissues, vascular tissues, blood and smooth muscle.

3. Appearance in Sections.

Young mesenchyme takes the form of a network of stellate cells.
The nucleus is vesicular and relatively large; the cytoplasm is scanty.
The interspaces between cells appear to be empty.
Old mesenchyme grades into the characteristics of mucous tissue (see beyond).

4. Functional Correlations.

Typically these cells are transient elements, awaiting differentiation.
They become the supporting tissues, vascular tissues and muscle.
A minority are retained as reserve elements and persist in adult tissues.
On demand these multipotential cells can differentiate in various directions.

B. MUCOUS TISSUE:

1. Occurrence.

It occurs transiently in the normal development of the supporting tissues.
Elsewhere its sole representative is the *Wharton's jelly* of the umbilical cord.
In this fetal appendage the packing tissue never progresses further.
(Its nearest counterpart in the adult is the *vitreous body* of the eye.)

2. Structure.

Typical mucous tissue is a gelatinous, semifluid mass.
A jelly, often feebly stained, comprises most of the bulk of the tissue.
Cells and scanty fibers are strewn throughout the jelly.
There are no intrinsic blood vessels, lymphatics or nerves.
A. CELLS.
The distinctive cell is a *fibroblast*, with wing-like processes.
In end view it appears stellate; in side view, spindle-shaped.
Many of the processes seem to fuse with those of neighboring cells.
The cell tends to flatten itself on the surface of fiber bundles.
Macrophages (phagocytes) and migratory lymphocytes are encountered rarely.
B. GROUND SUBSTANCE.
In the fresh condition it is homogeneous, like a slippery jelly.
Chemically it gives a mucin reaction, and belongs among the glycoproteins.
It stains deeply (and metachromatically) with toluidine blue.
C. FIBERS.
They vary in abundance with the age of the tissue.
Fine 'white' *fibrils* aggregate in compound bundles called *collagenous fibers*.
Other fiber types (reticular; elastic) are lacking.

3. Appearance in Sections.

The abundant jelly-substance is a highly distinctive feature.
It ordinarily stains palely, but shows better as the aperture of the microscope
diaphragm is reduced.
Yet some stains (thionine; Mallory) demonstrate it satisfactorily.
Shrinkage commonly produces gaps in the jelly.

Fibers vary in number and size with the age of the specimen.
>In the first half of pregnancy those of the umbilical cord are fine and scanty.
>In the last half of pregnancy they become coarser and more numerous.
>>In the vicinity of the umbilical vessels they group in wavy fiber-bundles.

4. Functional Correlations.

As an immature connective tissue, mucous tissue serves the embryo usefully.
>It provides a fibro-gelatinous packing substance.
In repair processes, young fibrous tissue duplicates the mucous-tissue condition as an
>intermediate stage of progress in the restoration of supporting tissues.
(In the vitreous body, transparency and refractivity are advantageous qualities.)

II. CONSTITUENTS OF THE ADULT CONNECTIVE TISSUES

The connective tissues, in general, possess characteristic constituents and qualities.
>Their representation varies widely in the several members of the group.
It is advantageous, nevertheless, to discuss these constituents in some detail before entering into
>a consideration of the peculiar features of each tissue-type.
Such a preliminary treatment involves *cells*, *fibers* and *intercellular substances*.
>These features are better seen in areolar tissue than in any other single type.

A. CONNECTIVE-TISSUE CELLS:

Ordinary sections, with routine staining, show the details of many cells poorly.
>Nuclei stain satisfactorily, but cytoplasmic details are often unsatisfactory.

1. Mesenchymal Cells.

Many authorities maintain that cells of this 'embryonic' type persist in the adult.
They resemble fibroblasts but tend to be smaller.
>In areolar tissue they usually lie along the wall of blood vessels.
When stimulated, these primitive cells differentiate into various cell types.
>Such responses are appropriate to local environmental conditions.
>This capacity is responsible for producing, under certain conditions, metaplasia.
>>*Metaplasia* is the seeming change of a tissue into a different kind.
>>Ordinarily it is the replacement of one kind by another, developing anew.
>(Fibroblasts are fully differentiated and cannot similarly create new cell types.)

2. Fibroblasts.

These cells are responsible for the formation of the several kinds of fibers.
>In a mature tissue they are almost immobile, and are often called *fibrocytes*.
>>Yet, following tissue injury, they become active and form new fibers.
>They also are believed to give rise to the glycoprotein of ground-substance.
>An obvious function is to keep the tissue in good metabolic condition.
They are large, flat, branching cells; they appear spindle-shaped in edge view.
>Nuclei are oval, pale (because of the finely granular chromatin) and larger than
>>any other in connective tissue; one or two nucleoli are conspicuous.
>The cytoplasm is nearly homogeneous and stains palely.
>>In sections it is often obscure, so that nuclei are chiefly seen.
Fibroblasts are the commonest cell of areolar tissue and the only cell of tendon.
>Endothelial cells (especially their nuclei) resemble them, but occur only in vessels.

3. Macrophages.

Among the many other names proposed, *histiocyte* is also frequently used.
These cells are most abundant in richly vascular areas.
  In loose connective tissue they are second only to fibroblasts in numbers.
The cell outline is irregular, but the cell processes are usually short and blunt.
  Sometimes they show branched processes.
      Nevertheless, they are normally immobile.
      For this reason the cells are often called *fixed macrophages*.
  Yet when activated by inflammation they can become ameboid.
The nucleus is oval (often indented), but smaller than that of a fibroblast.
  Chromatin forms a coarse pattern, so that the nucleus stains darkly.
  Nucleoli are not present as conspicuous features.
Macrophages are highly endowed with the ability to ingest particulate matter.
  Most remarkable is their capacity for taking up ultramicroscopic particles.
      Colloidal carbon and acid colloidal dyes, such as trypan blue, are phagocytosed
          and stored in cytoplasmic vacuoles.
  This greedy response distinguishes them sharply from all other cell types.
  Macrophages are important agents of defense by acting as scavengers.
      They engulf loose blood, bacteria, dead cells and foreign bodies.
      Ingested organic material is digested by cytoplasmic enzymes.
      Inert foreign substances may remain stored indefinitely.
          Example: soot particles in macrophages of the lung.
The mobilization of macrophages, under the stimulus of inflammation and at its site, is
    apparently brought about in several ways.
  Part of the increase is the result of mitoses among macrophages.
  Important additions come from the activation of fixed macrophages.
  Further recruits are gained from monocytes that leave the blood stream.
  Claims have been advanced for the transformation of still other cell types into ele-
      ments with all of the characteristics of macrophages.
Tissue macrophages are one component of the so-called *reticulo-endothelial system*.
  This larger category is known also as the *macrophage system*.
  All of the component cells respond phagocytically to inert, particulate matter.
  Representatives will be encountered in the spleen, liver and other organs.

4. Fat Cells.

These conspicuous elements are normal components of areolar tissue.
  They occur singly, or in clusters arranged along small blood vessels.
They are special cells, resembling fibroblasts, that store fat.
  Fat appears first as droplets which later merge into a common, fluid pool.
  Hence, adult fat cells are usually bloated with a huge fat vacuole.
These elements will be considered further under the topic of adipose tissue (p. 47).

5. Leucocytes.

Lymphocytes and monocytes may outwander into connective tissue.
  Some of these, however, arose in connective tissue and have remained there.
      Yet they can enter the circulation and sometimes do so.
Eosinophils emigrate from the blood stream into connective tissue.
  They are numerous in the lactating breast and in the respiratory and gastro-
      intestinal tracts.
Neutrophils, in particular, escape from capillaries in regions exhibiting inflammation
Some functions of leucocytes are summarized on p. 57.

6. Plasma Cells.

They are rare, except in serous membranes and lymphoid tissue.

They are plentiful in regions of chronic inflammation.

Plasma cells probably represent a special differentiation of the lymphocyte.

The nucleus is small; its chromatin is arranged like spokes or clock-figures.

The cytoplasm is basophilic and relatively abundant.

An area near the eccentric nucleus remains pale and unstained.

This is the region of the 'cell center' and its centriole.

Plasma cells are even more suspect than lymphocytes as the producers of antibodies.

7. Mast Cells.

These elements occur sparsely, often along the course of small blood vessels.

They are fairly large cells, but have relatively small, pale nuclei.

The cytoplasm is crowded with coarse, deeply basophilic granules.

The cell membrane ruptures readily during fixation and liberates the granules.

The granules are highly refractile and rather soluble in water.

These tissue basophils are entirely distinct from the basophils of the blood.

They contain histamine, heparin and serotonin.

8. Chromatophores.

Pigmented cells occur in the skin, pia mater and chorioid coat of the eye.

The cell body, containing brown melanin granules, extends into cytoplasmic processes.

Some (*melanoblasts*) manufacture pigment; others (*melanophores*) phagocytose it.

Other colors (red; yellow; colorless-iridescent) occur in lower animals.

Hence *chromatophore* is a general name for a pigmented cell, whereas *melanophore* (brown), *xanthophore* (yellow), etc., designate particular color bearers.

Known functions of melanin are limited to its role in absorbing light rays.

B. CONNECTIVE-TISSUE FIBERS:

Three kinds of fibers occur in adult connective tissue.

All are represented, to varying degrees, in each type of connective tissue.

1. Collagenous Fibers.

Another name, commonly used, is *white fiber*.

It is notable for being a compound fiber, composed of still finer fibrils.

A. GENERAL FEATURES.

Fibrils are 0.1 to 0.5 μ in diameter, but are uniform in size locally.

Electron micrographs indicate that they are composed of finer *protofibrils*.

These still thinner protofibrils are about 0.01 μ thick.

The fibrils run parallel courses which are actually more or less wavy.

Individual fibrils do not branch or unite with other fibrils.

They are believed to be held together by a cementing substance.

A *collagenous fiber* is a bundle, composed of a variable number of fibrils.

Hence the size of a fiber-bundle depends on the number of fibrils in it.

Bundle thickness ranges from a few microns to 100 microns or more.

A fiber-bundle is said to be encased in a thin covering of cement.

Bundles frequently branch and recombine, forming a network.

This arrangement is brought about by clusters of fibrils leaving one bundle and joining other bundles.

B. PHYSICAL PROPERTIES.

A fresh collagenous fiber is opaque, with a dull, pearly appearance.

That is, it is colorless (white) and has a low refractive index.

Pulling on a wavy fiber merely straightens it, without significant stretching.
> Its resistance to further pulling-force is remarkable.
>> When it yields, it breaks and frays irregularly, like a rope.

Electron micrographs show that fibrils are cross-banded.
> These bands occur at regular intervals of 0.064 μ.
> They are responsible for the birefringence shown under polarized light.

C. CHEMICAL CHARACTERISTICS.

These fibers consist of an albuminoid, *collagen*, which gives them their name.

Boiling dissolves the fibers into a colloidal solution of 'animal glue.'
> (This explains the name, collagen, which means 'glue producing.')
> Animal glue is really gelatin, which gels on cooling.

Weak acids and alkalies cause fibers to swell markedly.
> They swell unevenly and become transparent.

Strong acids and alkalies dissolve the fibers.
> Long action of weak solutions will do the same.
> This action is the basis of maceration processes.
>> The dissolving frees structures supported by white fibrous tissue.

Fibers are readily digested by an acid solution of pepsin (gastric juice).
> On the contrary, they resist the enzymes of pancreatic juice.

Tannic acid converts collagen into a tough, insoluble product.
> This reaction is the basis of the tanning of leather.

There is no specific stain for collagenous fibers.
> However, acid aniline dyes stain them strongly.
> The Mallory or Masson stain is a good practical test for these fibers.
>> The aniline-blue or light-green component colors them brilliantly.

2. Elastic Fibers.

A. PHYSICAL PROPERTIES.

Elastic fibers are always solitary, never occurring in bundles.

They branch and anastomose abundantly, thereby forming a network.
> In life they are stretched and under tension.

Stretching 1.5 times the relaxed length causes a fiber to break.
> The force required is one-tenth that for a collagenous fiber of equal size.
> Severed fibers break squarely across, like a rubber band.
>> They then retract and curl in a loose spiral.
> With advancing age these fibers lose their resiliency.

A fiber is much coarser than a collagenous fibril.
> Most, however, are definitely thinner than the thinnest collagenous fibers.

A fiber is optically homogeneous in structure, but actually contains fibrils.
> When fresh it appears microscopically as a bright thread.
> This appearance is due to its high refractivity.

Fresh, massed fibers have a yellowish color.
> Hence they are sometimes called *yellow fibers*.

B. CHEMICAL CHARACTERISTICS.

The fiber is composed of *elastin*, an albuminoid.
> Elastin resists boiling water and acids or alkalies.

The enzyme *elastase*, present in pancreatic juice, digests the fiber.
> It attacks the amorphous matrix, revealing fine fibrils.

Ordinary stains demonstrate elastic fibers poorly or erratically.
> Orcein or resorcin-fuchsin stain them deeply and electively.

3. Reticular Fibers.

A. PHYSICAL PROPERTIES.

The branching fibers unite in an irregular, fine mesh-work, or *reticulum*.

They are of different sizes, but all are relatively thin (0.2–1 μ).

Each consists of a bundle of fibrils whose thickness is about 0.01 μ.

This is the same size as the collagenous protofibril.

Reticular fibers are inelastic and lack some other characteristics of elastic tissue.

On the other hand, they have features in common with collagenous fibers.

In many locations the two blend and become continuous.

Most important is the identical banding revealed by electron micrographs.

The same periodic spacing (0.064 μ) is highly significant.

It means that the molecular arrangement is identical in both.

A chemical difference, under these circumstances, is not admissible.

B. CHEMICAL CHARACTERISTICS.

Reticular fibers are usually obscured in sections by other, crowding elements.

Ordinary stains show them poorly or not at all.

However, special silver techniques blacken them prominently and specifically.

Hence these fibers are called *argyrophilic*.

By contrast, the same silver techniques do not blacken collagen fibers.

They merely tinge them yellow to brown.

Chemical differences between the two fibers lack supporting evidence.

Hence the existence of a specific entity, *reticulin*, remains hypothetical.

It is, therefore, logical to ascribe the various contrasting characteristics to dissimilar physical natures of the two fiber types.

The different responses to silver have been attributed to thick and thin fiber-sizes.

A thin fiber has a larger surface in comparison to its mass.

Also the embedding cement varies in amount and, possibly, in quality.

Reticular fibers are the first connective-tissue fibers to appear in development.

They are still abundant in fetuses and the newborn.

But as development proceeds, many take on collagenous characteristics.

Some, however, remain permanently at the 'reticular' stage.

Such fibers can be interpreted as immature, arrested collagenous fibers.

C. AMORPHOUS SUBSTANCES:

1. Ground Substance.

Connective-tissue fibers and cells are embedded in an amorphous *ground substance*.

When fresh, it is optically homogeneous and transparent.

Hence it can be seen only when placed in media with a different refractive index.

It is extracted by ordinary fixatives, so is not seen in ordinary sections.

It can, nevertheless, be preserved by the freezing-drying method.

Ground substance varies in consistency between a semifluid and a jelly.

Such variations occur with activity, aging and injury.

It stains poorly or not at all with ordinary dyes.

Toluidine blue stains ground substance (metachromatically) a purple tone.

This response indicates the carbohydrate nature of the ground substance.

Two such carbohydrate components (acid mucopolysaccharides) are known.

Their viscosity is markedly decreased by enzymes, such as *hyaluronidase*.

This permits substances to spread faster through the tissues.

It is possible that still other unidentified glycoproteins are represented.

Fibroblasts are concerned in the production of the amorphous ground substance.

They contain granules that are the precursors of this material.

2. Tissue Fluid.

This liquid is a transudate derived from the plasma within blood vessels.

It constitutes one-third of the total body fluid, and is important functionally.

Tissue fluid contains proteins, crystalloids, metabolic products and gases.

The fluid apparently can exist in part as a free fluid within tissue spaces.

The extent to which such spaces exist normally is not surely known.

When there is tissue injury or inflammation, a rapid accumulation is obvious.

It seems that much water is bound to the ground substance in a colloidal state.

Dissolved substances diffuse through such an aqueous phase of the colloid.

III. THE LOOSE CONNECTIVE TISSUES

This group of adult tissues is characterized by the loose arrangement of its fibers.

A distinction between loose and dense, however, is arbitrary in some instances.

The members of this group include: reticular tissue; areolar tissue; adipose tissue.

A. RETICULAR TISSUE:

1. Occurrence.

It constitutes some, at least, of the framework of lymphoid organs, bone marrow and liver, and of alimentary and respiratory mucous membranes.

In other regions reticular fibers are associated with fibroblasts, rather than with reticular cells.

Example: fat cells; smooth muscle; capillaries; stroma of various nonlymphoid, parenchymatous organs.

This association is not 'reticular tissue' in the strict sense of that term.

2. Cells.

The *reticular cells* are stellate elements, somewhat resembling mesenchyme.

They have considerable cytoplasm and a large, pale nucleus.

Thin cytoplasmic extensions appear to join those of other cells.

The question of true continuity, as opposed to intimate contact, is similar to that presented by mesenchyme.

Some of these elements are the so-called *primitive reticular cells*.

They resemble embryonic mesenchyme rather closely.

They are not phagocytic, and can differentiate into diverse cell-types.

Those specializing to produce reticular fibers are a kind of fibroblast.

Other, larger elements are *phagocytic reticular cells*.

They have differentiated further than the primitive (more mesenchymal) type.

In so doing they have lost some of their earlier developmental potentialities.

These cells are *fixed macrophages;* they are actively phagocytic.

A fixed macrophage may become a *free macrophage* under certain conditions.

For example, when bacteria or other particulate matter are numerous.

(Additional information concerning macrophages will be found on p. 40.)

3. Fibers.

Reticular fibers are arranged as a fine lattice-work of branching threads.

Most of the protoplasmic processes of reticular cells are related to the fibers.

The processes wrap about or extend along the fibers.

Some have thought that the fibers actually lie inside the cell membrane.

Lymphocytes and other cells occupy the interstices of the meshwork.

4. Appearance in Sections.

   Reticular tissue is largely inconspicuous because of crowding cells of other types.

       Also the fibers do not color with ordinary stains.

   In open regions (*e.g.*, lymph glands) it appears as a network of markedly stellate cells.

       Cell processes are long; those lying in the proper plane seem to join.

       Occasionally the cytoplasm contains phagocytosed particles.

   The arrangement resembles embryonic mesenchyme.

       But the nuclei are relatively smaller and the cytoplasm more abundant.

       (Neighboring 'adult' tissues aid in identifying reticular tissue.)

   The interspaces of typical reticular tissue are commonly clogged with lymphocytes.

   In ordinary preparations of most organs it is seen less clearly than any other type of adult tissue.

5. Functional Correlations.

   Reticular fibers make delicate connecting and supporting frameworks.

       Beneath epithelia they enter into the composition of basement membranes.

   Primitive reticular cells, at least, produce lymphocytes and macrophages.

   Phagocytic reticular cells play important roles as scavengers and as agents of defense against bacteria.

B. AREOLAR TISSUE:

   The word 'areolar' refers to the 'little areas,' or spaces, within this tissue.

   It is a loosely arranged, fibro-elastic connective tissue.

1. Occurrence.

   Areolar tissue is the most widespread of all the connective tissues.

       Gross dissection is largely a matter of freeing areolar tissue from other things.

       It is encountered in every microscopical section of the body.

   It fastens down the skin and other membranes, conducts vessels and nerves, and binds together muscles and their component parts.

   It supplies a general bedding-substance (*stroma*) in the interior of many organs.

   Wherever organs or parts enjoy some mobility, areolar tissue occurs as a stretchy, anchoring and embedding medium.

       It also serves as a packing material, filling in the unused spaces between organs.

2. Gross Appearance.

   To the naked eye areolar tissue looks whitish to translucent.

   It is soft, pliable, slippery, stretchy and easily displaceable.

   With a hand lens it appears cobwebby; the fibers interlace loosely.

3. Structure.

   Areolar tissue consists of a ground substance that contains various kinds of cells and two principal kinds of fibers.

   A. GROUND SUBSTANCE.

       This is an amorphous jelly, holding coagulable tissue fluid.

       It is often described as occurring in sheets (*lamellae*).

           But even its existence is difficult to demonstrate.

   B. CELLS.

       All of the cells previously described (pp. 39–41) may be encountered.

       The two commonest by far are *fibroblasts* and *macrophages*.

c. FIBERS.

Collagenous fibers are far in excess, from the standpoint of total bulk.

These compound bundles branch and recombine; their ends cannot be found.

Elastic fibers also show a continuous branching network, without free endings.

In typical areolar tissue they are relatively inconspicuous.

Reticular fibers are also represented to some degree.

They occur where areolar tissue borders upon other structures.

Noteworthy is their contribution to basement membranes (p. 34).

4. Appearance in Sections.

There is no apparent plan to the interweaving tissue arrangement.

Shrinkage markedly reduces the interspaces of the living tissue.

The total tissue of the slice has a 'hashed' appearance.

Collagenous fibers, cut in random planes, intermingle without order.

They stain satisfactorily with ordinary acid dyes.

Fibers cut more or less lengthwise appear as wavy bands.

If well fixed, their component fibrils show as fine, longitudinal threads.

Acid fixatives cause fibrils to swell; their discreteness is then lost.

Fibers, cut across, present angular areas of irregular sizes and shapes.

With good preservation the component fibrils show as dots.

If swollen by fixatives, the sectioned fiber appears as a homogeneous disk.

Elastic fibers are shown poorly or not at all by ordinary stains.

If identifiable they resemble dots or short rods, smaller than white fibers.

Cells are squeezed in between fibers; only their nuclei are prominent.

The cytoplasm is often deformed and not well seen.

Ground substance is not demonstrable in ordinary preparations.

5. Functional Correlations.

A. MECHANICAL.

Areolar tissue both provides support and permits some mobility.

Displacement and stretching are followed by a return to the original position.

Thus it holds various tissues, organs and organ components in place.

Yet it permits considerable play between such parts.

It provides pathways for vessels and nerves.

It acts as a packing material between parts of the body, both large and small.

B. TRANSPORT OF METABOLITES.

Nutrient substances, gases and wastes traverse the interval between capillaries and the sites where tissue metabolism takes place.

Tissue fluid is the carrier of these substances.

The ground substance does not present a barrier to this transport.

C. DEFENSE.

Ground substance seems to act as a barrier against the spread of bacteria.

Its success in defense is in inverse relation to the ability of certain bacteria to form an enzyme that tends to liquefy this jelly.

Macrophages, and outwandered neutrophils and monocytes, mobilize on occasion.

Noxious substances, formed locally, are neutralized and destroyed by them.

Foreign bodies, micro-organisms and degenerating cells are ingested.

D. REPAIR.

Fibroblasts repair injuries produced by mechanical insult or disease.

They may even erect barriers against disease and wall-off foreign bodies.

The process of repair (wound healing) repeats fiber-formation, as in embryos.

C. ADIPOSE TISSUE:

Areolar tissue, in general, contains scattering fat cells.

Regions dominated by aggregations of these cells are designated *adipose tissue*.

Since fat is a storage tissue, its amount varies with the nutritional state.

1. Occurrence.

Fat is abundant beneath the skin, where it constitutes the *panniculus adiposus*.

  (This insulating layer is not present in mammals with a hairy coat.)

Other collections occur: around the kidneys and suprarenals; in the mesenteries and
     mediastinum; in the grooves of the heart; in bone marrow; in the cervical,
     axillary and inguinal regions.

  The different distributions in men and women suggest a genic and endocrine in-
     fluence on fat deposition.

It is absent from the nervous system, lungs, eyelids and penis.

2. Development and Involution.

Small droplets of fat accumulate in certain cells of the fetus (and of the adult).

The identification of these storage cells is not beyond dispute.

  Favored interpretations are: mesenchyme; specific *lipoblasts* set aside for this
     purpose; and fibroblasts departing from their usual fate.

  Such cells tend to collect along small blood vessels, and especially capillaries.

     They enlarge, withdraw their processes, and round up.

Further growth of the droplets is followed by their coalescence.

  This produces a bloated cell, containing a large fat-globule.

     The cytoplasm is thereby reduced to a thin, encompassing layer.

     The nucleus is pressed to the periphery and flattened.

In time of need, stored fat is given up through a reversal of the storage-events.

  Fat leaves a cell (as it also enters) not as fat, but as soluble components.

  As the fat is lost, the cell reverts to its original type.

     Such a depleted cell is capable of again storing fat.

  After losing fat, some cells may remain rounded and contain watery vacuoles.

     This is a type of atrophy, and the cells are named *serous fat cells*.

Certain adipose pads of the body retain their fat tenaciously.

  These give up fat only after long starvation.

  Example: orbit; joints; palm; sole.

3. Structure.

Fat is an atypical connective tissue, specialized for particular purposes.

  It is the cells, rather than interstitial substance, that dominate the scene.

     They comprise most of the tissue-bulk and impart its characteristic features.

A *fat cell* is a large, clear spherule that measures up to 120 μ in diameter.

  The fresh cell is highly refractive, bright and glistening.

  The fat of primates has a yellow color, due to lipochrome pigments.

The cytoplasm is a thin shell, somewhat more abundant about the flattened nucleus.

  It contains an oil drop which exudes when the cell is punctured.

A fine network of reticular fibers envelops each cell.

Chemically fat consists of a mixture of glycerides and fatty acids.

  Fat is insoluble in water and cold alcohol.

  It is soluble in ether, chloroform, benzol and xylol.

Hence fat has usually been dissolved out of sections prepared for study.

A vacant cavity is then left within the cytoplasm.

However, fat can be rendered insoluble and retained.

Several staining agents color the fatty component of adipose tissue.

The dyes named Sudan III and IV stain frozen-sectioned tissue red.

If these dyes are fed to an animal, its fat (and milk) become pink.

Yet there are no simple, specific stains for neutral fat.

Osmic acid preserves and blackens both fat and myelin.

Sudan Black also stains various lipids.

Scattering fat cells, free from mutual pressure, retain a spherical shape.

Compact fat differs, in that its cells are mutually compressed and deformed.

Between the fat cells are compressed connective-tissue cells, collagenous and elastic fibers, and capillaries.

Closely packed fat cells make up *lobules*, separated by fibrous *septa*.

A lobule is a territory supplied during its development by a single arteriole.

Throughout life it retains a fairly rich blood supply.

There is no intrinsic nerve supply, although nerves may be found in the tissue.

4. Brown Fat.

A peculiar type of fat occurs in certain locations in various mammals.

Such a fatty mass is light brown in color and has a glandular appearance.

The cells retain a polyhedral shape; the nucleus and cytoplasm are fairly typical.

Fat occurs as numerous droplets, distributed throughout the cytoplasm.

The fat-content is not readily affected by changes in the nutritional state.

It is, however, depleted rapidly after the hypophysis or suprarenals are removed.

This tissue is physiologically more active in certain regards than is ordinary fat.

It is distinctly lobulated and highly vascular.

Identifiable in the human fetus, brown fat is not distinguishable in the adult.

5. Appearance in Sections.

Ordinary sections consist largely of vacant spaces that vary in size.

Such spaces are bounded by exceedingly thin rims of cytoplasm.

When the nucleus happens to be included, it also is flattened and thin.

Scattered or loosely arranged cells have circular outlines.

Sections through the nucleus give a 'signet-ring' appearance.

Compact fat shows crowded cells, pressed into polygons (many are hexagons).

The nucleus is also distorted by the mutual pressure.

The tissue between cells is compressed beyond easy recognition.

Compact fat occurs in lobules, bounded by fibrous septa.

Little or no areolar tissue is seen within the lobule.

6. Functional Correlations.

Adipose tissue stores reserve nutritive material in the form of neutral fat.

But there is evidence of a fairly rapid turnover instead of a static deposit.

It forms soft elastic pads between organs and parts; some pads act as shock absorbers

It serves as a buffer tissue, as in bursae.

Fat is an efficient insulator against cold; that is, body heat is retained.

This is important to aquatic mammals, as is also its buoyancy.

It is also important to man, since an insulating hair-coat is lacking.

It has an esthetic value by padding the hollows of the body.

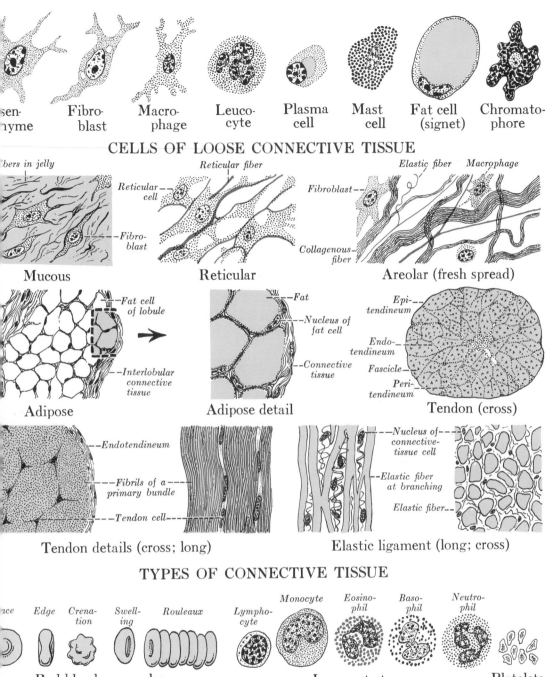

| sen-hyme | Fibro-blast | Macro-phage | Leuco-cyte | Plasma cell | Mast cell | Fat cell (signet) | Chromato-phore |

CELLS OF LOOSE CONNECTIVE TISSUE

bers in jelly

Reticular fiber

Elastic fiber   Macrophage

Reticular cell

Fibroblast

Fibro-blast

Collagenous fiber

Mucous   **Reticular**   **Areolar (fresh spread)**

Fat cell of lobule

Fat

Nucleus of fat cell

Epi-tendineum

Endo-tendineum

Connective tissue

Fascicle

Interlobular connective tissue

Peri-tendineum

Adipose   **Adipose detail**   **Tendon (cross)**

Endotendineum

Nucleus of connective-tissue cell

Fibrils of a primary bundle

Elastic fiber at branching

Tendon cell

Elastic fiber

Tendon details (cross; long)   **Elastic ligament (long; cross)**

TYPES OF CONNECTIVE TISSUE

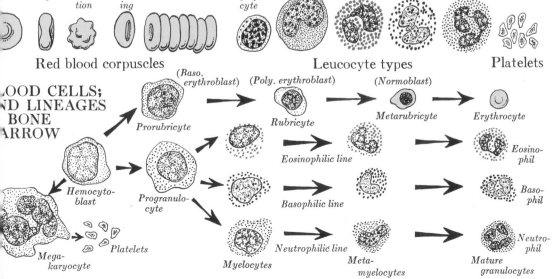

| ace | Edge | Crena-tion | Swell-ing | Rouleaux | Lympho-cyte | Monocyte | Eosino-phil | Baso-phil | Neutro-phil |

Red blood corpuscles   **Leucocyte types**   **Platelets**

OOD CELLS;
ND LINEAGES
BONE
ARROW

(Baso. erythroblast)   (Poly. erythroblast)   (Normoblast)

Prorubricyte

Rubricyte

Metarubricyte

Erythrocyte

Hemocyto-blast

Progranulo-cyte

Eosinophilic line

Eosino-phil

Basophilic line

Baso-phil

Mega-karyocyte

Platelets

Neutrophilic line

Myelocytes

Meta-myelocytes

Mature granulocytes

Neutro-phil

. REGENERATIVE ABILITY:
> The loose connective tissues, as a group, repair losses well.
> In reticular and areolar tissue the events repeat histogenesis in the fetus.
>> Reserve mesenchymal cells proliferate and differentiate into fibroblastic types.
>> First a mucinous ground substance is deposited.
>> In it new fibers are laid down, reticular and collagenous fibers forming promptly.
>>> Elastic fibers reappear slowly, and often incompletely.
> Fat cells do not divide; new fat cells differentiate from reserve mesenchymal elements.
> Other mesenchymal cells produce the fibrous tissue that embeds fat cells.

IV. THE DENSE CONNECTIVE TISSUES

hese tissues have an abundance of compactly arranged fibers.
> Cells are proportionately fewer than in loose connective tissue.
> Space available for ground substance and tissue fluid is extremely limited.
his group can be subdivided, on the basis of fiber direction, into two main categories.

. INTERLACED ARRANGEMENTS:
> The fibers are arranged so as to withstand tensions exerted from different directions.
>> Sometimes this category is designated as 'irregularly arranged' tissue.

1. Tissues Predominantly Collagenous.
> Most *fascias* are interwoven sheets with irregularly arranged bundles.
>> Example: deep fascias; (also dermis of the skin).
> Fibrous *capsules* of organs (spleen; testis), *sheaths* (periosteum of bone; epimysium of muscles; dura mater); *septa* and *trabeculae* (*i.e.*, partitions and beams within organs) are other examples of interlacing, dense tissue.
> All of these, and especially the most compact types, are notably whitish in color.

2. Tissues Predominantly Elastic.
> Networks of elastic fibers exist as tubular sheets within blood vessels.
> In the largest arteries elastic tissue consolidates into concentric, cylindrical, homogeneous *elastic membranes*.
> These are interrupted by irregular openings.

. PARALLEL ARRANGEMENTS:
> This category is sometimes designated as 'regularly arranged' tissue.
>> The fibers are oriented so as best to withstand tension exerted in one direction.

1. Tissues Predominantly Collagenous.
> The popular example is *tendon*, and this will be described as a type-form.
> The great majority of *ligaments* are similarly composed and constructed.
>> Their organization, however, is not quite so regular as that of tendon.
> *Aponeuroses* are organized like tendon, but are broad and flat.
>> Some show layering, with a different 'grain' in adjacent layers.
> A. STRUCTURE.
>> The unit of tendon structure is the so-called *primary tendon bundle*.
>>> This is merely a very large collagenous fiber, clasped by fibroblasts.
>>>> The designation of the fiber as a 'bundle' refers to its compound nature.
>>>> That is, the primary bundle is a collection of still finer fibrils.

Primary bundles run parallel, yet slightly wavy, courses.

Slanting anastomoses occur at acute angles, as in ordinary fibers.

Fine elastic networks have been described between bundles.

Tendon cells (fibroblasts) are located between primary bundles.

They are the only type of cell present here.

Their cytoplasm is compressed into thin, radiating wings.

These pass between the adjacent primary bundles.

Hence each *lamellar cell* is in a clasping relation to several bundles.

A variable number of primary bundles group together as a tendon *fascicle*.

This compound unit is also known as a *secondary tendon bundle*.

Fascicles are crowded and comprise most of the tendon substance.

Nevertheless, they are separated by some loose connective tissue.

B. TENDON AS AN ORGAN.

Tendons are rope-like cables that attach muscles to bones.

A total tendon is an entity that qualifies as a simple organ.

As such it possesses a distinctive plan of organization.

The entire tendon is composed of a variable number of *fascicles*.

The total number in any instance depends on the size of the tendon.

The whole tendon is ensheathed by a moderately compact fibrous tissue.

This external covering is given the name of *epitendineum*.

In larger tendons there are also radial plates of loose connective tissue.

Such coarse radial septa constitute the so-called *peritendineum*.

The individual fascicles are ensheathed, and thus separated from each other, b
loose connective tissue.

This ensheathing tissue, as a whole, is named the *endotendineum*.

Vessels and nerves course in the epi-, peri- and endotendineum.

They are sparse and never invade the fascicles.

Hence repair of injuries is notably slow.

C. APPEARANCE IN SECTIONS.

1. LONGITUDINAL SECTION.

Each tendon fiber (primary bundle) is a wavy band.

Its appearance is either homogeneous or longitudinally fibrillate.

This depends on whether or not the fixative preserved fibrils faithfully

Tendon cells occur in rows, squeezed in between the fibers.

Only their elongate nuclei usually show well.

Nothing else is seen between the tendon fibers.

Endotendineal septa show at intervals as strips of looser tissue.

2. TRANSVERSE SECTION.

A fiber takes the form of a prominent, angular area.

Tendon cells are stellate, with circular (or distorted) nuclei.

The cells are usually greatly shrunken and their processes short.

Often crack-like spaces (especially about cells) separate fibers.

In other instances fibers, swollen by technical procedures, tend to merge

Tendon fibrils should ideally show as tiny dots.

Commonly, however, the appearance is homogeneous and glassy.

This is due to swelling, produced by technical procedures.

On focusing, the fiber-areas usually shift position or rotate somewhat.

This is caused by focusing up and down wavy fibers, seen in end view.

Loose tissue of the endotendineum does not penetrate into a fascicle.

Tendon fibers and cells are the only things seen within a fascicle.

D. FUNCTIONAL CORRELATIONS.

This group of dense tissues provides tough, inelastic sheets and cords.

Each is constructed so as to satisfy the mechanical requirements imposed.

A tendon is flexible, yet highly resistant to a pulling force.

It has greater tensile strength than a bone of equal size.

A pencil-size tendon can sustain a weight of one-half ton before breaking.

Tendons are indirectly concerned with sensory reception (p. 303).

2. Tissues Predominantly Elastic.

These are much less numerous than the dense, collagenous type.

Examples: ligamenta flava (of the vertebrae); suspensory ligament of the penis; stylo-hyoid ligament; true vocal cords; ligamentum nuchae (of quadrupeds).

They are distinctly yellow in color because of their elastic-fiber content.

A. STRUCTURE.

In an elastic ligament the elastic fibers are coarse (up to 5 μ).

They run parallel courses, but branch frequently at acute angles.

Individual fibers are surrounded by a network of reticular fibers.

The elastic ligament is not organized as fully as is tendon.

Nevertheless, the fibers may tend to group into clusters.

Interspaces are occupied by scanty fibroblasts and fine white fibers.

Vessels and nerve fibers are relatively sparse.

B. APPEARANCE IN SECTIONS.

1. LONGITUDINAL SECTION.

An elastic ligament shows as loosely-spaced, often coarse bands.

These fibers branch and anastomose at short intervals.

Such connecting fibers are set at acute angles.

Hence the general fiber direction is nearly parallel.

A fiber is homogeneous and stains poorly in ordinary preparations.

Delicate connective tissue occupies the fiber interspaces.

2. TRANSVERSE SECTION.

Fibers are homogeneous areas, often arranged in groups.

The outline of a fiber is angular to rounded.

Delicate areolar tissue surrounds these groups (fascicles).

It also continues into a fascicle and surrounds individual fibers.

C. FUNCTIONAL CORRELATIONS.

Elastic ligaments maintain a state of tension when put on the stretch.

They yield to a pulling force, but recover when the tension ceases.

C. REGENERATIVE ABILITY:

If a tendon or ligament is torn or severed, it can repair the injury.

Fibroblasts and vessels grow in, and new collagenous fibers are laid down.

At first the new fibers are fine; subsequently they gradually coarsen.

The original fibrous tissue, at the cut ends, plays little or no role in repair.

Chapter VI. THE BLOOD AND LYMPH

I. THE BLOOD

Blood is a specialized and somewhat atypical connective tissue.

The ground substance is a fluid, the *blood plasma*.

Fibers make their appearance in the plasma as *fibrin*, but only when blood clots.

Previously they existed, potentially, in solution in the plasma.

Cells of two main types (red and white) are prominent constituents.

Red cells are so colored because they contain the respiratory pigment, *hemoglobin*.

Because of the fluid plasma, blood cells have no fixed positions.

Other visible particles suspended in the plasma are *blood platelets* and *chylomicrons*.

Blood constitutes about 7 per cent of body weight; a 150-pound man contains 5 quarts.

A. ERYTHROCYTES:

These elements are also called *erythroplastids* and *red blood corpuscles*.

In a strict sense the word 'erythrocyte' is inappropriate for mammals.

This is because the adult corpuscle lacks a nucleus and so is not a complete cell.

All vertebrates, other than mammals, have nucleated red cells, elliptical in shape.

In mammals the nucleus has been discarded; this enhances respiratory efficiency.

1. Shape.

In all mammals the shape is that of a biconcave disk.

This shape favors flexibility and the absorbing and releasing of gases quickly.

The outline is circular (except in the camel family, where it is oval).

Both surfaces of the disk are depressed, like large dimples, centrally.

Hence in edge view the outline is like that of a plump dumbbell.

Variant shapes occur pathologically, such as 'sickle cells.'

2. Size.

In man the living, undehydrated corpuscle is 8.5 μ in diameter.

In dry smears it measures 7.6 μ, and in sectioned tissues usually about 5.0 μ.

Size variations occur pathologically, both larger and smaller.

Most mammals have slightly smaller corpuscles than man.

The extremes are 9.4 μ (elephant) and 2.5 μ (musk deer).

(The largest erythrocytes in vertebrates occur in salamanders; up to 80 μ).

The total surface area available for respiratory exchanges is impressive.

For human corpuscles this amounts to 4200 square yards.

This area is nearly the size of a football field.

3. Number.

All statistics of frequencies refer to a volume of 1 cu. mm. of blood.

In human males the red-corpuscle count is 5,500,000; in females, 5,000,000.

The total number of corpuscles in an average-sized human is 25 million millions.

Placed in single file they could encircle the earth.

A marked decrease in number is encountered in pernicious anemia.

Increases in number follow chronic exposure to high altitudes or to carbon monoxide.

4. Color.

A single fresh corpuscle is pale greenish-yellow; massed corpuscles are red.

In conventionally stained blood smears the corpuscles take a pinkish tint.

5. Structure.

There is a peripheral membrane, but it is extremely thin (0.02μ).

It is a lipid-protein complex, making an elastic and semipermeable barrier.

The internal cytoplasm is apparently a homogeneous colloidal sol.

The nucleus and cytoplasmic organoids were lost in the later stages of development.

About 1 per cent of the corpuscles encountered are not quite mature.

These *reticulocytes* show a network-artefact stainable with brilliant cresyl blue.

6. Physical Properties.

A red corpuscle is soft, flexible and elastic.

It is frequently distorted momentarily when squeezing through capillaries.

Yet it is relatively firm, containing 40 per cent solids; (muscles, 20 per cent).

Rouleaux are columns of corpuscles, stacked like a pile of coins.

These occur spontaneously in a stagnant circulation or in drawn blood.

The adherence is apparently a surface tension effect.

It can be imitated by greased, weighted corks.

If plasma concentrates by evaporation, *crenation* of the corpuscle occurs.

This is a shriveling which produces a scalloped or prickly contour.

Water passes outward into the more concentrated (hypertonic) plasma.

If the plasma is diluted, the corpuscle imbibes fluid and swells.

Cup shapes become progressively fatter as the hypotonicity increases.

At a certain stage the hemoglobin leaves the corpuscle.

This outward passage of hemoglobin is called *hemolysis* or *laking*.

The pale corpuscle is then called a *blood shadow* or *blood ghost*.

Hemolysis is also accomplished by other agents that injure the plasma membrane.

Example: lipid solvents, such as ether; bile salts; snake venom.

Agglutination (*i.e.*, clumping) of corpuscles is induced by various agents.

Example: acid salt-solutions; glucose solution; agglutinins.

Agglutinins, present in the plasma, furnish the basis for the four blood types.

These are responsible for specific compatibilities and incompatibilities.

7. Chemical Composition.

The coloring pigment of red corpuscles is *hemoglobin*.

Hemoglobin is a complex protein, containing iron.

It crystallizes in rhombic plates.

These have characteristic shapes in different mammalian species.

Some lower animals use different metals in their respiratory pigments.

Example: molluscs, copper; tunicates, vanadium.

Hemoglobin hydrolyzes into *hematin* and *globin*.

The chloride of hematin is called *hemin*.

It crystallizes in brown rhombic plates, used as a test for blood.
This test, however, does not distinguish human from animal blood.
Hemoglobin can take up and bind 1.3 times its weight of oxygen.
This compound, *oxyhemoglobin*, is easily reduced by the tissues.
The amount carried is decreased in secondary anemias.

8. Life Span and Disposal.

The life span of the human red corpuscle is approximately 120 days.
This means that some 2,500,000 new corpuscles must enter the blood stream every
second, while an equal number is lost.
The total picture of normal red-corpuscle destruction is not known.
Damage is incurred mechanically by buffeting within the blood stream.
(During its life cycle a corpuscle travels about 700 miles.)
The plasma membrane is further damaged by constant O_2 and CO_2 transfers.
Both buffeting and tension changes facilitate rupture of the membrane.
It is known that whole corpuscles and fragments are engulfed by macrophages.
This occurs where there is reticulo-endothelium (liver; spleen; bone marrow).
The macrophages break up the hemoglobin into simpler products.
Bilirubin is excreted with the bile.
Iron is retained and used again in newly-developed red corpuscles.

9. Appearance in Sections.

The corpuscles are acidophilic disks of uniform size.
They are usually encountered within the blood vessels of tissues.
Ordinarily corpuscles do not occur free in the tissue spaces.
Their presence there may be due to rough handling in tissue-preparation.
Well preserved corpuscles are sharply defined disks (or often cups) in shape.
With inferior preservation there is agglutination, marked by the loss of clearly
defined corpuscular outlines.

10. Functional Correlations.

Blood is a fluid carrying a respiratory pigment.
The primary function of blood is to make possible tissue-respiration.
Red corpuscles carry oxygen from the lungs to the tissues.
In the lungs their hemoglobin combines with oxygen to form *oxyhemoglobin*.
In the tissues oxygen is given up and the oxyhemoglobin is reduced.
On the return journey they transport carbon dioxide from the tissues to the lungs.
RH antigen resides in the membrane of the red corpuscle.

B. LEUCOCYTES:

The white cells are true cells with ameboid ability; their general name is *leucocyte*.
They are much alike in all the vertebrate groups.

1. Classification.

There are two main groups, each with subgroups.
A. NONGRANULAR LEUCOCYTES.
1. Lymphocytes (25% ±).
2. Monocytes (5% ±).

B. GRANULAR LEUCOCYTES.

    1. Eosinophils (3% ±).

    2. Basophils (0.5% ±).

    3. Neutrophils (65% ±).

Nongranular leucocytes have a few inconstant, nonspecific granules in the cytoplasm.

    All cytoplasmic 'granules,' in life, are actually semifluid droplets.

    The nucleus is spherical to kidney shape.

Granular leucocytes have abundant, specific granules in the cytoplasm.

    The nucleus ranges from two lobes to a series of connected lumps.

2. Number.

    The average normal limits are 5000 and 9000 per cu. mm. in adults.

        The ratio of white cells to red corpuscles is about 1:700.

    The count in children is higher than in adults.

        At birth the number is approximately 16,000 per cu. mm.

    Marked variations from the normal number occur pathologically.

        An increase is *leucocytosis;* more than 12,000 indicates disease.

            This increase is out of proportion for one or more types.

                Example: lymphocytes increase in whooping cough; monocytes, in tuberculosis; neutrophils, in pus-forming infections; eosinophils, in allergies and parasitic infestations; basophils, in chicken pox.

        A decrease below 5000 is called *leucopoenia.*

            Example: in typhoid fever.

3. Structural Characteristics.

    Leucocytes are typical cells, somewhat resembling amebae.

    In fixed preparations their pseudopodia are withdrawn and do not show.

    Centrioles, mitochondria and Golgi apparatus are all demonstrable.

        Nongranular leucocytes also possess a nucleolus.

        None of these cell components show in stained smears.

    In smear preparations, cells flatten and appear larger than in life.

        Special stains, applied to smears, give the best blood picture.

        These stains contain eosin (acid), and methylene blue (basic).

            The methylene blue is in part oxidized into the azures (basic).

            Besides these three staining components there is an eosin-azure-methylene blue complex which is neutral.

A. LYMPHOCYTES.

    The commonest type in normal blood is known as the *small lymphocyte.*

    Most of them are slightly larger than a red blood corpuscle.

    The cell has a relatively large nucleus, enclosed by a thin layer of cytoplasm.

    The nucleus is nearly spherical; its slight indentation may not be noticed.

        It is very dense and dark because of heavy chromatin masses.

    The cytoplasm is basophilic and stains a clear blue color.

        It occasionally contains a few nonspecific, azurophil granules.

    Some lymphocytes are nearly twice the size of the ordinary small type.

        These are sometimes called *medium-sized lymphocytes.*

        They have the same structural characteristic as the small ones.

            But there is more cytoplasm in relation to the size of the nucleus.

        They are relatively scarce and are regarded merely as older cells.

    So-called *large lymphocytes* reside in the lymph nodes.

The largest are three times the size of the small type.

They are primitive, proliferative cells that give rise to lymphocytes.

Only under pathological conditions do they enter the blood stream.

B. MONOCYTES.

These cells have also been known as *large mononuclears* and *transitionals*.

They are larger (twice plus) than a red corpuscle.

The nucleus is ovoid-, kidney-, or U-shaped; these are age-stages.

It tends to be eccentric in position.

The chromatin is distributed in a more delicate network than in lymphocytes.

Hence the nucleus takes a paler stain.

The cytoplasm comprises more than half of the cell.

It may contain countless dust-like azurophil granules.

It stains a grayer or muddier blue than that of lymphocytes.

Rarely, intermediates between monocytes and medium-sized lymphocytes occur.

In this instance positive assignment to one group or the other is difficult.

C. EOSINOPHILS.

The diameter is nearly twice that of a red corpuscle.

This size-ratio is also true of basophils and neutrophils.

The nucleus is usually bilobed, with a connecting isthmus.

Its chromatin is fairly dense; the nucleus stains moderately well.

The cytoplasm constitutes considerably more than half of the bulk of the cell.

It is packed with coarse, round granules, uniform in size.

They stain electively with acid dyes (red to orange with blood-stains).

D. BASOPHILS.

The nucleus is usually elongate and somewhat bent.

It is partially constricted into two or three lobes.

The chromatin network is more loosely arranged than in eosinophils.

Hence the nucleus is relatively pale-staining.

The nucleus constitutes half of the cell bulk, or two-thirds its diameter.

The cytoplasmic granules are round, coarse and variable in number.

Some characteristically overlie the nucleus and tend to obscure it.

They are water-soluble, and so do not show in routinely stained sections.

They stain electively with basic dyes (dark blue to purple with blood-stains).

This cell-type is wholly distinct from the mast cell of connective tissue.

E. NEUTROPHILS.

The nucleus is markedly lobate (usually three, but as many as five, parts).

These masses are connected by thin chromatic threads into a distorted shape.

The degree of lobation increases progressively as the cells age.

The chromatin is rather compact and quite dark staining.

The abundant cytoplasm is closely packed with fine, inconspicuous granules.

These stain with neutral dyes, but give up the dye readily.

With blood-stains the color is lilac to lilac-pink.

The cytoplasm constitutes more than half the bulk of the cell.

4. Life Span and Disposal.

The total length of life is hard to determine because these cells leave the capillaries and spend their functional life in the tissue spaces.

The period spent in the blood stream is apparently brief.

Example: lymphocytes, probably only a few hours; granulocytes, longer.

The viable period after leaving the blood stream is uncertain.

Example: lymphocytes transplanted from lymph node, one week;
granulocytes cultured in artificial media, 3–12 days.

Probably macrophages (reticulo-endothelium) of the liver and spleen are the most active agents in removing aging leucocytes from the circulation.

Other leucocytes, outwandered into the connective tissues, disintegrate there.

Example: eosinophils congregate in the walls of the respiratory and gastro-intestinal tracts; neutrophils migrate into inflamed tissue, play a defensive role there and soon die.

Many lymphocytes enter the epithelia of the alimentary and respiratory tracts.

Their fate is presumably degeneration and death.

5. Appearance in Sections.

Leucocytes show well-stained nuclei; the cytoplasm rounds up about the nucleus.

The differential staining of cytoplasmic granules is inferior and incomplete.

Stained sections cannot compete with smears in this regard.

6. Functional Correlations.

Little beyond the obvious activities of leucocytes is known.

Information is based on experimental and pathological material.

Leucocytes appear to be largely inactive while in the blood stream.

They perform most of their functions outside the vessels in connective tissue.

A. AMEBOID MOVEMENT.

This is a crawling process on a substrate; swimming does not occur.

There is an active front end, producing pseudopodia.

At the temporary rear end there is a passive, trailing tail.

Neutrophils are the most active (up to 33 μ per minute).

Monocytes are only moderately active, while basophils are sluggish.

Lymphocytes are often immobile, but they can become remarkably active.

B. MIGRATORY ACTIVITIES.

There is a constant migration of leucocytes out of blood capillaries.

Some of these cells may return into the blood and lymph streams.

Emigration is greatly increased during periods of inflammation.

It is a specific response to chemotactic stimulation.

A leucocyte first attaches to the endothelium of a capillary.

It next sends a pseudopod through the wall and then slips through.

First neutrophils, and later monocytes, arrive at the site of irritation.

Eosinophils flock to the digestive and respiratory tracts in allergies.

Lymphocytes accumulate in the tissues at sites of chronic inflammation.

C. PHAGOCYTOSIS.

This is the ability to ingest foreign particles, bacteria, cells, etc.

Neutrophils are especially concerned with ingesting small, discrete particles.

Example: carbon particles; bacteria.

They are most active when outside the blood stream.

Some experiments indicate that basophils resemble neutrophils in these regards.

Eosinophils and lymphocytes are not known surely to be phagocytic.

Monocytes greedily engulf particulate matter, and coarse masses also.

They are the prime scavengers of cells and tissue debris.

Their activities are far greater outside of vessels than within them.

D. OTHER PROPERTIES.

All leucocytes increase in number in response to specific stimuli (p. 55).

Some information exists concerning the presence of enzymes in leucocytes.
Oxidases occur in granular leucocytes and monocytes.
Neutrophils contain phosphatases and liberate proteolytic enzymes.
Defense activities include phagocytosis, proteolysis, antibody formation, etc.
Neutrophils provide the first line of defense against invading organisms.
Some investigators believe that lymphocytes are a source of antibodies.

C. BLOOD PLATELETS:

1. Occurrence.

Blood platelets are protoplasmic disks that are characteristic of mammalian blood.
Lower vertebrates lack them, but have spindle cells named *thrombocytes*.
These seem to be generally similar in function.

2. Size and Shape.

Platelets are tiny disks, 2 to 3 μ in diameter.
Viewed on the flat, the shape is round to oval (often stellate when fixed).
In edge view the shape is like a spindle or rod.

3. Number.

The normal range is 200,000 to 350,000 per cu. mm.
Platelets are difficult to count accurately, partly because of their fragility.
Also they tend to clump together and stick to anything they touch.

4. Structure.

Blood stains demonstrate two regions in the platelet.
Centrally the protoplasm is granular and deeply basophilic.
Peripherally the protoplasm is pale and homogeneous.

5. Origin and Fate.

The dominant belief is that platelets arise as detached tips of processes extending from
the cytoplasm of the giant cells of bone marrow.
Their life span is probably not longer than a few days.
Their disposal is presumably by the phagocytic activity of macrophages in the liver,
spleen and bone marrow.

6. Appearance in Sections.

Occasionally platelets show within vessels, when preserved and stained properly.
They are tiny protoplasmic fragments with a basophilic staining preference.

7. Functional Correlations.

Platelets of circulating blood agglutinate and adhere to injured regions of vessels.
Such a *white thrombus* plugs leaks and covers injured spots.
Agglutinated platelets are associated with clotting, both inside and outside of vessels.
A plasma protein (*fibrinogen*), under enzymic influence, becomes threads of *fibrin*.
This meshwork entangles the blood cells and a jelly-like *clot* results.
Platelets seem to aid, at least, in the formation of the needed enzyme (*thrombin*).
A fibrin clot soon becomes smaller, firmer and stronger.
Knots of platelets throughout the mesh cause fibrin threads to twist and bend.
This clot-retraction is an important factor in stopping bleeding.

D. BLOOD PLASMA:

1. Composition.

Plasma constitutes 55 per cent of blood; cellular elements total 45 per cent.

Many substances are contained in the slightly alkaline plasma.

These include: gases; proteins; carbohydrates; lipids; inorganic salts; organic substances, such as enzymes and hormones.

Certain suspended particles are demonstrable by phase- or dark-field microscopy.

Chylomicrons are minute fat globules, more numerous after a fatty meal.

Hemoconia, or blood dust, probably represent cellular debris.

2. Appearance in Sections.

Acidophilic fibrin-threads and plasma show at times within vessels.

The fibrin occurs as delicate to coarse interlacing filaments.

The plasma is commonly a finely granular, but otherwise structureless, mass.

3. Functional Correlations.

Plasma activities are related to respiration, coagulation, temperature regulation, buffer mechanisms and fluid balance.

Plasma also transports hormones, foodstuffs, and excretory wastes.

Fibrin forms and blood coagulates when the circulation ceases or when blood escapes.

Plasma, defibrinated by clotting or whipping, is known as blood *serum.*

It is a clear, yellowish fluid, no longer capable of clotting.

This is because the fibrin and cellular elements are largely entangled in the clot.

II. THE LYMPH

Lymph is a fluid, collected from the tissues and returned to the blood stream.

Its origin is from the fluid that occupies the tissue spaces of the body.

The *tissue fluid* is material that has escaped through the wall of blood capillaries.

But the endothelium is a semipermeable membrane; hence the larger molecules of plasma, such as colloids and fats, are mostly retained by capillaries.

The dialyzed fluid loses nutrients and oxygen to the extravascular tissues.

The tissue fluid also acquires the waste end-products from tissue metabolism.

Hence it becomes quite different from the original dialysate.

Some tissue fluid is absorbed by blood capillaries (those tributary to venules).

The remainder is taken up by lymphatic capillaries, whereupon it is called *lymph.*

Lymphatic endothelium allows colloids to enter; most blood endothelium does not.

Lymph from the small intestine (*chyle*) is milky because of fat globules taken up.

Lymph from the liver is unusually rich in proteins.

The smallest lymphatic vessels carry a practically noncellular lymph.

On reaching the lymph nodes, cells (mostly small lymphocytes) are added.

Lymph coagulates, but the process advances slowly and the clot is soft.

Chapter VII. THE DEVELOPMENT OF BLOOD

Blood cells are short-lived, and are constantly being destroyed and replaced.

The process by which blood cells are formed is named *hemopoiesis.*

In the embryo and fetus total blood is formed successively in: the yolk sac; mesenchyme and blood vessels; liver; spleen, thymus and lymph nodes; bone marrow.

In the late fetus, and thereafter, blood is formed in the marrow and lymphoid tissues.

Under certain pathological conditions the liver, spleen and lymph nodes can take on functions like those of the bone marrow.

A. RIVAL INTERPRETATIONS:

Hemopoiesis is the area of greatest controversy in the entire field of histology.

Maximow and Sabin are the major proponents of rival, contesting schools of thought.

The chief points of disagreement involve the following:

    1. The identification of the mother cell(s) of the several lines of differentiation.

        Along with divergent opinions concerning cell characteristics and relationships go differences in terminology.

        Basically involved is the concept of all blood cells belonging to a single family-group versus the existence of separate, distinct families of cells.

    2. The development of all blood cells outside the vascular channels versus the development of leucocytes outside such channels and erythrocytes inside.

The theories of hemopoiesis can be summarized as follows:

    1. Unitarian (or monophyletic) theory.

        It derives all blood elements from a common mother cell.

    2. Dualistic (or diphyletic) theory.

        It derives nongranular leucocytes from one stem cell and granular leucocytes and erythrocytes from a different stem cell.

        (Some have used this term to designate a concept that assigns red cells to one developmental line and white cells to another line.)

    3. Trialistic (tri- or polyphyletic) theory.

        It derives blood cells from three distinct stem cells.

            These give rise to: lymphocytes; monocytes; granulocytes and erythrocytes.

Probably the best total evidence favors the unitarian theory.

Also this theory enjoys the support of a majority of hematologists.

Hence it will be simplest to base the following account on this interpretation.

It should be emphasized, however, that the controversies of the ultimate origins do not affect factual descriptions covering the structural features of the developmental stages of blood cells.

From this standpoint the disputed aspects of hemopoiesis are largely academic.

B. HEMOPOIETIC TISSUES:

In normal, postnatal life blood formation is less widespread than in the fetus.

After birth it is restricted to the lymphoid organs and red bone marrow.

These two different sources are implied when the terms *lymphoid* (for nongranular
leucocytes) and *myeloid* (for granulocytes and red corpuscles) are used.
But this convenient distinction is not realized at all times.
In early fetal stages such separate specialized sites do not exist.
In adults the separateness may again be lost under abnormal conditions.
This occurs in *myeloid metaplasia*, in which lymphoid organs imitate red marrow.

1. Lymphoid Hemopoietic Tissue.
Chief among the lymphoid organs engaged in hemopoiesis are the spleen and lymph
nodes.
Less important are the thymus, tonsils and more scattered nodular masses.
The lymphoid organs are the source of lymphocytes and monocytes.
Only a small number (about 5 per cent) of such cells arise in bone marrow.
For this reason, these derivatives of lymphoid organs are called *lymphoid elements*.

2. Myeloid Hemopoietic Tissue.
In the fetus and child, *red bone marrow* occurs in all the bones.
At about the time of puberty it begins to be replaced in some regions by fat.
This fatty marrow is then termed *yellow bone marrow*.
In adults red marrow is restricted to the spongy bone of: vertebrae; ribs; sternum;
cranium; clavicles; scapulae; pelvis.
There is almost none in the bones of the limbs.
The total marrow (red and white) accounts for about 5 per cent of body weight.
This is astonishing, since it weighs twice as much as the liver.
Yellow bone marrow typically is mostly fat; it contains some crowded marrow tissue.
Actually all intergrades between yellow and red marrow can occur.
Normally there is no evidence of hemopoietic activity in ordinary yellow marrow.
Nevertheless, this power is dormant and can be revived under stress.
Example: red marrow replaces yellow marrow after hemorrhages or in ane-
mias.
Red bone marrow consists of a supporting framework, vascular channels and free cells.
The framework is a typical reticulum, with reticular cells stretched along it.
Ordinary blood vessels connect with sinusoids lined with active macrophages.
This lining is a type of so-called *reticulo-endothelium*.
The distinctive marrow tissue is a pulpy mass of cells, both immature and mature.
These marrow cells collectively are called *myeloid elements*.
Interspersed are usually a varying number of fat cells.
The chief, characteristic components of myeloid tissue are the several stages in the
development of red blood corpuscles and granular leucocytes.
Giant cells (megakaryocytes) and blood platelets are further components.

C. STEM CELL:
It is plain that all blood cells trace their genealogy from mesenchymal progenitors.
It is equally clear that, sooner or later, various descendants acquire differences.
These specializations are not only structural but also in potentialities.
The main controversy hinges on whether the formative cells seen in lymphoid and myeloid
tissue are identical and interchangeable, or whether they are different in structure
and capacities.
Maximow, the chief advocate of the unitarian view, believed that the stem cell is a multi-
potent element that can be called a *hemocytoblast*.

It is present both in the lymphoid organs and in the bone marrow.

It is a large ameboid cell, identical with a medium-sized and large lymphocyte.

The cytoplasm is fairly abundant and is noticeably basophilic.

The nucleus is large, open-structured and contains one or more irregularly-shaped nucleoli; it is a relatively primitive (*i.e.*, undifferentiated) nucleus.

The hemocytoblast, in turn, is derived from a primitive reticular cell which is essentially a fixed, undifferentiated, nonphagocytic mesenchymal cell.

Maximow maintained that the small lymphocytes in blood-forming organs can grow larger.

This means that the small lymphocyte is potentially a hemocytoblast.

In its usual state it can be considered an inactive form of hemocytoblast.

D. DEVELOPMENT OF LYMPHOID ELEMENTS:

Nongranular leucocytes arise in lymphoid tissues and to a limited extent in red marrow.

Lymphocytes arise in the spleen and lymph nodes.

Monocytes differentiate chiefly in the venous sinuses of the spleen.

Others develop in the sinusoids of the liver and bone marrow.

According to Maximow, nongranular leucocytes differentiate from mitotic *hemocytoblasts*.

The intermediate stages of differentiation are not particularly distinctive.

Neither the nucleus nor cytoplasm undergoes marked changes.

The daughter *lymphocytes* become the ordinary small-sized ones encountered so abundantly.

The chromatin network is denser than in the mother cell; the nucleolus is single.

A few azurophil granules may develop in the cytoplasm.

Typical *monocytes* acquire a horseshoe-shaped nucleus; nucleoli are usually absent.

The cytoplasm remains basophilic, but stains a grayish blue.

It also may acquire many fine, pale-staining azurophil granules.

Many monocytes and lymphocytes pass into efferent channels and so reach the blood stream.

(According to Sabin, a 'primitive white blood cell' becomes a *lymphoblast* or a *monoblast*, depending on its environment; the lymphocyte, on the contrary, is an end-product, incapable of differentiating into anything else.)

Some further information on these matters will be found on pp. 138, 153.

E. DEVELOPMENT OF MYELOID ELEMENTS:

A minor activity of the red marrow is the production of lymphocytes and monocytes.

But the development of myeloid elements is the distinctive feature of this tissue.

These elements comprise the red-cell series, the granulocyte series and the giant cells of bone marrow (megakaryocytes).

According to Maximow, the stem cell of all three series is the *hemocytoblast*.

1. Erythrocytes.

Stages are characterized by a reduction in cell size, an increasing content of hemoglobin and a shrinking, progressively darker-staining nucleus that is finally discarded.

Cell division continues into the normoblast period.

A. PRORUBRICYTES (BASOPHILIC ERYTHROBLASTS).

This stage is smaller than the stem-cell (hemocytoblast).

Its nuclear network is slightly coarser; the cytoplasm is deeply basophilic.

The basophilia is due to the presence of ribonucleic acid.

B. RUBRICYTES (POLYCHROMATOPHILIC ERYTHROBLASTS).

Mitosis in the preceding stage has halved the size of the cells.

The nucleus is checkered with coarse chromatin masses.

The cytoplasm is losing its ribonucleic acid and is acquiring hemoglobin.

Hence it colors variably with both the acid and basic components of the stain.

The result (purplish; lilac; gray) explains the name 'polychromatophilic.'

C. METARUBRICYTES (NORMOBLASTS).

Mitosis again halves the size of the cell.

The nucleus becomes increasingly shrunken and pycnotic; mitosis ceases.

The cytoplasmic hemoglobin stains strongly acidophilic (almost maximally).

D. ERYTHROCYTES.

The nuclei of normoblasts have been lost by extrusion.

Red blood corpuscle is another term for this enucleated cell.

Immature stages contain a delicate network, composed of ribonucleic acid.

This becomes demonstrable by supravital staining or phase microscopy.

Such young forms are called *reticulocytes*.

Red corpuscles possibly enter the sinusoids through growth pressure from behind.

(According to Sabin, the stem cell of the erythrocyte series is a specific cell type, the *megaloblast*, derived from reticular cells that line the marrow sinusoids.)

2. Granulocytes.

According to Maximow, the common stem cell is a typical *hemocytoblast*.

The general name for various stages of differentiating daughter cells is *myelocyte*.

A. PROGRANULOCYTES.

The earliest type that is easily distinguishable is the *promyelocyte*.

This cell is ameboid and mitotic.

Nonspecific granules begin to appear in the basophilic cytoplasm.

B. MYELOCYTES.

The commonest cells in the granulocyte series are the *myelocytes*.

They proliferate repeatedly, but eventually become smaller and cease dividing.

Cytoplasmic basophilia decreases; specific granules appear in large numbers.

The kind of granule foreshadows an *eosinophil, basophil* or *neutrophil*.

Nuclei indent and assume a horseshoe shape; chromatin increases in density.

C. METAMYELOCYTES.

The cells following the final mitoses are called *metamyelocytes*.

These are juvenile types of leucocytes, with characteristic granular content.

The nucleus, at first horseshoe-shaped, gradually acquires its typical lobation.

D. MATURE GRANULOCYTES.

The terminal stage is that of the definitive granulocytes of the blood.

These mature cells enter the sinusoids and thus reach the blood stream.

Nonmotile forms are forced through the sinusoidal wall by tissue pressure.

(According to Sabin, the 'primitive white blood cell' produces a *myeloblast* which is the progenitor of the several granulocytes.)

3. Megakaryocytes.

According to Maximow, this giant cell takes origin from the *hemocytoblast*.

The nucleus enlarges and undergoes a peculiar multiple nuclear division.

The daughter nuclei merge and the same type of mitosis is repeated.

Concomitant cytoplasmic growth produces a giant cell, some 100 μ in diameter.

The nucleus is complexly lobed; the lobes may connect by thin strands.

The cytoplasm is finely granular, but has a clear ectoplasm at the periphery.

Processes extend into sinuses, and are said to pinch off their tips.

These cytoplasmic fragments are the *blood platelets*.

Megakaryocytes do not live long, and the cytoplasm disintegrates.

The shrunken nuclei are often carried to the heart and lodge in the lungs.
(Sabin derives these cells from reticular cells that line the marrow sinusoids.)

F. NUMERICAL RELATIONS:

The red marrow controls the proportions of cell-types present in the blood.
The relative numbers of the different kinds of these cells vary but little normally.
    This is true of both the marrow and the circulating blood.
Pathologically, however, these ratios may become altered.
    Example: in local infections neutrophils increase; in typhoid fever they decrease.
Correlated with the increase in cell numbers, by mitosis, goes a decrease in cell size.
    In other words, individual volumes are inversely related to numbers.
        Example: progranulocytes (large cells) comprise 5 per cent of nucleated marrow
            cells; metamyelocytes (smaller cells) comprise 22 per cent.
        Yet the volume of all metamyelocytes scarcely surpasses that of progranulocytes.
The total number of cells at each stage of a series remains at a quite constant level.
    This is owing to advancing stages and steady losses to the blood stream.
About 1.5 per cent of the cells of normal marrow are in mitosis at any given time.
    Under normal conditions the replacement demands are largely met by mitoses of im-
        mature forms rather than by the stem cells themselves.
    That is, hemocytoblasts are practically dormant and add few cells to the total yield.
        Under stress, on the other hand, hemocytoblasts are active since the ordinary
            supply is then inadequate.
The ratio of leucocytic forms to nucleated red cells is nearly 5:1.
    This is correlated with their longer stay in the marrow and shorter life when mature.

G. MARROW AS A TISSUE:

A general account of bone marrow, apart from its hemopoietic activities, will be found in
    a subsequent chapter (p. 77).

Chapter VIII. CARTILAGE

Cartilage, the 'gristle' of the body, is a special type of dense connective tissue.
  It is a fairly firm substance that will bear weight and give some rigidity.
  Like connective tissue, it consists of *cells, fibers* and *ground substance.*
      The ground substance and fibers, together, constitute the *matrix.*
Mature cartilage occurs in three subtypes:
  1. *Hyaline;* this is the fundamental and commonest kind.
  2. *Elastic;* this type specializes by adding elastic fibers to the matrix.
  3. *Fibrous;* this type specializes by emphasizing the collagenous fibers in its matrix.

A. HYALINE CARTILAGE:
  1. Occurrence.
      Ribs (ventral ends); long bones (articular ends).
      Nose; larynx; trachea; bronchi.
      External acoustic meatus.
      Fetal skeleton.

  2. Macroscopic Appearance.
      Cartilage occurs in plates, columns or irregular masses.
      It is solid, but somewhat flexible and elastic.
          It is easily cut with a knife.
      Hyaline cartilage is translucent, with a bluish to pearly tint.
          Hyaline means 'glassy'; this quality is a property of its matrix.
      It is enclosed within a fibrous envelope, except on articular surfaces.

  3. Microscopic Structure.
      A thin slice shows *cells* embedded in a clear, stainable *matrix.*
      The whole cartilage-slice is bordered by a fibrous strip, the *perichondrium.*
      A. PERICHONDRIUM.
          It is composed of coarse, firm connective tissue.
              This is densely interwoven and consists mostly of collagenous fibers.
          Next to the cartilage the perichondrium tends to be more cellular.
              This local specialization is not obvious after cartilage growth ceases.
          At the inner surface, its cells and fibers grade insensibly into cartilage tissue.
      B. CELLS.
          These *chondrocytes* are large (up to 40 μ), and tend toward a spherical shape.
              Mutual pressure, resulting from mitotic cell clusters, often distorts them.
              Near the perichondrium the cells are relatively young and flattened.
                  Here they gradate into the fibroblasts of the perichondrium.
              Under the free surface of a joint they also become flattened.

65

The basophilic cytoplasm contains fat droplets and glycogen.

On fixation it suffers marked shrinkage, vacuolation and distortion.

c. Cell Groups.

In young cartilage, before internal growth begins, cells occur singly.

Also near the perichondrium or a joint surface they remain single permanently

In somewhat older cartilage the cells usually occur in groups (2, 4, 8, etc.).

They then are arranged in rounded groups or in rows.

Between the compressed cells there may be a thin layer of matrix.

Such groupings are due to the process of internal growth (p. 67).

d. Matrix.

It appears to be homogeneous (but actually is not), and is basophilic.

Spaces in it, occupied by cartilage cells, are named *lacunae*.

In life a cartilage cell fills its lacuna fully.

Cell shrinkage, as commonly occurs in sections, reveals the lacuna.

It then shows as a smooth-walled cavity containing a shrunken chondro cyte.

1. physical structure.

The matrix appears to the eye to be amorphous and homogeneous.

Actually it is a stiff, gelatinous ground substance, permeated by a felt work of fine collagenous fibrils.

The fibrils are not visible in ordinary preparations, because their re fractive index is the same as that of the ground substance.

Thus the matrix is a basophilic substance masking fine acidophilic fibrils.

The gelatinous ground substance can be removed by tryptic digestion.

When this is done, the fibrillar framework is made plain.

Also the polarizing microscope will reveal these fibers in thin sections.

2. chemical composition.

Cartilage has a high water content (70 per cent).

The composition of cartilage matrix is complex.

One component is the collagen belonging to the collagenous fibers.

The ground substance includes: *chondromucoid; chondroitin-sulfuric acid; albumoid*.

Matrix dissolves in boiling water, forming *chondrin* or cartilage-glue.

Chondrin consists of gelatin, chondromucoid, albumoid, etc.

The distribution of the several chemical substances throughout the matri can be shown by differential staining reactions.

These specializations are correlated with growth and aging of the matrix

Nearest a cell is a refractile zone, the so-called *cartilage capsule*.

It is merely the youngest and most basophilic part of the matrix.

The deep staining is due to a high concentration of chondroitin sulfuric acid in this local region of the matrix.

Another zone is sometimes seen outside a single capsule, or surrounding group of capsules belonging to a cell cluster.

This is the *territory* or *chondrin ball*.

It is less basophilic than capsules, but more so than general matrix

In it mainly occur chondromucoid and chondroitin sulfuric acid.

The *general matrix*, between territories, is rich in albumoid.

It may take an acid stain, as does matrix beneath the perichondrium

This is because the collagenous fibers are not masked here by muc chondromucoid and chondroitin-sulfuric acid.

4. Nutrition.

In general, cartilage lacks intrinsic blood vessels, lymphatics and nerves.
>Vessels that occasionally become enclosed are passing to another destination.
>Only in large cartilages are there channels containing blood vessels.
>>These occur, for example, in the fetal skeleton.

Moreover, there are no canaliculi in the matrix along which fluids might pass.
>Hence nutrients, oxygen and cell wastes must seep through the matrix.
>>This diffusion is adequate, since the requirements of cartilage are not **high.**

Actual experiments show that dyes quickly permeate living cartilage.

5. Development and Growth.

Mesenchymal cells enlarge into crowded, vesicular cells.
>Such cells are surrounded by a mucinoid fluid.
>This preliminary tissue is named *precartilage*.
>Somewhat similar is the *notochordal tissue* that remains as the *pulpy nuclei* of inter-vertebral discs.

Thin plates of matrix appear between the cells and, like a honeycomb, enclose them.
>These cells, now *chondrocytes*, thereby become embedded in cartilage matrix.

Mesenchyme, surrounding the enlarging primordial mass of cartilage, is compressed.
>The resulting envelope becomes the fibrous *perichondrium*.

Continued growth of the cartilage is by two methods: *interstitial; appositional*.

A. INTERSTITIAL GROWTH.
>Cells that are well buried undergo mitosis and form groups of 2, 4, 8, etc.
>The deposition of matrix progressively separates the daughter cells and produces the so-called *capsules* about them.
>Continued laying down of matrix, by the cells, separates cells still further.
>>The 'capsule' proves to be merely a zone containing newly formed matrix.
>>Hence the first capsule loses its identity as newer matrix crowds it away.
>>>That is, the earlier capsules merge and become a *territory*.
>>>Still later the substance of a territory is, in turn, crowded away.
>>>>It then loses its identity as it blends with the general matrix.
>This method of growth occurs in relatively young, expansile cartilage.
>>The cell groups seen in old cartilage indicate the condition that existed when interstitial growth finally came to an end.

B. APPOSITIONAL GROWTH.
>This type of growth is from the perichondrium, as a tree grows from its bark.
>The innermost fibroblasts transform into cartilage cells.
>>These deposit matrix about them; in turn, they become overlaid by still newer cells and matrix, added from the perichondrium.
>This early method of growth continues until the cartilage reaches full maturity.

6. Regressive Changes.

Important changes occur wherever the cartilaginous skeleton is replaced by bone.

As cartilage ages there is cell loss and a decline in the basophilia of its matrix.

In old age the calcification of cartilages is a characteristic phenomenon.
>The matrix then becomes opaque, hard and brittle through lime deposits.
>Similarly, *calcified cartilage* appears as a temporary strengthening expedient during the replacement of cartilage by developing bone (pp. 85, 86).

A rarer secondary change is the formation of so-called *asbestos fibers*.

Silky, lustrous, parallel fibers are deposited.
>They do not have the properties of collagenous fibers.
Tissue softening, or even cavity formation, may result.

B. ELASTIC CARTILAGE:

1. Occurrence.

This type occurs in locations where support with flexibility is required, as follows:
External ear (auricle); auditory tube.
Epiglottis.
Larynx (corniculate, cuneiform and arytenoid cartilages).

2. Macroscopic Appearance.

It is yellow (because of elastic fibers), and more opaque than hyaline cartilage.
It is also more flexible and elastic.
An ensheathing perichondrium is present.

3. Microscopic Structure.

Elastic cartilage is fundamentally like the hyaline type.
The *cells*, singly and in groups, and their capsules are similar.
The general matrix also contains *ground substance* and masked *collagenous fibers*.
>But, in addition, it contains a meshwork of branching, *elastic fibers*.
The elastic fibers vary in thickness and abundance in different cartilages.
>They also are thicker and more closely packed in the interior of a cartilage.
>They may be so abundant locally as to obscure the ordinary matrix.
Growth occurs in the same ways as in hyaline cartilage.

C. FIBROCARTILAGE:

1. Occurrence.

This type occurs in locations where a tough support or tensile strength is desirable:
Intervertebral disks.
Pubic symphysis; some articular cartilages and capsules.
Lining of tendon grooves.
Insertions of some tendons and ligaments.
(Fibrocartilage never occurs alone, but merges insensibly with neighboring hyalin
cartilage or with fibrous tissue.)

2. Macroscopic Appearance.

This tissue has a firm, fibrous texture.
A perichondrium is lacking.

3. Microscopic Structure.

The *cartilage cells* are of the ordinary type.
>They occur as single cells, groups and rows.
The *matrix* shows a preponderance of obvious, coarse, *collagenous fibers*.
>These white fiber-bundles may interweave in an irregular pattern.
>Where tensile strength is featured, the fibers take parallel, wavy courses.
>>Between them are cartilage cells, commonly in rows.
The matrix is softer than in other cartilage types.
Little of ordinary hyaline matrix, lacking visible fibers, is seen.
>Near cells it is usually more abundant and takes a deeper basic stain.
>Intensely staining *capsules* commonly border the *lacunae*.

Ɔ. REGENERATIVE ABILITY:

Injuries are not repaired by the cartilage tissue itself.

This is because adult cells probably never divide.

Tissue from the perichondrium proliferates and fills in the defect or gap.

Fibroblasts convert into chondroblasts.

These cells deposit new matrix and become chondrocytes.

A fracture of a mature cartilage may become united by permanent fibrous tissue.

Some of this fibrous tissue, however, may be replaced by bone.

Ƹ. APPEARANCE IN SECTIONS:

Large cells (singly, in groups or in rows) occur in an abundant basophilic matrix.

Single cells are rounded when deeply located.

Near the cartilage surface they are flattened.

Cell groups in the interior are common and characteristic.

Mutually apposed surfaces are flattened.

The cartilage cells are shrunken and vacuolate, owing to loss of water and fat.

They often drop out of their opened matrix cavities (lacunae).

The matrix is basophilic and often stains more deeply in the vicinity of cells.

It varies in appearance in the three cartilage types.

In *hyaline cartilage* it is seemingly structureless.

In *elastic cartilage* it contains varying numbers of elastic fibers.

These are usually not well shown unless stained differentially.

In *fibrocartilage* the ground substance is largely replaced by collagenous fibers.

Ordinary matrix is seen only in the near vicinity of cells.

A fibrous, perichondral sheath envelops hyaline and elastic cartilage alone.

Ƒ. FUNCTIONAL CORRELATIONS:

Cartilage provides support that combines resiliency with fair rigidity.

It may specialize in the directions of elasticity and toughness.

It is a type of skeletal tissue that can grow rapidly enough to keep pace with the growth of a fetus, infant and child.

Cartilage produces provisional models of most of the future bones.

Within and around these models the replacing, definitive bones develop.

It also plays the leading role in the elongation of many bones.

Such growth centers (actually disks) produce secondary bony masses (epiphyses).

S^{35}, injected as sodium sulfate, appears first in cells and then in matrix.

This occurs in both growing and adult cartilage, suggesting a normal turn-over.

Chapter IX. BONE, BONE MARROW

AND JOINTS

I. BONE

Bone, or *osseous tissue*, represents the highest differentiation among supporting tissues.
It is a rigid tissue that constitutes most of the skeleton of higher vertebrates.

A 'bone,' as a total skeletal unit, is a simple, true organ.

Like other supporting tissues, bone consists of *cells*, *fibers* and a *ground substance*.

But a distinguishing feature is the presence in the ground substance of inorganic salts.

A. GENERAL FEATURES:

1. Macroscopic Appearance.

Bone consists of both compact and 'spongy' (*i.e.*, porous) hard-matter.

It is hard and tough, but somewhat elastic.

The color in life is a pinkish-blue.

Externally it is covered with a fibrous *periosteum*.

Internally its cavities are filled with *marrow tissue*.

A condensed layer, next to the bone, is the ill-defined *endosteum*.

2. Chemical Composition.

Earthy and animal components are intermixed in bone.

The inorganic components give hardness and rigidity.

The organic components give tenacity, elasticity, and resilience.

Pure earthy bone can be obtained by *calcination*.

On burning, bone first turns black as the animal parts carbonize.

Then it turns white and becomes brittle and chalky.

The loss by weight is one-third.

The general shape and internal arrangement are retained.

Analysis proves the earthy residue to consist of the following:

calcium phosphate (85%); calcium carbonate (10%); others (5%).

Pure animal bone may be obtained by steeping in dilute acid.

This treatment dissolves out the lime salts; it is called *decalcification*.

A tough, flexible substance remains that retains the form of the bone.

It is easily cut or bent; a slender bone can even be tied in a knot.

This residue retains faithfully most of the structural details.

For this reason decalcification is a preliminary step in preparing section

Decalcified bone consists of bone collagen, also known as *ossein*.

Ossein yields gelatin on boiling.

3. Spongy and Compact Bone.

Differences in the texture of bony regions are plain to the unaided eye.

Compact bone is external in position, whereas *spongy bone* is more internal.

Compact bone is solid, except for microscopic canals.

Spongy bone, also called *cancellous bone*, is a lattice-work.

It is composed of short bars, plates, tubes and globular shells.

The two types differ chiefly in their degree of porosity.

A long bone (*e.g.*, femur), sawed lengthwise, shows these relations well.

The two ends of the bone consist mostly of tissue that is obviously spongy.

Its irregular spaces continue into the main marrow cavity of the shaft.

All such cavities, large and small, lodge bone marrow.

By contrast, the 'shaft' is a hollow cylinder whose compact wall seems imporous.

4. Classification of Bones.

Every bone of the body contains both compact and spongy tissue.

The amounts of these and their local distributions vary.

There are several groups of bones, based on shape, as follows:

A. SHORT BONES.

These are roughly cuboidal in shape.

Example: bones of the wrist and ankle.

They consist of spongy bone enclosed within a shell of compact bone.

B. FLAT BONES.

Actually they are characterized by being thin, rather than flat.

Example: ribs; shoulder blade; bones of the cranial vault.

Two plates of compact bone enclose a middle layer of spongy bone.

In the cranium the flat plates are named *tables;* the spongy layer is the *diploë*.

C. LONG BONES.

This category includes bones of a somewhat cylindrical shape.

Example: most of the limb bones.

The main tubular shaft (*i.e.*, *diaphysis*) is chiefly compact bone.

Each end of the bone (*i.e.*, *epiphysis*) is chiefly spongy bone.

D. IRREGULAR BONES.

Bones of irregular and varied shapes, not belonging in the previous categories.

Example: vertebrae; many bones of the skull.

Like short bones, they consist of a spongy interior and a compact exterior.

B. STRUCTURAL ELEMENTS:

1. Bone Cells.

These faintly basophilic *osteocytes* are specialized, connective-tissue cells.

For a time, during bone development, they acted as formative cells (*osteoblasts*).

A little later they became imprisoned as matrix was progressively deposited.

Their size varies; they are approximately 10 x 35 μ, in flat view.

Their outline is irregularly oval (on the flat), or biconvex (on edge).

In life, bone cells fill little cavities (*lacunae*) in the bone matrix.

Fine cytoplasmic processes enter the angular bays of a lacuna.

In developing bone the processes of bone cells extend even farther.

That is, they occupy capillary tubes (*canaliculi*) radiating from the lacunae.

In this way bone cells interconnect temporarily by fine cytoplasmic processes.

In mature bone of mammals the processes apparently withdraw almost completely.

2. Bone Matrix.

Although apparently homogeneous, matrix really has a double structure.

The condition is something like that of a heavily starched cloth.

There are both a fibrillar basis and substances that mask this fabric.

One component is organic (*fibers*); the others, inorganic (*lime*) and organic (*cement*).

A. ORGANIC COMPONENTS.

The more obvious component is what seems to be typical collagenous fibrils.

The fibrils are fine, but are gathered in bundles 3 to 5 μ thick.

They are named *osteocollagenous fibers*.

The fibers are united by a special *cementing substance*.

This is the primary ground substance of the matrix.

It is a viscid substance of muco-albuminoid character.

B. INORGANIC SALTS.

The mineral salts of bone tissue are located solely in the cement between fibers.

They total 65 per cent of the weight of a bone.

Calcium phosphate comprises 85 per cent of this inorganic deposit.

C. LACUNAR CAPSULES.

Lacunae and canaliculi are bordered by a layer of special organic cement.

This forms a thin *lacunar capsule,* different from the rest of the cement.

It is homogeneous and the index of refraction is high.

In unstained sections the lacunar capsule appears as a shining ring.

Silver treatment blackens the capsule; basic dyes stain it also.

It is resistant to chemical attack, such as strong acids.

Hot alkali does not dissolve it, like ordinary matrix-cement.

3. Lamellae.

Bone matrix is characteristically arranged in layers (*lamellae*) 3 to 7 μ thick.

Such lamellae occur in parallel series, either flat or curved (concentric).

This results from the rhythmical manner in which matrix is deposited.

Lamellae are the most characteristic structural feature of adult bone.

The fiber components of each lamella interweave, yet are roughly parallel.

Their direction agrees with the long axes of lacunae in that lamella.

Adjacent lamellae of any series alternate in fiber direction.

That is, the fibers of one lamella course roughly at right angles to those of adjoining
lamellae, above and below.

It explains why lamellae appear to be so distinct, one from another.

This alternation gives maximum rigidity and strength.

Lamellae are arranged in sets (*Haversian systems; periosteal lamellae;* etc.).

Adjacent sets are delimited by a refractile *cement membrane.*

Example: an Haversian system and an abutting set of interstitial lamellae.

This cement is a thin layer of darkly staining binding-substance.

It is similar to the material of lacunar capsules.

Cement-deposit usually marks a pause between minor phases of local construction.

It may also mark the abandonment of a wave of uncompleted local destruction.

Even the trabeculae (*i.e.,* beams) of postnatal spongy bone consist of lamellae.

4. Lacunae.

A *lacuna* is shaped like a melon seed; its size averages 35 x 10 x 6 μ.

The arrangement of lacunae (and their canaliculi) is orderly.

The flat surface of a lacuna lies parallel to the lamellae.

But a lacuna may actually lie within a lamella, or largely between two lamellae.
The long axis agrees with the direction of fibers in its containing lamella.
Tiny tubes, or *canaliculi*, project from all surfaces of a lacuna; many are long.
Some bend, and all pass in a perpendicular direction through the lamellae.
Canaliculi branch and anastomose freely with those of other lacunae.
Canaliculi, next to periosteal and endosteal surfaces, open onto them.
Others, adjacent to Haversian canals, open into those canals.

C. BONE ARCHITECTURE:

1. Periosteum.

A. RELATIONS.

This fibrous sheath envelops bone, except on articular surfaces.
Its union with the underlying bone varies in strength.
It is firm on short bones, epiphyses and where tendons and ligaments insert.
The bolting-down is accomplished by *Sharpey's fibers* (see beyond).

B. STRUCTURE.

Two layers are described, but they are not sharply demarcated.
The outer layer is dense, fibrous and vascular.
It contains mostly collagenous fibers.
The inner layer is looser, more elastic and more cellular.
It appears clearest, as a distinct zone, during the developmental period.
At this time bone-forming cells are a characteristic component.
In the normal adult it does not contain such demonstrable osteoblasts.
Yet, on stimulation (*e.g*, by fracture), it becomes reactivated.
Osteoblasts then reappear.
Vessels and nerves, from the external layer, pass through to the bone.
Sharpey's fibers leave the inner layer and embed in the bone matrix.

C. SHARPEY'S FIBERS.

These are coarse collagenous fibers (or bundles of fibers).
They turn inward from the inner periosteum and enter the bone matrix.
Here they pass through the periosteal lamellae, like spikes.
They are sometimes called *perforating fibers*.
Their general course is perpendicular to lamellae.
Sharpey's fibers serve to bolt periosteum to bone.
Some perforating fibers, elastic in nature, have been described also.
Sharpey's fibers also occur in some sets of interstitial lamellae.
These represent buried fragments of earlier periosteal lamellae.
They never occur in Haversian systems or endosteal lamellae.

2. Compact Bone.

This type consists of lamellae, in orderly arrangements, and of minute canals.

A. PERIOSTEAL AND ENDOSTEAL LAMELLAE.

These are series of parallel lamellae lying next the periosteum or endosteum.
In tubular bones they have a concentric, cylindrical arrangement.
They are traversed, either vertically or at an angle, by *Volkmann's canals*.
Such canals contain blood vessels, lymphatics and nerves.
In one direction they communicate with the periosteum or marrow cavity.
In the opposite direction they connect with *Haversian canals* (see beyond).

B. HAVERSIAN CANALS.

Compact bone is really quite vascular, although microscopically so.

Haversian canals conduct blood vessels, lymphatics and nerves through bone.
> They are abundant in compact bone, acting as the axes of Haversian systems
The largest canals are 0.1 mm. in diameter.
> Their commonest course follows the long axis of the bone.
They branch and anastomose; in this manner they become continuous with the
> Volkmann's canals of the periosteal and endosteal lamellae.
Some cross connections between Haversian canals have been called Volkmann's
> canals.
> These pass radially and actually pierce the lamellae at an angle.
> On the other hand, an Haversian canal is surrounded by concentric lamellae

c. HAVERSIAN SYSTEMS.
These are cylindrical branching tubes, present only in compact bone.
> Each *Haversian system* is arranged about an Haversian canal.
> Its wall is thick, whereas its lumen (the Haversian canal) is narrow.
An Haversian system consists of concentric tubular layers.
> Each bony layer, 3 to 7 μ thick, is known as an *Haversian lamella*.
> The total number of lamellae in a system varies between 4 and 20.
Bone cells are distributed in roughly concentric layers also.
> Those canaliculi that border an Haversian canal communicate with its cavity
> Those located at the periphery of a system almost always loop back.
> Only rarely do they end blindly or connect with canaliculi of another system

d. INTERSTITIAL LAMELLAE.
These sets of lamellae fill in the spaces between Haversian systems.
> They are irregular in size and in shape.
The orientation of the component lamellae varies greatly.
> Some sets are parallel to the surface of the bone and curve but little.
> > These are remnants of earlier periosteal lamellae.
> Others are distinctly curved remnants of Haversian systems.
> > They survived destruction during a wave of bone remodeling.

3. Spongy Bone.
This type is simpler and less regularly organized than compact bone.

a. ARRANGEMENT.
The total bony mass is enclosed within a variably thick layer of compact bone.
The spongy mass is composed of trabeculae, plates, tubules and globular shells.
All of the interspaces are filled with vascular marrow.

b. STRUCTURE.
The fundamental composition of postnatal, spongy bone is lamellar.
> But the arrangement is more irregular than in compact bone.
Some cylindrical cavities occur, bounded by concentric lamellae.
> These simulate Haversian systems, as do sections cut through globular shells
Spongy and compact bone blend in structure where they become continuous.

4. Endosteum.
This delicate layer lines the marrow cavities, covers the irregular surfaces of spongy bone
> and extends, as a lining, into the canal system of compact bone.
In adult bone it consists merely of condensed reticular tissue.
Endosteum is analogous to the thick periosteum in its formative powers only.
> During the period of bone development it contains active osteoblasts.
> > In the adult these cells are not identifiable as such.
> Yet, like periosteum, it retains the latent capacity to form and dissolve bone.

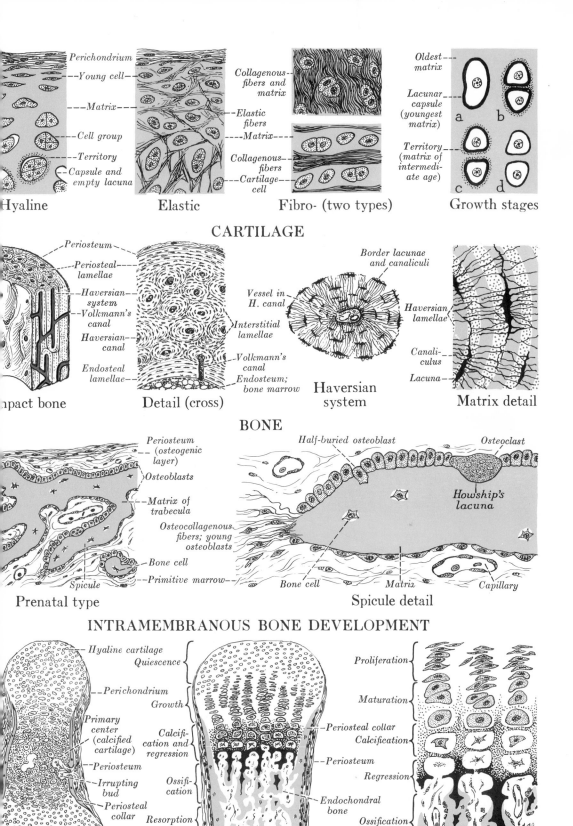

Perichondrium
Young cell
Matrix
Cell group
Territory
Capsule and empty lacuna

Hyaline

Collagenous fibers and matrix
Elastic fibers
Matrix
Collagenous fibers
Cartilage cell

Elastic

Fibro- (two types)

Oldest matrix
Lacunar capsule (youngest matrix)
a   b
Territory (matrix of intermediate age)
c   d

Growth stages

CARTILAGE

Periosteum
Periosteal lamellae
Haversian system
Volkmann's canal
Haversian canal
Endosteal lamellae

Compact bone

Vessel in H. canal
Interstitial lamellae
Volkmann's canal
Endosteum; bone marrow

Detail (cross)

Border lacunae and canaliculi
Haversian lamellae

Haversian system

Border lacunae and canaliculi
Haversian lamellae
Canaliculus
Lacuna

Matrix detail

BONE

Periosteum (osteogenic layer)
Osteoblasts
Matrix of trabecula
Osteocollagenous fibers; young osteoblasts
Bone cell
Spicule
Primitive marrow

Prenatal type

Half-buried osteoblast
Osteoclast
Howship's lacuna
Bone cell
Matrix
Capillary

Spicule detail

INTRAMEMBRANOUS BONE DEVELOPMENT

Hyaline cartilage
Quiescence
Perichondrium
Growth
Primary center (calcified cartilage)
Calcification and regression
Periosteum
Irrupting bud
Ossification
Periosteal collar
Resorption
Nutrient artery

Beginning stage

Periosteal collar
Periosteum
Endochondral bone
Marrow cavity

Later stage

Proliferation
Maturation
Calcification
Regression
Ossification

Ossification detail

INTRACARTILAGINOUS BONE DEVELOPMENT

5. Bone Marrow.

This tissue will be described in a separate topic (p. 77).

). VESSELS AND NERVES:

In bones, in general, *arterioles* enter from the periosteum at many points.

They course within the Volkmann and Haversian canals.

After supplying the bone they reach the marrow.

Some *venules* retrace the arterial course.

These arterioles and venules are largely capillary-like in actual structure.

In long bones one or more larger arteries also enter about midway of the shaft.

These *nutrient arteries* course in a prominent, oblique canal directly to the marrow.

Here they branch into proximal and distal divisions.

Nutrient veins retrace the arterial course.

Nevertheless, most of the blood of the marrow and spongy bone leaves by another route.

Numerous veins find exits at the extremities of the bone.

Lymphatic vessels exist in the various canals (nutrient; Haversian; Volkmann).

Many sensory *nerves* occur in the periosteum.

Other nerves, presumably vasomotor, accompany the arterial vessels.

. METABOLIC PATHWAYS:

Bone is rich in small vessels, yet no capillary mesh exists within bone matrix itself.

In compact bone, vessels are restricted to the external and internal surfaces, and to the conducting canals within the bone itself.

In spongy bone the vessels mostly course in the marrow spaces, between bony masses.

In bone the dense matrix does not permit the diffusion of nutrients, gases and wastes.

Instead, canaliculi establish communications between lacunae and neighboring canals, and between lacunae and adjacent periosteum and marrow.

More precisely, the canaliculi connect with tissue spaces located near capillaries.

(In the canals, the so-called arterioles and venules are much like capillaries.)

Diffusion within the continuous, communicating system provides for interchanges.

Oxygen and nutrients leave the capillaries and enter the tissue fluid outside.

Diffusion carries them through the fluid-filled canaliculi to lacunae.

Here bone cells take up what is needed and pass the remainder on to other cells.

Catabolic wastes leave the cells and diffuse in a reverse course.

This method of interchange is relatively inefficient, but is adequate.

A saving factor is the modest requirement of the relatively inactive bone cells.

Moreover, the farthest bone cells are usually less than 0.1 mm. from a capillary.

About 0.2 mm. is the farthest from a capillary that a bone cell can survive.

In spongy bone completely solid trabeculae are not more than about 0.2 mm. thick.

Thicker trabeculae are supplied with canals and blood vessels.

. REGENERATIVE ABILITY:

This topic is treated on p. 90.

. APPEARANCE IN SECTIONS:

1. Osseous Tissue.

Practically all bone is lamellated; its layered arrangement is distinctive.

The appearance in sections depends on how the component fibers are cut.

A lamella cut 'with the grain' shows longitudinal fibrillations.

A lamella cut 'across the grain' shows granular dots.

Decalcified bone usually suffers from a marked blurring of details.
　　This is due to swelling of osteocollagenous fibers by the reagents used.
　　The decalcified matrix takes an acidophilic stain, like any collagenous fibers.
　　Bone cells are shrunken, and canaliculi are more or less obscured.
Ground sections of dry bone present a picture of lifeless matrix.
　　The details of matrix structure, however, are shown at their best.
　　Bone cells have disappeared and their lacunae contain air.
　　　　By direct light, lacunae are bright; by transmitted light, dark.
　　　　This is because of the low refractive index of air.
　　Lacunae differ in shape, depending on the plane of section.
　　　　Cut parallel with lamellae, the lacunae are oval.
　　　　Cut vertical to lamellae, either a long or short oval is seen.
　　　　　　This depends on whether the long or short cell-axis is cut across.
　　Canaliculi are similarly dark by transmitted light.
　　　　They appear either as hair-lines or as dots.
　　　　This depends on whether they are cut lengthwise or across.

2. Transverse Section through Shaft of a Long Bone.

Periosteal and endosteal lamellae occur in parallel series.
Haversian systems form sets of concentric rings about central canals.
　　Each resembles a tree-trunk, with rings and a hollow center.
Interstitial lamellae have irregular locations between Haversian systems.
Bone cells, within lacunae, occur in fairly regular rows in adult bone.
　　However, they may be situated between lamellae or in them.
Sections, cut through the main shaft, show a central marrow cavity free (or nearly free)
　　of spongy bone and filled with bone marrow.
Sections, cut near the ends, show marrow interspersed with much spongy bone.

3. Longitudinal Section through Shaft of a Long Bone.

Periosteal and endosteal lamellae appear much as in transverse sections.
The changed appearance of Haversian systems is striking.
　　They are less conspicuous because the ringed arrangement is lost.
　　Parallel lamellae, flanking an elongate canal-space, are seen.
　　Branching and anastomosis between systems occur here and there.
　　Canals are not seen nearly so abundantly as are the bony walls of the systems.
Cement membranes may furnish the only clue to the boundary between systems o
　　Haversian and interstitial lamellae.

4. Vertical Section of a Flat Bone.

Next to the free surface, above and below, is compact bone bordered by periosteum.
　　This upper and lower layer may be thick (*e.g.*, tables), or extremely thin.
　　Each layer consists of a series of parallel lamellae.
　　Haversian systems occur, but they are not abundant.
Connecting the compact layers is a varying amount of spongy bone (*e.g.*, the diploë
　　Marrow tissue occupies the spaces of the spongy bone.
The best representatives of this type are the bones of the cranial vault.

5. Vertical Section of Short and Irregular Bones.

Beneath the periosteum there is a varying amount of compact bone.
　　Whether thin or thick, it is always lamellated.
The interior consists of spongy bone and marrow.

I. FUNCTIONAL CORRELATIONS:

Bones provide skeletal support to the body.

Bone architecture is directly related to the functional stresses encountered.

Maximum support is furnished with the least material and weight.

Protection is afforded to vital organs in the head, chest and pelvis.

Leverage action is effected through muscles acting upon bones.

Movement is accomplished by the presence of joints at the ends of bones.

Locomotion and movements of parts of the body are thus made possible.

A lodging place is provided for bone marrow.

Bone is not an inert tissue, even though it has a low metabolic rate.

It is plastic, and remodeling can take place to accommodate changed stresses.

This occurs after a badly set fracture, or following disuse or increased use.

Bones store calcium, but this deposit is labile (especially that of spongy bone).

There is a normal, physiological turnover of the calcium salts.

Much of the skeleton replaces its mineral salts over a period of months.

Also the calcium store is a reserve that can be drawn on rapidly.

This occurs in meeting needs in other tissues; it may be excessive in pregnancy.

Bone cells are relatively dormant in mature bone; they are incapable of mitosis.

Yet they are responsible for the well-being and maintenance of the matrix.

Periosteum helps to anchor tendons and ligaments.

It conducts blood vessels and nerves to the bone.

The periosteum plays an important part in bone development.

It is also actively concerned in the repair of injuries to bone matrix.

II. THE BONE MARROW

The marrow cavity of compact shaft-bone and the intervening spaces of spongy bone are filled with soft, vascular marrow tissue.

Until the prepuberal period all marrow is of the hemopoietic type (*i.e., red bone marrow*).

During puberty and adolescence much of the red marrow is replaced by fat cells.

This inactivated tissue is called *yellow bone marrow*.

Under stress, however, it can return to active hemopoiesis.

In the normal adult, red marrow occurs chiefly in the sternum, ribs, vertebrae and cranium.

It consists of a highly vascular supporting framework, and of free cells occupying the meshes of the framework.

There is no need for the amount of red marrow that would fill a total adult skeleton.

In aged or emaciated persons the yellow bone marrow undergoes changes.

The fat cells lose their oil content.

The tissue then acquires a reddish tint and a gelatinous consistency.

It is then called *gelatinous bone marrow*.

A. FRAMEWORK:

Reticular fibers make a rather loose latticework or spongework.

Lying along these fibers are primitive and phagocytic reticular cells.

Sparse fat cells also are scattered about in this stroma.

B. VASCULAR RELATIONS:

Large, tortuous sinusoids occur abundantly, specialized in the reticular framework.

These channels are lined by flattened, phagocytic reticular cells.

Another name given to these cells is *fixed macrophages*.

Such cells may detach and become free in the sinusoidal blood.

The sinusoidal wall permits newly-formed blood cells to slip through.

Thus gaining the lumen, they are added to the blood stream.

Nutrient marrow-arterioles reduce to capillaries which, in turn, empty into sinusoids.

Sinusoids then converge into venules which leave the marrow by several routes.

Lymphatic vessels have not been demonstrated in bone marrow.

C. FREE CELLS:

These cells, lying free in the meshes of the reticulum, are blood cells.

Represented are all stages in the maturation of red and white elements (p. 62).

D. APPEARANCE IN SECTIONS:

In decalcified bone the topographical relation of marrow to bone is characteristic.

Spongy bone shows irregular bony plates embedded in red or yellow bone marrow.

A shaft of a long bone shows compact bone enclosing a central mass of yellow marrow

Typical yellow bone marrow is scarcely distinguishable from adipose tissue.

The crowded residue of marrow tissue is wholly inconspicuous.

In some instances little clusters of marrow cells occur among the fat cells.

Red bone marrow is notable for its cellularity and (usually) scattered fat cells.

Megakaryocytes and stages in the maturation of blood cells are uniquely diagnostic.

Among the stages seen, basophilic myelocytes are usually notably absent.

This is because their granules dissolve in aqueous fixatives.

E. FUNCTIONAL CORRELATIONS:

Yellow marrow in the adult is a dormant tissue hemopoietically.

The potentiality of returning to the functional state, however, is not lost.

Red marrow is the chief hemopoietic center of the adult.

It is the normal site where red corpuscles and granular leucocytes differentiate.

The relative numbers of the different kinds of cells vary but little normally.

The macrophages function like those elsewhere in the reticulo-endothelial system (p. 40)

III. THE JOINTS

Bones are connected by *articulations;* this region of union is also called a *joint.*

By means of these connections the individual bones co-operate in forming a skeleton.

A. SYNARTHROSES:

These are immovable (or only slightly movable) joints.

1. Syndesmosis.

The union is by dense fibrous tissue (collagenous or elastic).

Example: the sutures of the skull are collagenous tissue; the ligamenta flava,
uniting vertebral arches, are dense elastic tissue.

In a cranial *suture* the fibers are largely continuations of Sharpey's fibers.

2. Synchondrosis.

The connection is by cartilage (hyaline or fibrocartilage).

Example: union of growing epiphysis and diaphysis (hyaline); pubic symphysis
(fibrocartilage); intervertebral disk (mostly fibro-, but hyaline nearest the
bone).

3. Synostosis.

The union of originally separate bones is by osseous tissue.

These bones were earlier joined by cartilage or by fibrous tissue.

Example: union of mature epiphysis and diaphysis; aging sutures of the skull.

The zone of union of an epiphysis and diaphysis is sometimes called the *metaphysis*.

. DIARTHROSES:

These are freely movable joints, with a *joint cavity* interposed between the bones.

Articular cartilages cover the ends of the bones; their maximum thickness is 0.5 mm.

They are usually hyaline cartilage, spared from the general ossification.

Superficial cells are flat; deeper cells tend to be arranged in vertical columns.

The deepest layer, adjoining bone, is calcified.

Perichondrium is absent wherever opposing cartilages touch.

The *joint capsule* envelops the articulation, like a collar.

Its outer layer, continuous with the periosteum, is densely fibrous.

The inner layer, the *synovial membrane*, lines the joint cavity.

This is a looser vascular layer, surfaced discontinuously with fibroblasts.

It is sometimes called a 'false epithelium' (p. 26).

The membrane may be thrown into folds or processes (*synovial villi*).

Glairy, lubricating *synovial fluid* originates from the membrane.

It arises largely as a dialysate of the blood plasma and lymph.

An *articular disk, articular meniscus* or a ligament may project into the joint cavity.

They lie within a protruding, wedge-shaped portion of the synovial membrane.

The disks usually convert into fibrocartilage.

Synovial membrane is lacking in regions where rubbing occurs.

Blood vessels and lymphatics supply the capsule, and especially the synovial membrane.

Nerves and nerve endings occur chiefly in the outer, fibrous layer of the capsule.

. FUNCTIONAL CORRELATIONS:

Articulations connect the individual bones into a skeletal system.

A wide range of movement is made possible, depending on local requirements.

Nevertheless, movement is not an essential characteristic of joints in general.

Some joints are as immobile as the bones they connect.

They provide an opportunity for long bones to grow in length near the joint region.

In doing this, the epiphyseal growth zone is unhampered by pressure and contact.

Flat and irregular bones expand by growth in connective tissue at articular margins.

Chapter X. THE DEVELOPMENT
AND GROWTH OF BONES

A. SOME UNIQUE QUALITIES OF BONE:

As bone evolved, several new features appeared, not found in cartilage.
Nature had experimented with stiffening cartilage by calcifying its matrix.
This tissue was not a success because it could not metabolize properly.
The very deposit of lime salts presented a barrier to diffusive interchanges.
Bone solved the problem of rigid support and introduced four distinctive features.

1. A Canalicular System.

Capillary tubes within the matrix provide a means of diffusive communication.
Also, at boundaries, the adjacent canaliculi open into tissue spaces.
In this way the tissue fluid in these spaces becomes continuous with fluid within the entire canalicular system.
Thus the means is provided for carrying out metabolism within osseous tissue.

2. Internal Vascularity.

The canalicular system can operate effectively only through distances about 0.2 mm away from sources of tissue fluid.
Hence bone acquired a vascular supply within its matrix.
These internal vessels are carried in special canals (Haversian and Volkmann).
The co-operative action of (1) and (2) permits bone to live indefinitely.

3. A New Type of Appositional Growth.

Interstitial growth, as in cartilage, became impossible for bone.
This is because the amorphous ground substance becomes stiff with lime immediately after its formation.
Growth in thickness follows the general appositional plan used by cartilage.
By contrast, a new type of appositional growth was perfected to care for elongation.
The new method employs a special plate of cartilage, the *epiphyseal disk.*
This disk grows progressively near its outer surface.
Its inner surface is correspondingly destroyed and replaced by bone.

4. Reconstruction.

Fetal (mostly spongy) bone is destroyed locally and reformed, again and again.
After birth, newly-formed matrix is deposited in layers (lamellae).
This bone is also eroded and reconstructed repeatedly.
During the reconstructions Haversian systems are fashioned in some bones.
Finally parallel systems of lamellae (periosteal; endosteal) are laid down.

OSSIFICATION FUNDAMENTALS:

The histogenesis of bone, or *osteogenesis*, is the same wherever it occurs.

Two types (*intramembranous* and *intracartilaginous*) are traditionally described.

These merely refer to particular environments in which bone happens to develop.

For this reason some generalities concerning the process of ossification can be presented at the outset as fundamental concepts.

Afterward, certain special problems confronting developing bones can be considered.

These pertain to development in membrane and cartilage, and to continuing growth.

1. Distinctive Specialized Cells.

Two cell types, distinctive for osseous tissue, make their appearance.

A. OSTEOBLASTS.

These differentiate from mesenchymal cells and specialize as bone-formers.

They are medium-sized cells that tend to associate in a continuous layer, next to the expanding bone matrix.

This 'epithelioid' sheet resembles a simple cuboidal epithelium.

There is, however, a wide range in cell shape at different locations.

Apparently the flatter, paler cells are depleted and inactive elements.

Active *osteoblasts* have deeply basophilic cytoplasm, and special granules in it.

Both conditions are held to relate to the synthesis of ground substance.

The collagenous fibers of the matrix are named *osteocollagenous fibers*.

The cytoplasm also contains the enzyme, *alkaline phosphatase*.

It plays an important role in the deposition of matrix.

Osteoblasts have delicate processes; many connect with those of adjacent cells.

As bone deposition proceeds, many osteoblasts become imprisoned in the matrix.

These become bone cells (*osteocytes*), located within individual lacunae.

The retention of cytoplasmic processes during cell-entombment accounts for the establishment of intercommunicating canaliculi in bone matrix.

After an osteoblast becomes a bone cell, its matrix-forming activities cease.

Except, apparently, for the deposition of the *lacunar capsule*.

The recruitment of osteoblasts is from the mesenchyme in formative regions.

There is no significant number of mitoses among differentiated osteoblasts.

B. OSTEOCLASTS.

These elements are also known as the *giant cells of bone development*.

They are large multinucleate cells, with pale to acidophilic, foamy cytoplasm.

The cell may measure up to 100 μ; nuclei number from several to dozens.

Osteoclasts are commonly seen in regions where bone is being resorbed.

In regions of calcified cartilage they are often called *chondroclasts*.

They sometimes occupy shallow pits in bone known as *Howship's lacunae*.

The cytoplasm sometimes is separated from bone matrix by a fringe.

Is it a kind of striate border or only a fringe of exposed matrix-fibers?

The osteoclast ('bone breaker') was so named because it was supposed to be responsible for the dissolution of bone matrix.

Except for their common presence in resorbing regions, direct evidence fails.

Serious doubts can be cast on their active role in the resorptive process.

Bone resorption sometimes proceeds in their complete absence.

Howship's lacunae may be merely spots of easy or concentrated erosion.

The presence or absence of osteoclasts in them may be incidental.

Evidence favoring secretory or absorptive activities is wholly inadequate.

They are not phagocytic to particulate matter, as are macrophages.

The origin of the osteoclast is multiple, and may vary with circumstances.
It is the product of cell fusions, not of repeated nuclear division.
Mesenchymal cells of the marrow stroma produce some osteoclasts.
Inactive osteoblasts also merge to form such giant cells.
Bone cells, becoming free by bone dissolution, are added as well.
In the absence of a special cell to preside over bone resorption, it may be asked
how the process would take place, often in a localized manner.
It is known that the cells which normally lie next to bone matrix (young or
mature) can elaborate phosphatase.
It is possible that bone maintenance requires contact with such cells.
If, then, a bony surface becomes exposed directly to tissue fluid, or if 'foreign'
cells are in contact with matrix, stability would be lost.
Under these conditions, resorption would occur.
Thus an osteoclast, at best, would play merely a passive role.
Bone matrix, in contact with it, could not maintain its integrity.

2. Tissue Participants.

A. PRIMITIVE MARROW.

Vascular mesenchyme, in the region where a so-called membrane bone will
develop, provides the osteoblasts and vessels concerned in bone
deposition there.
It is responsible presently for the formation of spongy bone.
The perichondrium of a so-called cartilage bone sends a bud of vascularized tissue
into the cartilaginous model of a future bone.
(Such perichondrium is called *periosteum* as soon as it overlies bone.)
Cartilage melts away before this advancing *irruptive tissue*.
This tissue differentiates into *primitive marrow*, including osteoblasts.
It at once engages in the formation of spongy bone in the newly excavated
cavities of the cartilage.

B. PERIOSTEUM.

The inner layer of the primitive periosteum of every bone becomes osteogenic.
This general activity supplements the furnishing of early irruptive buds.
On its internal surface a sheet of osteoblasts arises and deposits bone there.
Early *periosteal bone* is spongy; later it is deposited in compact layers.
At times resorption occurs along the surface where periosteum and bone meet.

C. ENDOSTEUM.

The peripheral layer of marrow tissue is osteogenic (*i.e.*, bone-producing).
It contributes bone; notable are the late, definitive, *endosteal lamellae*.
But an endosteal surface is also a site of extensive resorption.
The acquisition of the huge *marrow cavity* in the shaft of a long bone is through
resorptive activities at the junction of marrow tissue and bone.

D. CARTILAGE.

Cartilage is well adapted to serve as a provisional model for future bones.
It is sufficiently rigid to act as a temporary fetal skeleton.
Unlike bone, it develops rapidly and can keep up with rapid fetal growth.
Cartilage also provides the unique *epiphyseal disks* in many bones.
Such plates occur in long bones, and in some flat and irregular bones.
Here continued cartilage proliferation, followed by destruction and bone
deposition, accomplishes growth in length.

3. Osteogenesis.

A. SPICULAR BONE.

Early bone, almost everywhere, makes its appearance in the form of *spicules*.

These 'little spikes' arise at multiple points.

Osteoblasts, differentiating at local sites, make a start on matrix formation.

At first, the matrix consists of *osteocollagenous fibers* intermingled with amorphous *ground substance*.

Such provisional matrix is soft, and is sometimes called *osteoid tissue*.

Directly following, there is a deposition of lime salts in the osteoid mass.

This stiffening substance completes the definitive *matrix*.

As a spicule becomes of appreciable size, osteoblasts clothe it on all sides.

Continued matrix formation, beneath the snugly fitting epithelioid layer of osteoblasts leads to an increase in spicule thickness.

Laggard osteoblasts are trapped and imprisoned as *bone cells*.

Osteoblastic replacements come from differentiating mesenchymal cells.

The deposition of matrix produces lacunae about cell bodies and canaliculi about cell processes.

At the tip of a spicule, osteoblasts and developing osteocollagenous fibers make a brush-like arrangement.

Here the bone grows, often rapidly, and adds to the length of spicules.

B. SPONGY BONE.

Elongation and branching lead to unions between previously separate spicules.

In this way, *spongy bone* arises and takes form wherever it is to exist.

Continued deposition makes the *trabeculae* (beams) of the bony spongework thicker and the whole system increasingly compact.

Such early bone is not laid down in layers, and its fibers run in random, interlacing directions.

C. LAMELLAR BONE.

After birth the bone of the fetal skeleton is replaced.

Previously the bone was of an irregularly interwoven, unlayered type.

This is the case, despite repeated erosions and replacements of the matrix.

By contrast, the definitive type of bone is lamellated (*lamellar bone*).

This is true both of compact and of spongy bone.

C. INTRAMEMBRANOUS DEVELOPMENT OF BONE:

The details of osteogenesis will not be described again in the remaining topics.

Indeed, only the development of bone into an organ (organogenesis) will be discussed.

Still to be considered are two specific problems confronting a developing bone.

One is the way osteogenesis adapts to the particular environment encountered.

That is, within a membranous or cartilaginous forerunner of the future bone.

The other is the adaptation of matrix to meet local needs (mechanical; metabolic).

This has to do with the remodeling of matrix into a bone that is competent to meet the requirements of postnatal life.

The present account will deal only with the general organogenesis of membrane bones.

In later topics the remodeling in response to functional demands will be described.

The products of intramembranous ossification are often called *membrane bones*.

The name merely implies that the bone arose in mature mesenchyme.

Such tissue constitutes a cellular and fibrillar plate or 'membrane.'

1. Occurrence of Membrane Bones.

A. Pure Membrane Bones.

Flat bones of cranial vault; irregular bones of the face.

B. Mixed Membrane and Cartilage Bones.

Occipital; temporal; sphenoid.

(In addition, it should be emphasized that every cartilage bone in the body ends its development by becoming membrane bone, through secondary replacements.

2. Early Development.

The site of a future bone is a sheet of primitive connective tissue (old mesenchyme).

Each bone starts its development at one or more points (*ossification centers*).

This has already begun in the eighth week of fetal life.

A center becomes richly vascularized and is actively proliferative.

Spicules appear at a center and soon elongate in a radiating manner.

Continued spreading produces a wheel-like pattern, within the membranous model

Branching and anastomosis soon make this a spongy meshwork of trabeculae.

Thickness is subordinated to rapid, centrifugal (*i.e.*, spreading) growth.

Hence the preponderant growth parallels the flat surfaces of the membrane

By birth the cranial bones have met along most of their margins.

They are surrounded by connective tissue which organized early as a *periosteum*

Osteoblasts on its inner surface have helped thicken the total bony mass.

Thickening of trabeculae has reduced greatly the earlier interspaces.

These contain vessels and marrow, but the bone is a fairly compact plate.

3. Later Development.

For some time after birth the cranial bones are simple, bony plates—wholly spongy.

Gradually the periosteum begins to lay down parallel lamellae.

Thus in childhood are produced the characteristic *tables* made of compact bone

Thinning of the thick, central trabeculae produces the widely spaced *diploë*.

As the brain enlarges, the calvarium has to make additional room.

Also the calvarium acquires a more gentle curvature.

During these readjustments appositional growth is largely on the outer surface, whereas resorption occurs mostly on the inner surface.

During the period of reconstruction some *Haversian systems* are created in the compact bone of the tables.

Their manner of formation, in general, will be described on p. 88.

D. INTRACARTILAGINOUS DEVELOPMENT OF BONE:

Most of the bones of the skeleton are preceded by cartilaginous models.

Thus there is an intermediate stage not encountered in developing membrane bones.

This cartilage is, however, a provisional tissue that is eroded and replaced by bone.

It is this feature that gives additional complexity to the history of these bones.

During the replacement of cartilage, ossification occurs within the eroding mass.

This fact explains why the terms *intracartilaginous* and *endochondral* are used.

Yet, as the bone continues to grow and becomes reconstructed, the final osseous tissue in a mature bone is almost wholly a direct deposition, as in membrane bones.

The simplest events characterize short bones, since these have no epiphyses.

The most complex history is found among the irregular bones.

These may have multiple centers of ossification, both primary and secondary.

A typical long bone of the forearm or leg shows all of the essential features simplest.

There is one primary center for the shaft, or *diaphysis*, and one secondary center for each end, or *epiphysis*.

Hence this type of bone will serve as a basis for the descriptions in subtopics 1–5.

Primary ossification centers appear in some cartilages of the primitive skeleton as early as the second fetal month.

The latest primary centers (wrist; ankle) do not arise until childhood.

A few *secondary (epiphyseal) centers* are present in cartilages before birth.

The great majority, however, do not appear until childhood or adolescence.

1. Early History of Cartilaginous Model.

A condensed mass of mesenchyme is the first indication of a future bone.

This differentiates into precartilage and then into typical hyaline cartilage.

At the periphery is a fibrous sheath, the *perichondrium*.

A. PRIMARY CENTER.

The site of the first ossification center is indicated by changes in cartilage cells, located internally and midway of the shaft of a long bone.

Hence this center is also called the *diaphyseal center*.

These cells enlarge and the intervening matrix is correspondingly thinned.

Such large, mature cells are able to secrete alkaline phosphatase.

At the same time, lime salts are deposited in the adjacent matrix.

This *calcified cartilage* stains intensely with basic dyes.

The enlarged cartilage cells soon die because they have walled themselves off from nutrients diffusing through the matrix.

When they die the calcified matrix becomes unstable and begins to dissolve.

This leaves irregular cavities within the matrix.

Intermingled with the cavities are undissolved calcified spicules and disintegrating cartilage cells.

B. PERIOSTEAL COLLAR.

Meanwhile the inner, cellular layer of the perichondrium is becoming active.

Some cells differentiate into osteoblasts and produce an *osteogenic layer*.

A thin, cylindrical *collar* of bone matrix is deposited about the cartilage.

This collar encloses approximately the middle third of the cartilage model.

Henceforth the overlying, former perichondrium must be called *periosteum*.

The bone, forming in a typically intramembranous manner, is *periosteal bone*.

It acts as a splint to compensate for strength lost by cartilage dissolution.

C. IRRUPTIVE PERIOSTEAL BUDS.

Vascular connective tissue from the periosteum pushes through one or more breaks in the bony collar and is known as an *irruptive periosteal bud*.

It soon encounters the altered cartilage about the primary center.

As a bud advances, the thinned partitions between cartilage cells dissolve.

The cartilage cells perish by the time their distended lacunae open up.

Arriving at the center, the tissues of the bud proliferate rapidly.

This tissue-mass progressively occupies the spaces made available by the destruction of cartilage cells and matrix.

Some of the mesenchymal cells differentiate into osteoblasts.

This invading tissue is now called *primary marrow*.

D. EARLY ENDOCHONDRAL BONE.

Osteoblasts gather on the undestroyed remnants of the calcified cartilage, using these as a scaffolding on which to work.

They straightway proceed to encrust them with bone.

Since the surviving calcified cartilage was in the form of an irregular mesh-work, the encrusting bone is spongy as well.

Its trabeculae are characterized by having cores of calcified cartilage.

The osseous mass, thus established, is the *primary ossification center.*

Located midway of the shaft, it is also known as the *diaphyseal center.*

2. Growth in Length.

A. ADVANCE OF OSSIFICATION FROM PRIMARY CENTER.

Elongation of the cartilaginous model results from interstitial growth.

As endochondral ossification spreads toward the ends of the cartilage, the events are similar to those in establishing the primary center.

But the stages are more clearly segregated in a series of transverse zones.

Of course, each zone changes character as ossification advances on it.

That is, the same cells forming zones 1, 2, 3 (as listed below) soon comprise 2, 3, 4 and still later 3, 4, 5, etc.

Passing from the ends of a cartilage toward the primary center of ossification, a series of gradual stages can be recognized that illustrates the processes.

1. QUIESCENT (OR RESERVE) ZONE.

Nearest the ends is primitive hyaline cartilage, showing slight, slow growth.

At first this zone is relatively extensive, but it shortens progressively as steadily advancing ossification encroaches on it.

2. PROLIFERATIVE ZONE.

Next centralward in the cartilage is an active, mitotic zone.

A cell divides and the daughter cells repeat, forming conspicuous rows.

These rows are arranged parallel with the long axis of the cartilage.

A row grows chiefly by adding cells at and near its distal, free end.

The cells of a row are crowded, flattened and separated by little matrix.

There is much more matrix between adjacent total rows.

Such columns of young cells, oriented in the long axis of the cartilage, tend to add length rather than breadth to the cartilage-mass.

3. MATURATION ZONE.

Here mitoses cease, but the cells and lacunae enlarge to a cuboidal shape.

This increases still further the length of cell rows and their matrix.

All such growth is interstitial, expanding growth.

The maturing cells produce increasing amounts of phosphatase and glycogen.

4. CALCIFICATION ZONE.

Deeply basophilic, calcified matrix features this relatively narrow zone.

The cells of this level have reached the peak in their life cycle.

5. REGRESSIVE ZONE.

Here the cartilage cells are dying or undergoing actual dissolution.

The matrix between successive cells is dissolving, thus opening up lacunae.

These spaces add to existing tubular channels in the matrix.

The thicker plates of cartilage between cell rows (*i.e.*, the walls of the tubular channels) are not eroded significantly.

Vascular primary marrow is extending into the newly opened spaces.

Osteoblasts differentiate from mesenchymal cells of the marrow tissue.

6. OSSIFICATION ZONE.

Osteoblasts gather on the exposed plates of calcified cartilage.

They promptly clothe them with an encrustation of bone.

This addition extends significantly the spongy bone already present.

7. OSSEOUS ZONE.

At first a zone of endochrondral bone extends from the region undergoing ossification all the way to the primary center.

It might seem that this zone would continuously increase in length.

Actually this is not the case, as the next paragraph will explain.

8. RESORPTIVE ZONE.

The advance of ossification toward the ends of the cartilages is offset by a compensatory resorption of bone.

Resorption is chiefly at the oldest (or proximal) end of the bony mass.

This keeps the mass of spongy bone nearly constant in length.

B. PERIOSTEAL-ENDOCHONDRAL RELATIONS.

The clearing away of endochondral bone leaves an increasingly large 'cavity.'

Actually this common central space fills with differentiating tissue.

This tissue is the *secondary marrow* (or definitive red marrow).

The progressive removal of endochondral bone is matched with periosteal activity.

The bony, periosteal collar not only thickens but also extends at each end.

These new deposits compensate for the loss of endochondral bone.

Henceforth, at any level that has lost its endochondral bone, the periosteal collar must provide all of the required strength and support.

C. OSSIFICATION IN SECONDARY CENTERS.

After birth, *secondary ossification centers* arise in the remaining cartilage.

A center organizes within the cartilage at each end of a typical long bone.

These two secondary centers are also called *epiphyseal centers*.

They will produce the permanent bony *epiphyses*.

The sequence of changes follows that already described for the shaft.

But the proliferating cartilage cells form irregular clusters, not rows.

Vascular osteogenic tissue tunnels through from the cavity in the shaft.

It reaches the center of an organizing epiphysis, and here osteoblasts lay down bone on the exposed calcified cartilage.

Ossification then spreads peripherally in all directions.

All of the cartilage is not replaced by spongy bone, and this is important.

About the free end enough is spared to constitute the *articular cartilage*.

Also a plate is left between the epiphyseal and diaphyseal bone.

This transverse plate is known as the *epiphyseal disk*.

It is a temporary synchondrosis; *metaphysis* is a name given this region.

D. GROWTH FROM EPIPHYSEAL DISKS.

All future elongation of a long bone emanates from the two epiphyseal disks.

Except at the start, when the epiphysis is still establishing itself, bone is not added from the distal (epiphyseal) surface of the disk.

Active growth does continue at the proximal surface, facing the diaphysis.

Hence the disk proliferates cartilage steadily near its distal surface and replaces older cartilage by bone at its proximal surface.

The formation of axial rows of cells, the calcification of cartilage and the deposit of bone on these calcified plates continues, as earlier in the shaft.

Cartilage growth and bony replacement just balance each other in the disk.

As a result, the thickness of the epiphyseal disk remains constant.

When final growth is attained, proliferation in the disk ends.

Its cartilage is then wholly replaced by bone.

Diaphysis and epiphysis finally unite by a bony union; it is a *synostosis*.

This plane is marked permanently by the so-called *epiphyseal line*.
Henceforth, any further elongation is impossible.

3. Growth in Thickness, or Diameter.

Long bones increase in diameter by the deposition of new periosteal bone.
This is *appositional growth*, carried out by intramembranous ossification.
The periosteum retreats outward, like the bark of a growing tree.
If this process continued indefinitely, bones would be too thick-walled and heavy.
Also the marrow cavity would be no wider than in a young fetus.
To avoid this result, new bone is added progressively to the outside, while a somewhat less amount is being resorbed from the oldest bone on the inside.
In this way the bony wall thickens, but in a controlled manner.
An accompanying benefit is an increase in the diameter of the marrow cavity.
The *primary marrow cavity* arose as the endochondral bone was removed.
The permanent *secondary marrow cavity* consists of the primary cavity plus extensive additions gained from the erosion of periosteal bone.
Toward the epiphyses spongy bone is retained as a permanent feature.
The marrow cavity, as such, does not extend into these regions.

4. Gross Remodeling.

Bone is a plastic tissue that can adapt its external shape and internal architecture so as to meet new requirements advantageously.
Changed stresses result from accidents, disease, use and disuse.
They also may derive from planned, clinical intervention.
Even in fetal life, bones modify the shape of earlier roughly modeled stages.
Also it is plain that, as a bone elongates, its thick ends recently lay at levels where now there is thin shaft.
These problems are solved by extensive remodeling programs.
But remodeling is not accomplished as a sculptor might push and reshape clay.
It can result only from resorptions in some regions and depositions elsewhere.

5. Internal Reorganization.

Gross changes, necessitated by growth and altered environment, lead to internal reorganization of the bone substance.
These changes utilize bone destruction and new deposition.
The alterations are carried out in an experimental, indecisive manner.
Alternate waves of construction and destruction repeat in the same region.
In this way over-deposits and over-resorptions are gradually corrected.
Reorganizations accompany the maturing of a bone and alter it greatly.
During fetal life all osseous tissue is spongy and nonlamellar.
After birth periosteal bone is laid down in compact, distinct layers (*lamellae*).
Also *Haversian systems* become established as a characteristic feature.
They serve to distribute vessels advantageously throughout compact bone.
Haversian systems always course lengthwise in the wall of the shaft.
They have several different sources of origin.
Some earlier ones form in the longitudinal tunnels produced from the peripheral region of the advancing epiphyseal disk.
These are called *primitive Haversian systems*.

Others are made possible by the filling-in of cylindrical canals that are secondarily dissolved out of the compact bone of the shaft.

Still others arise as longitudinal grooves just beneath the periosteum.

Such are closed over and buried by later-formed bone.

The tunnels, formed in this way, are then converted into Haversian systems.

Regardless of the source of their tunnel, all Haversian systems develop alike.

At the outset, the tunnel preceding any future system is lined by osteoblasts.

It also contains at least one blood vessel.

Successive layers of bone are deposited in the tunnel, from the outside inward.

Finally the spacious tunnel is reduced to a slender canal about the vessel.

The processes of construction and destruction alternate as long as bones grow.

Former Haversian systems are destroyed and rebuilt repeatedly.

In doing this, parts may escape destruction and become *interstitial lamellae*, filling-
in between new systems.

Other interstitial series represent fragments of former periosteal lamellae.

As bone growth nears completion, definitive *periosteal* and *endosteal lamellae* are laid
down that persist, undisturbed, as complete concentric layers.

The periosteum is predominantly concerned with deposition and the endosteum with
resorption, but these roles can be reversed.

This happens notably where the shaft swells into the end of a bone.

As the bone elongates further, this region has to reduce to a slender shaft.

The internal rebuilding of bone continues, at a slower rate, throughout life.

As a result, the internal pattern becomes more and more complex.

It is a mosaic made of a steadily increasing number of fragments.

6. Short and Irregular Bones.

The foregoing descriptions were based on conditions in a typical long bone.

Little additional need be said about other types of cartilage bones.

A. SHORT BONES.

From a center of ossification, spongy-bone formation spreads in all directions.

At the periphery a thin layer of cartilage is spared.

This serves as a proliferative zone, beneath which ossification progressively
takes place in an expanding manner.

When this phase of internal growth is completed, the external shell of cartilage is
also replaced by bone.

The fibrous envelope, now periosteum, next deposits additional spongy bone.

This layer varies in thickness in different short bones.

Later its spongy structure becomes compact.

B. IRREGULAR BONES.

The variety of shapes and component parts can be suggested by two examples.

A *vertebra*, modeled in cartilage, exhibits several centers.

The body develops much like a short bone from a single center.

But there are also an epiphyseal center and disk at each end.

Each vertebral arch has a center from which bone grows out.

This growth also spreads into its several protuberant 'processes.'

In addition, there are three secondary centers and disks.

The *scapula* is mostly a flat bone that develops from two centers.

But, in addition, there are seven secondary centers.

E. REGENERATIVE ABILITY:

Osseous tissue (bone cells and matrix) is not able to repair losses directly.

It cannot, of itself, heal local injuries or gross fractures.

But from associated tissues the repair can be accomplished.

At the time of a *fracture* there is hemorrhage from torn vessels, and clotting.

Proliferating fibroblasts and budding capillaries invade the clot.

The clot becomes organized by this *granulation tissue*.

The resulting *procallus* consolidates, and cartilage develops within it.

This product is the *temporary callus;* it unites the fractured bones strongly.

Osteoblasts appear in the deep layer of the periosteum and also in the endosteum.

Spongy bone is laid down which progressively replaces the callus.

Cartilage invasion is accompanied by calcification and erosion.

The process repeats the steps seen in fetal endochondral ossification.

Bony union is restored, after which the *bony callus* becomes compact.

Internal reorganization then takes place and bony excesses are resorbed.

Bone *grafts* are commonly used to bridge gross defects or for plastic reconstructions.

This bone does not persist, and its periosteum is only a minor contribution to repair.

Osteogenic tissue of the host is the significant reparative agency.

New bone spreads over the dead ends of the host bone and over the transplant.

Eventually both the dead ends and the transplant are replaced by new bone.

Hence the transplant serves merely as a temporary bridge and pathway.

F. CONTROLLING FACTORS:

The genetic constitution is a basic factor in osteogenesis and morphogenesis.

Genes control the occurrence of osteogenesis and the presence or absence of cartilage.

They also determine the normal timing and order in which ossification centers appear

They likewise superintend the fusion of epiphyses and the cessation of growth.

Vitamins play important roles in conditioning normal ossification.

D-deficiency is accompanied by faulty absorption of calcium from foods.

This leads to *rickets*, in which cartilage cells hypertrophy and persist, so that the epiphyseal disks become thick and irregular.

Also neither the cartilage matrix nor the osteoid tissue calcifies to any degree.

C-deficiency leads to the condition known as *scurvy*.

This is marked by an impaired production of fibers and ground substance.

Calcification is also affected because of reduced phosphatase production.

A-deficiency interferes chiefly with the remodeling of growing bones.

They become thick through lack of compensatory resorption.

Hormones are participants in the growth and maintenance of bone.

The hypophyseal growth-promoting hormone is essential to normal bone growth.

But this is only one phase of its general influence on body growth.

Oversecretion and undersecretion lead to *gigantism* and *dwarfism*, respectively.

Thyroid hormone has a nonspecific influence on the growth of bone.

The effect is probably due to its controlling role on the general metabolic rate.

Sex hormones (male and female) are, in general, antagonistic in their effects on the development of bone in either sex.

The gonadal hormone of each sex has important relations to the growth rate.

The appearance of centers, rate of maturation and closing of epiphyses are correlated with the normal or abnormal developmental rate of the gonads.

Parathyroid hormone regulates the life-long resorption of spongy bone.

This resorption, in turn, controls the normal release of calcium to the blood in the physiological turn-over of calcium stored in bones.

Excess hormone production is accompanied by pathological osseous resorption.

G. APPEARANCE IN SECTIONS:

A developing bone is characterized by spongy bone, bone marrow and periosteum.

The cut surfaces of spongy bone appear as branching trabeculae.

In active regions osteoblasts occur in rows along trabeculae.

The marrow tissue is variable in appearance, depending on its age.

It may be primitive and simply organized, or congested and specialized red marrow.

At the periphery of the bony mass the periosteum occurs as a condensed, fibrous zone.

Compact bone, layered bone and Haversian systems are late (postnatal) features.

A membrane bone is notable for its lack of cartilage.

A cartilage bone is distinguished by cartilage and stages in its replacement.

Cartilage cells are multiplying, enlarging and disintegrating.

Cartilage matrix, in the vicinity of enlarged cells, is calcifying.

This is made evident by increased basophilic staining there.

Cartilage erosion, leaving spike-like remnants, is a feature.

Bone deposition in this region is upon such calcified remnants.

Secondary (epiphyseal) centers are late (mostly postnatal) features.

Chapter XI. THE MUSCULAR TISSUES

Muscle comprises the 'flesh' of the body, and much of the walls of hollow organs.
It is a tissue through which movements of the body and its parts are made possible.
   To this end, cells have specialized in the protoplasmic property of contractility.
   These cells also are rather efficient in the protoplasmic quality of conductivity.
Muscle cells are elongate elements, and contraction operates in this long axis.
   Thread-like shape and functional polarity make contraction maximally effective.
The unit of muscle tissue is a cell that is usually called a *muscle fiber*.
   This usage (*i.e.*, an entire cell is a 'fiber') is unique for muscle.
   By contrast, a connective-tissue fiber is noncellular; a nerve fiber is a cell process.
The protoplasm of a muscle cell is given a special name, *sarcoplasm*.
   This term is applied especially to the unspecialized cytoplasm.
The contractile elements are the minute thread-like *myofilaments* within the fiber.
   These, grouped as *myofibrils*, are cytoplasmic specializations, distinctive of muscle.
Muscle is classified on both a functional and a structural basis.
   Functionally it is either *involuntary* or *voluntary*.
      The distinction depends on whether or not its action is controlled by the will.
   Structurally it is either *striated* (cross-striped) or *smooth* (unstriped).
      The distinction rests upon the presence or absence of serial banding of the fiber.
   The two classifications can be combined, as follows:
      1. Smooth involuntary muscle; this is *smooth muscle*, mostly present in hollow organs.
      2. Striated involuntary muscle; this is *cardiac muscle* of the heart wall.
      3. Striated voluntary muscle; this is *skeletal muscle*, attached to the various bones.
Muscular tissue enters into the composition of many organs as building material.
   But a skeletal muscle, considered as a structural and functional unit, is an organ.

I. SMOOTH MUSCLE

This type is also called nonstriated, unstriped and involuntary.
It has the simplest structure among the three kinds of muscle.

1. Occurrence.
   Walls of hollow viscera (except heart), of ducts and vessels.
   Skin; spleen; eye; penis; broad ligament; visceral pleura.

2. Shape.
   The individual fibers are elongate, tapering spindles.
      In some special locations, forked or star-shaped fibers occur.
   Sections almost never include the full length of a fiber.
      Maceration loosens and isolates fibers, and so demonstrates their true length.

3. Size.

There is marked variation in length (18 to 200 μ) in different regions.

In the pregnant uterus they enlarge from 70 to 500 μ.

The greatest diameter is also variable (3 to 8 μ).

4. Structure.

A. NUCLEUS.

The shape is elongate (ovoid to cigar-shape), depending on fiber length.

The nucleus lies midway of its fiber, where the fiber is broadest.

It is almost centrally located, and extends in the long axis of the fiber.

The nucleus shortens when the muscle cell contracts.

It then tends to wrinkle or twist by passive distortion.

B. CYTOPLASM.

The cell membrane is delicate, and not visible with the light microscope.

It is far thinner (0.015 μ) than the sheath of a striated muscle fiber.

The cytoplasm appears homogeneous when fresh, and usually after fixation.

The electron microscope, however, demonstrates *myofilaments*, about 0.01 μ thick.

These basic elements belong among the differentiations known as organoids (p. 13).

The myofilament is an unstriped thread coursing lengthwise in the fiber.

Chemically it is similar to those in other types of muscle (p. 96).

It is believed to be more solid than the general sarcoplasm.

Clusters of myofilaments may appear after fixation as *myofibrils*, about 0.3 μ thick.

Such are said to be artefacts, produced by clumping.

Coarser *border fibrils* often occur beneath the cell membrane.

Their nature and significance are not wholly clear.

The unspecialized *sarcoplasm* is scanty in amount.

It is not noticeable between the closely packed myofibrils.

It is visible about the nucleus, and especially extending beyond its ends.

5. Grouping of Fibers.

Some solitary fibers or loose networks occur, as in certain regions of the skin.

However, the common, functional unit is a *fascicle* (*i.e.*, bundle) of fibers.

Its fibers pack together in an arrangement that is economical of space.

Thick middle regions and thin ends alternate in adjacent fibers.

A. ISOLATED BUNDLE.

Example: erector muscles of hairs.

B. AGGREGATED BUNDLES (forming sheets).

A layer is well defined when its component bundles orient similarly.

Example: intestine; ductus deferens.

A layer is ill-defined when its bundles interlace or take different directions.

Example: stomach; bladder; uterus.

6. Inter-relation of Fibers and Bundles.

Each fiber is surrounded by delicate reticular and elastic nets, and nothing else.

Bundles and sheets of muscle fibers are separated by ordinary areolar tissue.

In these ways the smooth muscle of a structural unit is united into a functional unit.

The pull of one fiber is transmitted to another, and of one fascicle to another.

The result is a unified action rather than localized twitches of individual fibers.

7. Stretching and Contraction.

When a hollow organ dilates, the muscle cells seem to glide past each other.
This passive response to stretching thins the layers considerably.
Muscle contraction is slow, sustained and resistant to fatigue.
The whole fiber may contract as a unit, or local waves may pass along it.
The latter produce swollen, dark-staining *contraction nodes*.
These tend to align, wave-like, across a sheet of muscle.
Contraction may maintain a constant muscular tension (*i.e.*, *tone*) in an organ.
At times it also may exert a more vigorous, propulsive force.

8. Vessels and Nerves.

Smooth muscle is only moderately well supplied with *blood vessels*.
Capillaries course in the connective tissue that surrounds bundles of fibers.
But they do not invade bundles and supply individual fibers.
The capillary mesh is elongate, in agreement with general fiber direction.
Autonomic *nerve fibers* branch and end on some muscle cells.
Yet relatively few of all the muscle fibers receive a terminal nerve twig.
The mechanism of excitation-spread to uninnervated fibers is not surely known.
It presumably involves the inherent irritability of sarcoplasm.

9. Regenerative Ability.

Adult fibers sometimes show evidence of proliferation.
Also reserve mesenchymal cells can apparently differentiate into smooth muscle fibers.
Nevertheless, these activities and capacities are, at best, limited.
Large injuries are filled-in by connective tissue that becomes a scar.

10. Appearance in Sections.

A. LONGITUDINAL SECTION.
The fibers appear like parallel bands which taper as they end.
Adjacent fibers tend to overlap in a staggered fashion.
Their full length is never demonstrable in a single section.
The length of a fiber, as seen, depends upon several factors:
The actual length of the particular fibers examined.
The plane of section with respect to the axis of the fiber.
The straightness of the fiber with respect to the plane of section.
Only the faintest fibrillation, at best, is discernible within fibers.
Dark-staining, crosswise bands sometimes show in a muscle or on individual fibers.
These are regions of local contraction, 'set' by fixation.
The nucleus is moderately to highly elongate.
It lies midway of the fiber length.
B. TRANSVERSE SECTION.
The fibers show as circular or polygonal disks of variable size.
These sizes range from the full fiber breadth to mere dots.
This depends on the level of section through each fiber.
Only some of the largest disks include a nucleus.
The nucleus is located at or near the center of the disk.
The cytoplasm appears homogeneous at ordinary magnification.
No distinct stippling (*i.e.*, sections of cut myofibrils) is seen.
A delicate reticulum separates the fibers from each other.

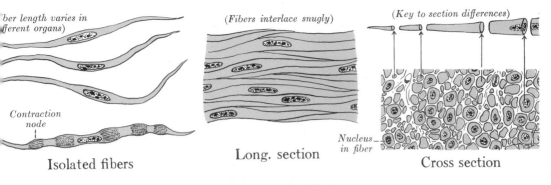

ber length varies in ferent organs)

Contraction node

Isolated fibers

(Fibers interlace snugly)

Long. section

(Key to section differences)

Nucleus in fiber

Cross section

SMOOTH MUSCLE

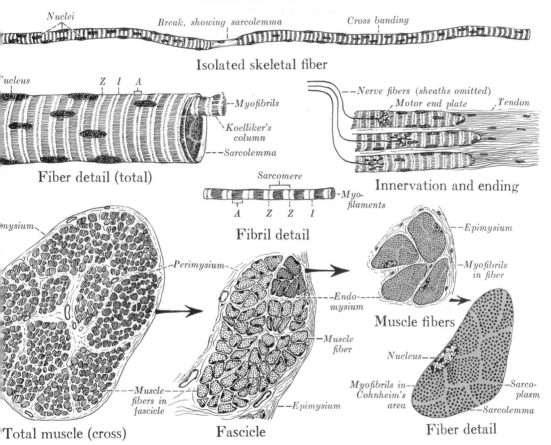

Nuclei   *Break, showing sarcolemma*   *Cross banding*

Isolated skeletal fiber

Nucleus   Z I A

—Myofibrils

—Koelliker's column

—Sarcolemma

Fiber detail (total)

—Nerve fibers (sheaths omitted)
—Motor end plate —Tendon

Innervation and ending

Sarcomere

—Myo-filaments

A   Z   Z   I

Fibril detail

mysium—

—Perimysium—

—Endo-mysium

—Muscle fiber

—Muscle fibers in fascicle

—Epimysium

Total muscle (cross)

Fascicle

—Epimysium

—Myofibrils in fiber

Muscle fibers

Nucleus—

Myofibrils in—Cohnheim's area

—Sarco-plasm

—Sarcolemma

Fiber detail

SKELETAL MUSCLE

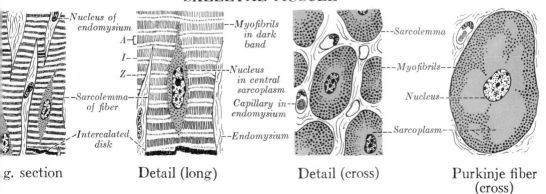

—Nucleus of endomysium

A—
I—
Z—

—Sarcolemma of fiber

—Intercalated disk

g. section

—Myofibrils in dark band

—Nucleus in central sarcoplasm

Capillary in endomysium

—Endomysium

Detail (long)

—Sarcolemma

—Myofibrils—

Nucleus—

—Sarcoplasm—

Detail (cross)

Purkinje fiber (cross)

CARDIAC MUSCLE

With ordinary staining this fine network is not demonstrated clearly.
Bundles or sheets of fibers are separated by areolar tissue.

C. DIFFERENTIATION OF SMOOTH MUSCLE FROM CONNECTIVE TISSUE.

Muscle fibers are protoplasmic and commonly stain darker with eosin.

Nuclei lie inside muscle fibers, but occur between connective-tissue fibers.

In longitudinal sections, muscle nuclei are larger and often wrinkle.

No other kinds of cells occur between the muscle fibers within a bundle or sheet.

In other words, such smooth muscle is notably a 'pure culture.'

Some stains differentiate smooth muscle from connective tissue sharply.

These stains are especially valuable where intermingling occurs.

The Mallory stain colors collagenous fibers a bright blue.

Smooth muscle is stained feebly pinkish.

The Milligan stain colors smooth muscle a magenta hue and collagenous fibers in sharply contrasted blue or emerald green.

II. SKELETAL MUSCLE

Skeletal muscle is a voluntary, striate type of muscle.

It comprises the 'flesh' attached to the vertebrate skeleton.

But only in mammals does it have a deep red color.

The unit of structure is the *skeletal muscle fiber*, a multinucleate cell.

1. General Features.

A *muscle fiber* is an extremely long, and fairly thick, multinucleate cell.

Some of these thread-like elements are almost visible to the naked eye.

A single living fiber is yellowish; massed fibers are red.

The fiber is contained within a tough, structureless sheath.

This is a specialized cell membrane, known as the *sarcolemma*.

The numerous *nuclei* are arranged about the periphery of a mammalian fiber.

The fiber contains dozens to hundreds of *myofibrils*.

These are prominently cross-banded (alternating dark bands and light bands).

Between the myofibrils there is unspecialized *sarcoplasm*.

2. Shape.

Each fiber is a single, long, protoplasmic thread.

Its general shape is cylindrical (or prismatic through pressure).

Toward the extreme ends there is gradual tapering.

In some instances the ends bifurcate or branch.

Example: tongue; skin of face.

3. Size.

A. LENGTH.

An individual muscle fiber is usually said to be between 1 and 40 mm. long.

The total length of human fibers would then be tens of thousands of miles.

It is claimed that much longer fibers occur in nontapering muscles (*e.g.*, sartorius).

B. DIAMETER.

The ordinary limits lie between 10 and 100 μ.

The thickness varies with the type of muscle, and even within the same muscle.

Example: the gluteus has coarse fibers; the ocular muscles, fine fibers.

The diameter of fibers increases with age, exercise and male-hormone influence.

An adult fiber may be as much as ten times its diameter at birth.
Even in old age fibers are thicker, though less numerous, than earlier.
Exercise will increase fiber thickness by 25 per cent.
The augmented muscularity of adolescent boys is attributable to testosterone.
The diameter of fibers decreases in a period of emaciation.

4. Nuclei.

These are numerous (about 35 per mm.), the total number depending on fiber length.
The nucleus is ovoid to fairly elongate and is oriented lengthwise of the fiber.
In mammals its characteristic position is peripheral, close beneath the sarcolemma.
Yet in many 'red fibers' (see beyond) the nuclei are scattered, taking any position.

5. Sarcolemma.

This is a sharply outlined, close-fitting, tubular sheath.
It stains poorly and is best seen where a fiber is crushed, torn or shrunken.
It is structureless, transparent, elastic and tough; its thickness is 0.1 μ.
The inherent elasticity makes it conform to changing fiber shape.
The sarcolemma is a modified and specialized cell membrane.
The electron microscope shows it to be double, separated by a space.
The outer layer stains like a basement membrane.

6. Sarcoplasm.

This comprises the relatively undifferentiated cytoplasm between myofibrils.
It is clear and less refractile than any region of the myofibrils.
It is most abundant in the intervals between clusters of myofibrils and about nuclei.
The amount of sarcoplasm varies considerably in different fibers.
Some are rich in sarcoplasm; these have coarse fibrils, weakly cross-striped.
Others are poor in sarcoplasm; these have thinner fibrils, with well defined striping.
In some animals (*e.g.*, rabbit) the various muscles fall into two color-categories.
Red muscles (or 'dark' muscles) have fibers rich in sarcoplasm.
White muscles (or 'light' muscles) are poor in sarcoplasm.
In most mammals, including man, both kinds of fibers mingle in the same muscle.
One or the other predominates, but no muscle is actually pale.
Sarcoplasm is fundamentally a clear protoplasm, but it contains various specializations:
Mitochondria; Golgi network; glycogen 'granules'; fat droplets.
Sarcoplasmic reticulum, a system of specialized endoplasmic reticulum (p. 13).
Perhaps it transmits excitatory impulses delivered to the sarcolemma.
Pigment; *myoglobin* is much like hemoglobin and gives color to the fiber.

7. Myofibrils.

These are unbranched, parallel filaments that extend the length of a fiber.
Their average thickness ranges between 1 and 2 μ; the thinnest are 0.2 μ.
The fibrils often occur in bundles, called *Koelliker's columns*, probably not artefacts.
Such bundles are separated from each other by relatively abundant sarcoplasm.
A Koelliker's column in cross section is called a *Cohnheim's area*.
Electron micrographs demonstrate that each myofibril is a compound thread.
It contains fundamental units, the *myofilaments*, of two sizes and lengths.
Each consists of chains of long protein molecules of *actin* or of *myosin*.
The thicker filaments (myosin) are restricted to the extent of the dark band.
The thin filaments (actin) extend throughout the light band.
They also continue for a varying distance into the dark band (p. 98).

Myofibrillar Banding.

Each fibril bears alternate *dark* and *light bands*, about 300 to each millimeter.

Actually these 'bands' are regional cylinders, and not mere surface markings.

The corresponding bands on all fibrils agree in position at any particular level.

Hence the total appearance of a fiber is that of a long riband (actually a rod).

crossed by alternating stripes (actually disks) in good alignment.

It is notable that the sarcoplasm does not participate in this banding at all.

A. DARK BAND.

It is also called the *anisotropic*, or *A disk*.

Another term is the *Q disk* (abbreviation for Querscheibe).

This disk is strongly refractile and dark in the living fibril.

It is doubly refractive (anisotropic) to polarized light.

Viewed under the polarizing microscope the dark band appears bright, while the light band is invisible.

The birefringence is a property of the myosin of the thick myofilaments.

The A disk consists of a more concentrated substance that resists stretching.

This portion of the fibril stains well.

The middle region of the A disk is paler, and is called the *H disk*.

Another name is Hensen's disk; H also stands for 'helle,' meaning clear.

It represents a region into which actin myofilaments do not extend.

B. LIGHT BAND.

It is also called the *isotropic disk*, or *I disk*.

This disk is poorly refractile and pale in the living fibril.

It is singly refractile (isotropic) to polarized light.

Only the thin myofilaments (actin) occur in this disk.

However, they continue on and enter the A disk.

This light band contains more water than the dark band, and stretches easily.

It does not stain with ordinary dyes.

C. ADDITIONAL MARKINGS.

A thin *Z membrane* (Z for Zwischenscheibe) bisects each I disk transversely.

Actually it is a web-like set of threads on which actin filaments insert.

An attachment to the sarcolemma is doubtful.

Electron microscopy has demonstrated the presence of two still feebler stripes.

The *M line* (M for Mittelscheibe) bisects the H disk.

The *N line* (N for Nebenscheibe) crosses the I disk, between Z and A.

The exact nature of these two markings is poorly understood.

The Sarcomere.

In relaxed muscle, the A, H, I and Z disks are plainly visible.

The entire muscle fiber bears these markings, repeated in identical sequence.

During contraction the appearance of these parts undergoes change (p. 98).

In practice, it is customary to consider the fiber as a series of fundamental units.

Each of these structural units is a *sarcomere*.

A sarcomere is any segment of the fiber included between successive Z membranes.

It contains all of an A disk and one-half of the I disks that border on A.

Mild trypsin digestion destroys the Z membranes.

The fiber then fractures into sarcomere segments.

A sarcomere is the unit of histological structure and physiological action.

To understand one sarcomere completely would be to understand skeletal muscle
both as to its significant structural basis and its correlated functioning.

10. Structural Changes During Contraction.
Active contractility resides in the myofibrils.
   Contraction can shorten a relaxed fiber up to one-half its former length.
   The fiber then thickens and the sarcomeres shorten.
In contraction, as followed in stained sections, the following events are noted:
   The distance between the Z membranes lessens progressively.
      The region of the Z membrane becomes relatively thick and stains deeply.
      This is because of the accumulation of sarcoplasmic elements there.
   The length of the I disk seems to diminish progressively.
      This brings the Z membranes nearer the A disk.
   The A disk loses its stainability and is not distinguished from I.
      Yet its length remains constant, as the polarizing microscope proves.
The electron microscope indicates that only one active shift takes place.
   This is done by the thin (actin) myofilaments.
   They slide along the thick (myosin) myofilaments of the A disk.
   As the two actin sets approach, the H disk shortens and obliterates.
   Actin attachment to the Z membranes draws the latter in tow passively.
   Thus the entire sarcomere becomes shorter.

11. Functional Correlations.
Skeletal muscle contracts faster than does smooth muscle.
   But it fatigues easier and its action is less sustained.
   It is set off by a smaller stimulus, yet consumes more energy.
Muscles that are most constantly active have more red fibers, rich in sarcoplasm.
   These withstand fatigue better.
   Example: ocular; respiratory; masticatory.
Muscles capable of quicker and more powerful contraction have more white fibers.
   These fibers are rich in myofibrils, but exhaustion enters sooner in them.
   Example: digital muscles; biceps.
The size increase of exercised muscles is due to an increased amount of sarcoplasm.
The total mechanism of muscular contraction is understood but partially.
   Discovery of the shift of actin filaments has aided understanding somewhat.
      Yet changing relations at the side linkages between filaments are obscure.
   Energy for this action is liberated through a series of known oxidizing reactions.
      This energy-store is converted into kinetic energy without significant heat.
      How the protein filaments accomplish this has not been explained.

12. Muscle as an Organ.
A. STRUCTURAL PLAN.
   Muscle fibers are aggregated into functional groups known as *muscles*.
      The number of fibers in a muscle depends chiefly on its size.
         Example: biceps, 260,000 fibers; stapedius, 1,500 fibers.
      The muscle fibers are grouped into bundles, called *fascicles*.
         Some muscles have large fascicles, and thus show a coarse grain.
            Example: gluteus maximus; deltoid.
         Others, such as the ocular muscles, have a very fine grain.
         In many muscles no fascicle extends the full length of the muscle.

Connective tissue embeds fibers, surrounds fascicles, and encloses the muscle.
  (The toughness of meat depends mostly on the amount of this tissue present.)
  The delicate connective tissue between the muscle fibers is called *endomysium*.
  The fibrous sheath around each fascicle is *perimysium* (or internal perimysium).
      Portions along radii tend to produce septa, subdividing the muscle.
  The fibrous sheath around the whole muscle is *epimysium* (or external perimysium).

B. ARRANGEMENT OF MUSCLE FIBERS.
  Some fibers extend the entire length of a fascicle and attach at each end.
  Some fibers attach at one end of a fascicle and terminate freely within it.
  Some fibers lie wholly within the fascicle, attaching to neither end.
  It is commonly said that fascicles longer than 5 cm. contain no fibers that extend
      through their entire length.

C. UNION OF MUSCLE WITH TENDON.
  The connective tissue of a muscle makes a continuous system of fibrous tissue.
      That is, epi-, peri-, and endomysium are local portions of a sheath-system.
      This 'harness' merges with the fibrous tissue that anchors a muscle in place.
          Such attachments, on which a pull is exerted, are tendon, periosteum, etc.
  In addition, the ends of muscle fibers themselves become firmly anchored.
  The manner of union of muscle with tendon has been debated for many years.
      Electron micrographs now show that there is no direct continuity of these fibers.
      Instead, tendon fibrils insert onto the wrinkled tip of the sarcolemma.

. **Vessels and Nerves.**
Blood vessels follow the connective tissue into muscle.
  In the endomysium a rich, elongated network of capillaries surrounds each fiber.
Lymphatics occur in the epimysium and in the perimysial septa only.
Muscle sensibility is mediated through sensory *muscle spindles* (p. 302).
Motor activity is mediated through specialized *motor end-plates*.
  Motor nerve fibers that supply a muscle branch repeatedly within the muscle.
      A terminal twig from such branching ends about midway along some muscle fiber.
      It then loses its myelin sheath and its neurolemma in part.
      The axonal-twig ends in a 'crow-foot' pattern directly on the sarcolemma.
          Here the sarcolemma overlies a local mass of sarcoplasm, containing nuclei.
  Every muscle fiber receives one of these specialized motor endings.
      In most instances a single, branching nerve fiber innervates many muscle fibers.
          This set of muscle fibers is arranged in a compact group, often a fascicle.
          It constitutes a separate functional contractile unit (up to 100 fibers).
      In muscles with delicate precise movements, individual nerve fibers branch less.
          In one ocular muscle each nerve fiber innervates a single muscle fiber only.
Neurons exert a trophic influence which maintains muscle fibers in good condition.
  Motor-nerve injury leads to muscle atrophy (as in infantile paralysis).

. **Regenerative Ability.**
Remnants of injured or degenerated muscle fibers can regenerate to a certain extent.
Large injuries to a muscle are filled-in and healed by a connective-tissue scar.

. **Appearance in Sections.**
  A. LONGITUDINAL SECTION.
  Fibers are solitary acidophilic bands, both long and relatively thick.

The fibers of any given muscle are fairly uniform in size.
Cross-striping is bold and conspicuous under moderately high magnification.
But locally, or under certain conditions, striations may show poorly (if at all).
A longitudinal, fibrillar arrangement is usually apparent within a fiber.
Nuclei may appear to occupy any position with respect to fiber breadth.
But more are seen at the sides; all actually occupy border regions of a fiber.

B. TRANSVERSE SECTION.

Fibers show as more or less rounded polygons, prominent and fairly equal in size.
Fibrils are cut across and appear as distinct dots.
These dots may be grouped in clusters (Cohnheim's areas).
The sarcolemma is a thin, limiting line.
Nuclei lie close beneath the sarcolemma; an interior position is exceptional.
Delicate connective tissue (endomysium) separates the fibers.
Coarser connective tissue encloses bundles of fibers (fascicles).

III. CARDIAC MUSCLE

This involuntary, striate muscle is peculiar to the myocardium of the heart.
It also extends onto the roots of the large vessels joining the heart.
Cardiac muscle is much like skeletal muscle in structure.
But in development, innervation and function it resembles smooth muscle.

1. General Features.

Cardiac muscle consists of short columns, united into a close meshwork.
The meshwork simulates a syncytium because cell junctions are obscure.
Actually each column consists of discrete cells, arranged in a single row.
Plasma membranes, where cells abut, are resolved only with the electron micr
cope.
The main columns of the mesh in any local region extend in a common direction.
These are connected by thinner, slanting branches.
The term *cardiac muscle fiber* is used to designate any local muscle column.
Connective tissue fills-in the slit-like interstices of the meshwork.
This *endomysium* is well pronounced in mammals alone.
Fibers contain *nuclei, sarcoplasm* and *myofibrils*, much as the skeletal muscle.

2. Diameter.

The diameter of cardiac fibers varies between 9 and 22 μ.
The thickest are not much larger than the thinnest skeletal fibers.

3. Nuclei.

The shape is ovoid and the orientation agrees with the long axis of the fiber.
Nuclei retain a central position within the fibers, as in embryonic stages.
They are usually spaced a fair distance apart.

4. Sarcolemma.

A very thin sheath that encapsulates the fibers serves as a *sarcolemma*.
It is much more delicate than that of skeletal muscle.
Yet in sections it appears as a thin, limiting line.

. Sarcoplasm.
This is rather abundant; it is correlated with a capacity to withstand fatigue.
(The heart does enough work daily to lift itself a distance of 35 miles.)
Sarcoplasm embeds the nucleus and extends beyond it in a spindle-shaped mass.
This axial accumulation is devoid of myofibrils.
Elsewhere sarcoplasm surrounds individual myofibrils and myofibril-clusters.
Mitochondria are abundant and fat droplets are numerous.

. Myofibrils.
The *myofibrillae* are distinct, but less robust than those of skeletal muscle.
Their extent is restricted to individual cells, but endings are not plain.
Fibrillar striping is like that in skeletal muscle, but closer and fainter.
During contraction a similar sequence of events occurs.
The myofibrils are sometimes gathered into *Koelliker's columns*.
Transverse sections of these columns show as *Cohnheim's areas*.

. Intercalated Disks.
Prominent markings pass across cardiac fibers at irregular intervals.
They may not transect the entire fiber, and may take a stepped or zig-zag course.
Such *intercalated disks* are blackened by silver nitrate and stained by some dyes.
Intercalated disks occur only where delicate plasma membranes demark contiguous cells.
Actually cardiac muscle is cellular, and the two abutting membranes are sinuous.
Maceration with potassium hydroxide produces a separation at this level.
Dense substance next to the irregular, transverse boundaries tends to stain deeply.
Such a result, at its maximum, produces a relatively thick, compound 'disk.'
Only the electron microscope demonstrates all these details correctly.
Intercalated disks first become evident late in fetal life.
The number seen increases with age, and especially in overworked hearts.
They represent zones of weakness at which separation may take place.
This occurs pathologically in 'myocardial segmentation.'

. Purkinje Fibers.
Despite its cellularity, cardiac muscle is a good conductor of excitation impulses.
This property provides a basis for the spread of contraction waves.
There is also an *impulse-conduction system* made of specialized cardiac fibers.
This network lies close to the endocardium.
Its component *Purkinje fibers* are thick, with abundant central sarcoplasm.
Their fibrils are relatively few and occupy a peripheral position in the fibers.
The most prominent part of the system is the *atrio-ventricular bundle*.
Its function is to co-ordinate the atrial and ventricular rhythms.

. Gross Arrangement of Muscle.
The meshwork of muscle fibers is partially segregated by thicker connective tissue.
This segregation produces bundles and plates of muscle.
Many of these layers interconnect the right and left halves of the heart.
The fibers of any such layer take a common lengthwise direction.
In general, layers located at different levels in the wall course in different directions.
Hence any slice through the heart shows fiber groups cut in various planes.

10. Vessels and Nerves.

Blood capillaries form plexuses in the endomysial connective tissue about fibers.
>This supply is about twice as rich as in skeletal muscle.

Lymphatic capillaries are also present in the endomysium.

Autonomic *nerves* end in simple brushes on (or possibly in) cardiac muscle fibers.
>These are much like those on smooth muscle.

11. Regenerative Ability.

This is even less evident than in skeletal muscle; healing is by scar tissue.

Cardiac muscle is more resistant to injuries than other types of muscle.

12. Appearance in Sections.

A. LONGITUDINAL.

>There is a system of branching strands, bearing fine cross-striations.
>>This banding may show poorly, or not at all, in local regions.
>
>There is considerable variation in the width of fibers seen in any region.
>Intercalated disks are diagnostic features, but sometimes show poorly.
>Nuclei occur in the axis of the band, not marginally.
>Endomysial connective tissue is rather plentiful.

B. TRANSVERSE.

>Irregularly-shaped areas are separated by considerable connective tissue.
>>These areas are variable in size, but smaller than ordinary skeletal fibers.
>
>The nucleus, when included, is central and relatively large.
>>Some sections of fibers, lacking a nucleus, show a central mass of sarcoplasm
>
>Cohnheim's areas often are arranged like radiating wedges.

13. Comparison of the Three Muscle Types.

A. LONGITUDINAL SECTION.

>Smooth-muscle fibers are relatively small spindles; cardiac fibers, a coarsely branch-
>>ing network; skeletal fibers, very large solitary bands.
>
>Smooth muscle is unstriped; cardiac, weakly striped; skeletal, strongly striped.
>Smooth-muscle nuclei are slenderer and more elongate than the other two.

B. TRANSVERSE SECTION.

>Smooth-muscle fibers are much smaller than the other two.
>>Skeletal fibers are larger than cardiac.
>
>Smooth-muscle fibers show wide size variation; cardiac fibers, moderate variation
>>skeletal fibers, fair uniformity in any given muscle.
>
>Smooth-muscle fibers lack any evident stippling (myofibrils); cardiac and skeletal
>>fibers show fibrils as plainly visible dots.
>
>Smooth- and cardiac fibers have central nuclei; skeletal fibers, peripheral nuclei
>Smooth-muscle nuclei are largest, relative to fiber diameter; skeletal are smallest
>Cardiac and skeletal muscle are embedded in connective tissue (endomysium).
>>Smooth muscle packs tightly; there is no obvious tissue between fibers.

Chapter XII. NERVOUS TISSUE

Irritability and conductivity are inherent properties of protoplasm.
    Irritability is sensitivity to stimuli, with the setting up of an impulse-response.
    Conductivity is the transmission of such a wave of excitation.
    These qualities reach their highest expression in the nervous tissue.
Nerve cells are massed in, or near, the *central nervous system* (brain; spinal cord).
Nerve-cell processes are capable of transmitting impulses over long distances.
    Some lie wholly within the central nervous system.
    Others extend beyond the brain and cord, or lie largely or wholly outside of them.
        They constitute the *peripheral nervous system.*

I. THE NEURON CONCEPT

A. NEURON:
    A *neuron* is a nerve cell, consisting of a cell body and all of its processes.
        It arises from a single embryonic cell, the *neuroblast.*
            (Formerly it was thought that it arose from a chain of cells or out of a syncytium.)
        It retains its physical independence throughout life.
        It connects with other neuron-units by contact only.
        It is the structural and functional unit of the nervous system.
    Many years elapsed before these fundamental concepts were established.
        Much of the controversy centered around the seeming improbability that nerve fibers,
            some measurable in inches or feet, could be merely elongated cell processes.
        It has proved convenient to retain some of the old terminology.
            The main cell-body of a neuron is often called the *nerve cell.*
            The thread-like cell processes are called *nerve fibers.*
            (Originally these terms implied a separateness, somewhat like connective-tissue
                cells and fibers.)

B. SYNAPSE:
    Neurons intermingle and come into intimate relations with each other.
    Any apparent protoplasmic continuity between neurons is held to be a deception.
        On the contrary, intimate contact is the closest relation that exists.
        The neuron units are still separated by intact plasma membranes.
    This region of physiological junction is named the *synapse.*
        Further details concerning it are given on p. 113.

II. THE CELL BODY (OR PERIKARYON)

The portion of a total neuron that looks like an ordinary cell is the *cell body.*
    For convenience it is often called the *nerve cell.*
    A technical name is the *perikaryon* (*i.e.,* the region of a cell about the nucleus).

A. GENERAL FEATURES:

1. Size.

Nerve cells are mostly large in comparison with other body-cells.
In man the extremes in diameter are 4 and 135 μ.

2. Shape.

Cell shape is dependent on the number and arrangement of cell processes.
    A. UNIPOLAR CELL. A nearly globular cell, with a single process that bifurcates.
        Example: cells in the ganglia alongside the brain and spinal cord.
    B. BIPOLAR CELL. A spindle-shaped cell with a process at each end.
        Example: cells of acoustic ganglia; some retinal neurons; olfactory neurons.
    C. MULTIPOLAR CELL. A cell with several to many processes.
        This is the commonest type of all.
        Variant shapes are illustrated by stellate-, pyramidal- and pear-shaped cells.
            Example: cells in the central nervous system and autonomic ganglia.

3. Numbers.

A computation has been made of the total number of nerve cells in one region.
    In the cortex of the brain alone this number is given as 14,000,000,000.

4. Nucleus.

Usually there is but one *nucleus*, located more or less centrally.
It is large and spherical, with a distinct nuclear membrane.
    There is one (rarely more) prominent *nucleolus*, centrally located.
    Chromatin makes a scanty network; *nuclear sap* is clear and abundant.

5. Cytoplasm.

    A. CELL MEMBRANE.
        There is a limiting border of condensed cytoplasm.
        It constitutes a thin and not very definite *plasma membrane*.
    B. NEUROPLASM.
        This name denotes the general, relatively unspecialized cytoplasm.
        Living *neuroplasm* usually appears homogeneous.
            Dark-field or phase microscopy reveals the presence of granules.
            Staining proves it to be basophilic, and demonstrates other constituents.
    C. ORGANOIDS.
        Mitochondria and the *Golgi complex* are present in typical form.
        A centriole is present in neuroblasts, but not in mature cells.
            This lack is correlated with the inability of the neuron to divide.
        Neurofibrils are specialized organoids, peculiar to the neuron.
            Like the neuroplasm, they exist in both the cell body and cell processes.
            Neurofibrils are firm, protoplasmic threads, embedded in the neuroplasm.
            Each fibril represents a bundle of much finer (0.008 μ) filaments.
                Only the electron microscope resolves these *neuroprotofibrils*.
            Neurofibrils have apparently been demonstrated in some living cells.
                They are, however, shown best by special silver techniques.
                They are not solitary threads, but they branch and anastomose.
            The utility of neurofibrils to the neuron still remains undetermined.
                Some histologists even believe that they are precipitation artefacts.
                Nevertheless, polarizing studies show that living axons are fibrillar.

Nissl bodies are a flaky material (as seen in sections), characteristic of neurons.

Another name for them is *chromophil substance*.

Phase microscopy demonstrates their existence as discrete clumps in living cells.

Electron microscopy reveals parallel, flat sacs and densely massed ribosomes.

Each belongs to the chromidial group in the system of endoplasmic reticulum.

Nissl bodies are present in the cell body and branching dendrons.

They are absent from most axons and their conical base (axon hillock).

Basic aniline dyes stain the granules strongly.

This is owing to their content of ribonucleic acid, like nucleoli.

The presence of this acid implies the occurrence of protein synthesis.

Cytoplasm is synthesized continuously; intensely in regenerating fibers.

After injury to the axon, Nissl bodies disappear, at first centrally.

On recovery of the neuron, they reappear.

In certain pathological conditions they apparently dissolve and diffuse.

The neuroplasm then stains darkly.

The dissolution and loss of Nissl bodies is called *chromatolysis*.

D. INCLUSIONS.

Granules and fat droplets are fairly common constituents.

Pigment granules are of widespread occurrence in man.

Brownish-black, coarse granules (*melanin*) occur in primates, in general.

They are present only in certain cells of definite regions.

Example: substantia nigra of the midbrain; some ganglion cells.

Yellow to brownish granules occur mainly in the larger nerve cells of man.

They are fine and tend to aggregate as they become numerous.

They represent a *lipochrome pigment* of a special fatty nature.

Such pigment increases with age, and probably represents metabolic slag.

6. Appearance in Sections.

Nerve cells are mostly large; they are usually cut into several slices.

Hence the nucleus is not included in every section observed.

The most common cell shape is rounded or irregularly angular.

The cytoplasm is basophilic and granular.

Usually there is some indication of the flaky Nissl substance.

The nucleus is large and round; it contains scanty chromatin.

There is a prominent, rounded, basophilic nucleolus.

B. NERVE CELLS OF CENTRAL SYSTEM:

These cell bodies are multipolar, but vary in size and shape.

The anterior-column cells (stellate) of cord, Purkinje cells (pear-shaped) of cerebellum, and pyramidal cells of motor cortex illustrate the range in form.

Cells, similar in type and function, tend to aggregate in local groups, called *nuclei*.

Their naked cell bodies are embedded in nerve fibers and neuroglial tissue.

C. NERVE CELLS OF PERIPHERAL NERVOUS SYSTEM:

These cell bodies are associated in groups that are known as *ganglia*.

Since ganglia are major features of the nervous system and consist of more than bare nerve cells, they will be described in the following, separate topic.

III. THE GANGLIA

The essential feature of a *ganglion* is a group of cell bodies belonging to neurons.
> These are located outside the central system, and are associated with either the cranio-spinal
>> or the autonomic system.

A. GENERAL FEATURES:

A *ganglion* is supported and surrounded by connective tissue.

Nerve fibers are present, many or all of which belong to the ganglion cell bodies.
> Other fibers enter some ganglia and synapse with its neurons.
> Still others may merely pass through, seeking other destinations.

The larger ganglia are prominent swellings that contain up to 50,000 *ganglion cells.*
> By contrast, the smallest consist of but few cells.

All ganglion cell-bodies are enveloped by a thin cellular *capsule.*
> This consists of special *satellite cells,* also called *capsule cells.*
>> These cells make a single-layered, cellular envelope.
>> Their embryonic mother cell was similar to that of the ganglion cell.
>>> The daughter cells of each merely took different lines of specialization.
>> Satellite cells are continuous with the neurolemma sheath of the cell process.
> In life only a thin film of tissue fluid separates capsule from ganglion cell.

The cellular capsule is reinforced by a connective-tissue sheath.
> This blends with the vascular stroma, which embeds nerve fibers as well.

B. CRANIO-SPINAL GANGLIA:

They occur in the dorsal (posterior) roots of the spinal nerves.
> They make nodular enlargements on some of the cranial nerves.

1. Cell Shape.

The cells are unipolar and hence are fairly globular in shape.
The acoustic ganglia are exceptional in retaining bipolar, embryonic-type cells.
> In addition, these cells lack a capsule.

2. Cell Size.

The cells fall into two groups, small and large.
Small cells range between 15 and 25 μ; they have unmyelinated fiber-processes.
Large cells range up to 100 μ; their associated nerve fibers are myelinated.

3. Cell Structure.

The cell body exhibits no unusual features.
There is a single stem-process which presently bifurcates T- or Y-fashion.
> Both of these branches have the structure of an efferent process (an axon).

Nevertheless, the thicker peripheral process is functionally afferent (a dendron).
> It enters a peripheral nerve and terminates as a sensory receptor.
> The thinner, central process is an axon; it passes into the spinal cord or brain.
> No fibers of other neurons traverse the ganglion.

The main process of large cells may wander within the capsular space before emerging.
> It occasionally arises by more than one root, or gives off short collaterals.

C. AUTONOMIC GANGLIA:

Some make a series of enlargements along the sympathetic trunks.
> Others occur on the more peripheral plexuses and within the walls of visceral organs.

1. Cell Shape.

Typical ganglion cells are multipolar; the only common shape is stellate.
A few bipolar and unipolar cells also occur.

2. Cell Size.

They are smaller (15 to 45 μ) than the larger representatives of the cranio-spinal series.

3. Cell Structure.

The cell body has the structure of typical nerve cells.
Its cytoplasm often contains prominent masses of pigment.
Nuclei tend to be eccentric, and two (or more) sometimes occur.
The several cell processes usually pierce the capsule.
But sometimes short dendrons ramify and remain inside the capsule.
This *glomerulus* is in synaptic relation with entering axons from other cells.
Sometimes, but not always, the axons and dendrons are distinguishable.
The axon (called a *postganglionic fiber*) lacks a myelin sheath.
In the outlying ganglia, typical capsules may be lacking about the cell body.
Instead, the ganglion cells are enmeshed in an interlacing system of cells.
These spindle-shaped elements are equivalent to capsule cells.
All autonomic ganglion cells are apparently motor in function.
Most of them (perhaps all) enter into synapse with a *preganglionic fiber*, whose cell body lies within the central nervous system.

D. APPEARANCE OF GANGLIA IN SECTIONS:

Large, encapsulated cells intermingle with nerve fibers and connective tissue.
Connective tissue also envelops the whole ganglion.
Some of the tiniest cell groups lack this envelope.
The capsule is the distinguishing feature of ganglion cells in general.
Its epithelioid cells have nuclei far smaller than that of a ganglion cell.
A space is frequently seen between capsule and ganglion cell.
In silver preparations this space is greatly exaggerated by shrinkage.
Ganglion cells are large elements, cranio-spinal cells showing a greater size range than do autonomic cells.
Cranio-spinal cells are rounded to slightly pear shape and have one main process.
This process pierces the capsule to gain the outside and become free.
(Naturally many sections miss it by passing in the wrong plane.)
Prominent tracts of nerve fibers course through the total ganglion.
Autonomic cells are angular in shape (*i.e.*, multipolar).
The cell body commonly contains prominent pigment masses.
Cell processes are multiple and pierce the capsule at various points.
Only after silver staining is this determinable.
Groups of cells and fibers intermingle confusedly; fiber tracts do not occur.

IV. CELL PROCESSES (NERVE FIBERS)

To provide long conduction paths, cell cytoplasm is drawn out into thread-like processes.
These are variable in number, arrangement and degree of branching.
One to several processes (*dendrons,* or dendrites) conduct impulses toward the cell.
A single process (*axon,* or axis cylinder) conducts impulses away from the cell.

When the receptive and emissive ends are both far away from the cell body, then axon and dendron are structurally alike (*i.e.*, axon-like).

This occurs in the two processes of cranio-spinal ganglion cells.

A cell process may be very long with respect to the size of its cell body.

Example: the length of a fiber from the lower spinal cord to the foot is some 20,000 times the diameter of its cell of origin.

Also cell processes may contain a relatively huge amount of cytoplasm.

Example: an axon can have several hundred times as much cytoplasm as the cell body.

The general cytoplasm is *neuroplasm;* it contains neurofibrils and may contain Nissl bodies.

1. Dendrons.

Multipolar cells, as befits the name, have several to many dendrons.

By contrast, a uni- or bipolar cell has but one process that functions as a dendron.

Such a dendron, however, is atypical and is structurally like an axon.

A typical dendron is distinguished by its form (dendron means 'tree').

It arises by a broad stem that branches freely into a bush-like process.

The branches dwindle rapidly in size and end not far from the cell body.

The branches of a dendron are often contorted, varicose and thorny.

The spiny appearance is due to lateral twigs, called *gemmules.*

These are usually swollen or knobbed at their ends.

Dendrons terminate in contact with the axons (and cell bodies) of other neurons.

They make up much of the felty 'neuropil' of the spinal cord and brain.

They acquire no sheaths and do not build any nerve tracts.

Dendrons are virtually short, branching extensions of the cell body.

Their internal structure is like that of the cell body itself.

That is, it is typically fibrillar and granular (including Nissl bodies).

2. Axon.

There is but one axon; it is usually longer and slenderer than the dendrons.

In some interconnecting neurons the axon is short and difficult to distinguish.

The axon of a multipolar cell usually begins as an elevation on the cell body.

This conical projection is known as the *axon hillock.*

The larger ones are devoid of Nissl substance, like the axon itself.

The axon maintains a nearly uniform size throughout its length.

It may bifurcate, but does not decrease in size because of this.

The contour is smooth and not spiny.

Nevertheless, some slender lateral branches (*collaterals*) do occur.

An axon usually ends in twig-like arborizations named *telodendria.*

Many axons acquire accessory sheaths along most of their course.

An axon and its sheaths are commonly called a *nerve fiber.*

Nerve fibers tend to run in bundles, termed *tracts* in the central system and termed *nerves* in the peripheral system.

The most important component of a fiber is the *axon* (or axis cylinder).

This is a protoplasmic, thread-like extension of the cell body.

The sheaths of an axis cylinder are of two different kinds.

One is a fatty sheath, made of formed substance and named the *myelin sheath.*

The other is a cellular sheath (of Schwann), or the *neurolemma.*

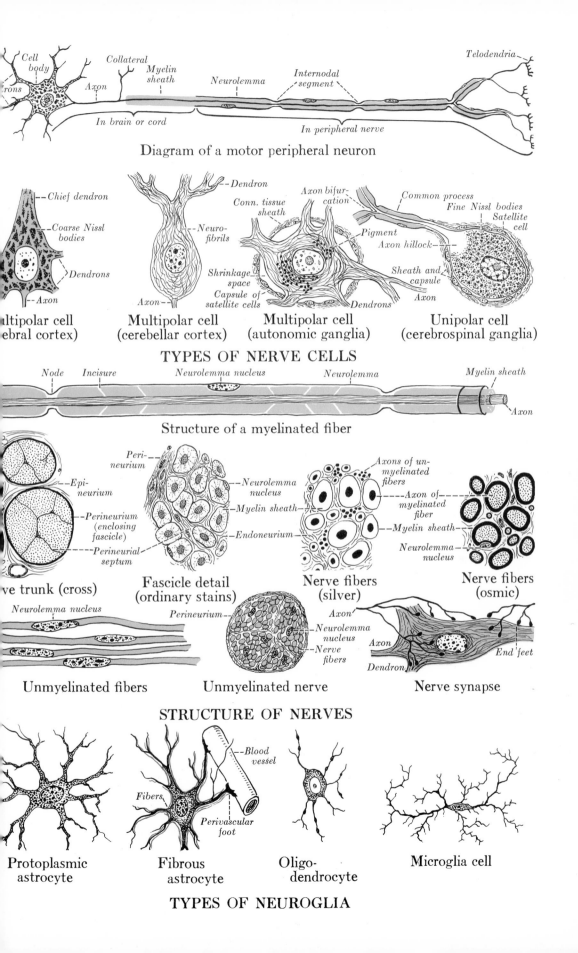

Diagram of a motor peripheral neuron

TYPES OF NERVE CELLS

Multipolar cell (cerebral cortex)

Multipolar cell (cerebellar cortex)

Multipolar cell (autonomic ganglia)

Unipolar cell (cerebrospinal ganglia)

Structure of a myelinated fiber

Nerve trunk (cross)

Fascicle detail (ordinary stains)

Nerve fibers (silver)

Nerve fibers (osmic)

Unmyelinated fibers

Unmyelinated nerve

Nerve synapse

STRUCTURE OF NERVES

Protoplasmic astrocyte

Fibrous astrocyte

Oligo-dendrocyte

Microglia cell

TYPES OF NEUROGLIA

V. CLASSIFICATION OF NERVE FIBERS

he presence or absence of sheaths furnishes a basis for the classification of nerve fibers.

1. Myelinated Nerve Fibers.
 A. WITH A NEUROLEMMA.
  Such fibers are common in the peripheral nerves of the cranio-spinal series.
  The tubular myelin sheath is interrupted at intervals in regions called *nodes*.
 B. WITHOUT A NEUROLEMMA.
  These fibers occur in the white substance of the brain and spinal cord.
  Here the myelin sheath appears to be an uninterrupted cylinder.
   Actually, nodes and other clefts (incisures) occur, but are not plainly seen.
  Neuroglial cells in association with fibers take the place of a neurolemma.

2. Unmyelinated Nerve Fibers.
 A. WITH A NEUROLEMMA.
  The axons of autonomic ganglia are all of this type.
  Also included are most of the small fibers of the cranio-spinal nerves.
  Myelinated peripheral fibers, near their terminations, furnish local examples.
   That is, the myelin sheath has been lost already, whereas the neurolemma
    sheath comes to an end somewhat farther on.
 B. WITHOUT A NEUROLEMMA.
  Axons within the gray substance of the brain and cord are naked threads.
  The final terminations of all nerve fibers are devoid of sheaths.
  Some tracts in the brain and spinal cord lack sheaths throughout their entire course.

VI. THE STRUCTURE OF PERIPHERAL NERVES

ll of the fibers of peripheral nerves are organized as typical axons.
 Actually, however, the sensory fibers are functional dendrons.
he following descriptions apply to the main extent of peripheral nerve fibers.
 They do not include the terminal simplifications through loss of sheaths.

. MYELINATED FIBERS:
 A fresh *fiber* appears to be a homogeneous, shiny, semitransparent tube.
  The wall is thick and interrupted at intervals by constrictions, or *nodes*.
  Branching may occur at these nodal levels.
 No further details are visible without staining.
  The stained appearance varies with the technique used.
 The thickness of fibers lies between 2 and 20 μ.
  This size-variation depends on the type of nerve and animal examined.
  Large fibers conduct impulses faster, and probably run longer courses.

1. Axon.
 In life the *axon* (or *axis cylinder*) is a soft, elastic, homogeneous-appearing jelly.
  The unspecialized cytoplasm of an axon (*i.e.*, neuroplasm) is called *axoplasm*.
  It is semifluid, and a continuous replacing-flow of it is claimed.
  Axoplasm embeds the more solid neurofibrils and mitochondria, but nothing else.
  The *neurofibrils* are continuous with those located in the cell body.

The surface membrane of the axoplasm is believed to be the part most directly con‐
cerned with the transmission of the nerve impulse; it is the *axolemma.*
The living axon is several times thicker than the myelin wall which encloses it.
(Most fixatives have the fault of shrinking the axis cylinder to a thin thread.)

2. Myelin Sheath.

The axon is surrounded by a tubular *myelin sheath,* containing fatty *myelin.*
In a fresh fiber the sheath is glistening, white and highly refractive.
Its presence is responsible for the 'white substance' of the spinal cord and brain.
Myelin is more fluid than the axoplasm of the axon itself.
Postmortem changes quickly break down the labile myelin into droplets.
Electron-microscope studies indicate that the myelin is arranged in spiraling layers.
Dark and light layers alternate; the total ranges up to 50 or more.
Their exact relation to myelin and *neurokeratin* is unclear.
The spiralling arrangement resembles that of a jelly roll.
Myelin is a complex mixture of lipids and protein.
It is dissolved out by lipid solvents (ether, alcohol, etc.).
Osmic acid blackens myelin; hematoxylin, after bichromation, also stains it well.
The tubular sheath is interrupted at intervals of 0.08 to 0.6 mm.
This produces constrictions along the fiber, called the *nodes of Ranvier.*
The total fiber resembles a sausage-chain, whose 'links' are *internodal segments.*
Their length is proportional to the length and thickness of a fiber.
Other breaks or interruptions are the *incisures* or clefts (of Schmidt-Lantermann).
These oblique, circular clefts subdivide the myelin sheath into *myelin segments.*
Such slanting segments fit together funnel-fashion; they arise as shearing defects
A spongy framework is visible in the sheath after myelin extraction.
This *neurokeratin network* is a precipitated and insoluble protein fraction.
The insulating function of myelin has long been advocated.
There is evidence that myelin also speeds impulse conduction.

3. Neurolemma.

The neurolemma is the toughest and most rigid part of a nerve fiber.
It dips inward at the nodes and there touches the axon.
Actually it consists of a series of separate, linked units.
Each unit is a single cell that extends between two nodes.
The ordinary microscope shows this *sheath of Schwann* as a long, thin tube.
Intervening between it and the axon is the series of myelin tubes.
The neurolemma is transparent and refractive; it displays little obvious structure
The exposed surface of the sheath is a modified plasma membrane.
Just within this membrane lies a thin, discontinuous layer of cytoplasm.
It is represented best about midway between two nodes.
Here is also located a single nucleus—oval and somewhat flattened.
From this center the cytoplasm radiates in interconnecting strands.
The electron microscope reveals that each unit of the sheath is a spiral wrapping.
A developing sheath cell encloses the axon, producing a concentric spiral.
Fusion of directly apposed membranes creates a mesentery-like *mesaxon.*
Myelin replaces the cytoplasm except at the extreme periphery.
Sheath cells are ectodermal; they originate from primitive ganglionic tissue.
In the central nervous system, oligodendroglia substitute for sheath cells.
The neurolemma is essential to the life and functioning of a peripheral fiber.

Presumably the sheath affords protection to the nerve fiber, as well.
The cells deposit myelin and are requisite to fiber regeneration.

4. Appearance in Sections.
A. LONGITUDINAL SECTION.
The fibers are pale bands, often of considerable width, grouped in bundles.
(Both smooth muscle and collagenous fibers take ordinary stains better.)
The myelin sheath is pale, but may show a network of neurokeratin.
Neurolemma nuclei are elongate and numerous.
Axons show as axial, well spaced threads when fibers are cut along the center.
They are acidophilic; with silver techniques they are brown to black.
Osmic acid stains the myelin sheath, which shows as parallel, blackened bands.
Shrinkage of the fiber-bundle (fascicle) commonly produces a zig-zag course.
B. TRANSVERSE SECTION.
The neurolemma shows as a sharply defined line about a fiber.
Occasionally a neurolemma nucleus is included, causing a local bulge.
The myelin sheath is a thick, usually unstained (or empty) ring.
Osmic acid stains the sheath, which then shows as a blackened ring.
The axon is a small, acidophilic central spot; it is blackened by silver methods.
The bundling of fibers to make a circular, ensheathed fascicle is distinctive.
(Neither smooth muscle nor tendon duplicates this arrangement.)
On changing the microscopical focus, a nerve fiber (myelinated or not) maintains
its size and remains in focus; artefacts usually do not.
That is, a fiber extends through the entire thickness of the section.
The images of the fibers often shift position on focusing.
This is because such fibers pass slantingly through the section.

B. UNMYELINATED FIBERS:
These are also called *Remak's fibers*.
They are thin, gray-colored fibers, 1 to 2 μ thick.
The ordinary appearance is of anastomosing strands, nucleated at intervals.
Actually each strand is a bundle of fine axons, with a common sheath.
Perhaps every fiber is invested with some myelin, even though too thin to stain.
All fibers contain doubly refractive material, as the polarizing microscope proves.

1. Axon.
Several axons course together as a compound fiber-cluster.
The group as a whole shares a common neurolemmal ensheathment.
Each axis cylinder is so slender that little structure is revealed.

2. Neurolemma.
This is a syncytial, nucleated sheath of ectodermal (neural crest) origin.
Each strand contains several to many tiny tubular grooves, opening to the exterior.
Coursing in each channel, and filling it, is an individual axon.
More rarely there is a solitary fiber with an individual sheath.

3. Appearance in Sections.
Ordinary staining methods color unmyelinated fibers but palely.
Methylene blue or silver techniques demonstrate axons clearly.

A. LONGITUDINAL SECTION.

A compound 'fiber' is a pale band with prominent, elongate nuclei at intervals.

These sheath nuclei seem to occupy the full fiber breadth and interrupt it.

The fibers are grouped in a long bundle (fascicle), paler than connective tissue.

In silver preparations, the axis cylinders are fine, black, crowded threads.

B. TRANSVERSE SECTION.

Individual 'fibers' appear as small, pale, circular areas.

Nuclei, when encountered, are rounded and prominent.

In silver preparations each axon shows as a black dot; these occur in clusters

The fibers occur in definite fascicles, ensheathed with connective tissue.

All connective tissue colors more deeply with routine stains than do axons.

C. NERVE AS AN ORGAN:

A peripheral nerve, taken as a whole, is an organ (as is a muscle or bone).

It has, therefore, a distinctive pattern of organization.

1. Structural Plan.

Individual nerve fibers are separated by fine collagenous fibers.

This interstitial connective tissue comprises the *endoneurium*.

That portion of it closest to each nerve fiber adheres to the neurolemma.

It constitutes a sort of fibrous covering, and is named *Henle's sheath*.

Nerve fibers are gathered into distinct *fascicles* (or funiculi).

Each fascicle is enclosed within a dense fibrous sheath, named the *perineurium*.

Wings from the perineurium often invade a fascicle; each is a *perineurial septum*.

Fascicles are bundled together as a *nerve*, or nerve trunk.

This is accomplished by loose areolar tissue, designated as *epineurium*.

It contains fat cells, blood vessels, lymphatics and some nerve fibers.

Most nerves consist of several to many fascicles; tiny nerves may have but one.

Nerve trunks frequently branch by the divergence of intact fascicles.

Each subgroup then serves as a separate, smaller trunk.

In small nerves, fascicles themselves may branch.

Through the branching and recombination of fascicles, *nerve plexuses* are created

Most peripheral nerves are mixed, containing both myelinated and unmyelinated fibers

The color of a fresh nerve depends on the nature of its component fibers.

Cranio-spinal nerves appear white because of their dominant myelinated fibers.

Autonomic nerves appear gray because of their unmyelinated fibers.

2. Vessels and Nerves.

Blood vessels and *lymphatics* occur in the epineurial tissue.

These vessels ramify and some reach the interior of fascicles.

Nerve twigs in the epineurium supply fibers to the blood vessels related to fascicles.

Such vasomotor fibers are called *nervi nervorum*.

VII. THE SYNAPSE AND OTHER ENDINGS

The axonal process of many nerve cells ends in relation to another neuron (or neurons).

This association constitutes the *synapse*, a local region of impulse transference.

Other axonal terminations are on muscle or glands, where activation is brought about.

Axons (functional dendrons) of ganglion cells serve as receptors of sensory excitation.

Some of these endings are attuned to general sensibility; others serve the special senses.

. The Synapse.

This is a specialization for communication between an axon and another neuron.

The contact usually is between an axon and the cell body or its dendrons.

Much more rarely it is between two axons.

As many as several thousand axonal terminals may bring impulses to one neuron.

The possible different routes of interneural transmission are prodigious.

The form of the axonal ending at a synapse exhibits many variations.

Commonly these endings swell into tiny, button-like *end feet* (or *boutons*).

Other types are *brushes* or *baskets* that adhere to a second neuron, or clasp it.

In every instance the association of the two neurons is intimate, but one of contact only.

The barrier consists of two thin surface membranes, 0.02 μ apart.

These are portions of the plasma membrane of each synapsing neuron.

The evidence is based on actual cytological observation.

It is also supported by a measurable delay in impulse-transmission here, and the failure of neuronal degeneration to pass a synapse.

Some neurons receive only a few terminations; others receive thousands.

A single axon may supply more than one ending on a second neuron.

But many neurons may contribute to the total number of synapses on a single neuron.

Nerve impulses pass equally well in either direction along a neuron.

It is the excited synapse that exerts a dynamic polarization.

It acts like a one-way valve, so the impulse can escape in one direction only.

This is from an axon to the dendrons or to the cell body of the next neuron.

. Motor Peripheral Endings.

Terminations on the three types of muscle have already been discussed (pp. 94, 99, 102).

Endings on glandular epithelium are described on p. 167.

. Sensory Peripheral Endings.

These receptors occur in relation to epithelium, connective tissue, muscle and tendon.

Some are related to general sensibility and others to the special senses.

They will be treated in Chapter XXV, which deals with sense organs of all kinds.

VIII. AUXILIARY TISSUES OF THE NERVOUS SYSTEM

. NEUROLEMMA AND CAPSULE CELLS:

These ensheathing elements of peripheral neurons are ectodermal (neural crest) in origin.

They form a continuous epithelioid layer over ganglia and peripheral fibers (pp. 106, 110).

. EPENDYMA:

The non-nervous *ependymal cells* are derived from the primitive neural ectoderm.

They remain, much like an epithelium, lining the cavities of the brain and spinal cord.

Embryonic ependyma is ciliated, and some cells retain cilia permanently.

Radiating from the central cavity, the cell tapers and ends in the neural wall.

The tapering end may branch; it becomes a long, thread-like process.

The ependymal process contains fibrils of the glial type.

In some regions they are specially modified, as in the chorioid plexuses (p. 118).

C. NEUROGLIA:

Non-nervous auxiliary cells, of ectodermal origin, occur wholly within the neural wall.
These are *neuroglia*, among which three main types are recognizable.

1. Astrocytes (or Astroglia).

This group consists of star-shaped cells with branching processes, hence the name.
A. PROTOPLASMIC ASTROCYTE.
It occurs chiefly in the gray substance of the brain and spinal cord.
The cell body bears fairly thick processes which branch repeatedly.
Both cell body and processes contain granular cytoplasm.
Some processes attach to blood vessels by expanded *perivascular feet*.
Some smaller astrocytes are satellite cells about neuronal cell bodies.
B. FIBROUS ASTROCYTE.
It occurs chiefly between the fiber tracts of the white substance.
The cell bears fewer but longer processes than the protoplasmic type.
They are thinner, straighter and branch but little; some attach to vessels.
Long, unbranched fibrils develop within the cytoplasm.

2. Oligodendroglia (or Oligodendrocytes).

These elements occur in both the gray and white substance of the brain and cord.
They are more abundant in the white substance and form rows between nerve fibers.
In the gray substance they serve as satellites to the cell bodies of neurons.
There is scanty cytoplasm about the nucleus, and but few cell processes.
The processes are small, beaded and not much branched.

3. Microglia.

Since these cells seem to be mesenchymal invaders, they are also called *mesoglia*.
Microglia are found throughout the brain and spinal cord.
They occur near nerve cells and blood vessels.
Their nucleus is small; it is elongate or irregular, and stains darkly.
The cytoplasm is scanty, but is drawn out at opposite ends of the cell.
These end-processes branch twistingly and are thorny in appearance.

D. APPEARANCE IN SECTIONS:

After ordinary staining many relatively small nuclei show in the central system.
They lack nucleoli, and thus differ from the nuclei of nerve cells.
Astrocytes have the largest oval nuclei and may show some perinuclear cytoplasm.
Oligodendroglia have smaller, rounded nuclei.
Microglia have small, irregular to elongate nuclei.
With the Golgi technique, two types of cell are demonstrated.
Spider cells (astrocytes) have long, branching, radiating processes.
Mossy cells (oligodendroglia; microglia) have short, varicose processes.
With the silver carbonate technique, individual characteristics are revealed faithfully.
The cell types and their diagnostic features are as described above.

E. FUNCTIONAL CORRELATIONS:

Ependyma subserves a supporting role, at least in the fetal brain and cord.
Neuroglia constitute an interstitial, auxiliary tissue of the central system.
They are suspected of playing an important role in the metabolic activities of neurons.
They react in definite ways when neurons are affected by a pathological process.

Astrocytes are supporting elements, with apparent insulating functions, as well.

Both types have processes in intimate contact with blood vessels.

Small astrocytes serve as satellites to nerve cells.

Oligodendroglia seem to substitute as sheath cells to myelinated nerve fibers.

Microglia can become migratory and highly phagocytic elements.

They are the macrophages of the central nervous system.

IX. MICROSCOPIC ANATOMY OF THE BRAIN AND CORD

he organization of the central system, as to both general architecture and structural details, has become the specific property of a branch of anatomy known as *neurology*.

ince these topics are treated in special textbooks, no duplication will be attempted here.

X. NERVE STAINS

)rdinary stained sections do not yield satisfactory information on most details.

Neither will any single, special stain serve as an all-purpose method.

fence individual techniques have been devised to reveal the various neuronal features.

Neurocytology records the composite information gained through their use.

1. Basic Dyes.

Dyes, such as *cresyl violet*, stain well the Nissl substance and all nuclei.

Chromatolysis (p. 105), following axon injury, is used to identify cells of origin.

In this way the cells belonging to definite fiber tracts can be traced.

Methylene blue is excellent as a supravital stain for the axon and nerve endings.

Hematoxylin, following mordanting in potassium bichromate, stains myelin.

The myelin sheath stains deep blue; all other tissue elements remain unstained.

2. Silver Reduction Methods.

A. GOLGI METHODS produce a coarse, black deposit of a silver salt.

The tissue itself is the prime reducing agent, but the response is commonly spotty.

Those neurons that do respond often are delineated in their entirety.

External form, but not internal structure, is made visible in exquisite detail.

Neuroglia also are sometimes demonstrated.

B. CAJAL METHODS utilize photographic developers as reducing agents.

The entire neuron is impregnated with a reduced silver compound.

In addition, neurofibrils are rendered visible.

C. SILVER CARBONATE REDUCTION, followed by gold toning, is used as a neuroglia stain.

The result is a selective staining of neuroglia and microglia.

3. Osmic Acid.

This reagent oxidizes, blackens and renders myelin insoluble.

Combined with potassium bichromate, it blackens the myelin droplets of degenerating fibers, whereas the myelin of healthy fibers colors yellow.

This method (of *Marchi*) is used in tracing the course of fibers distal to an injury.

XI. PROLIFERATIVE AND REGULATORY ABILITIES

euroglia, neurolemma and capsule cells can proliferate throughout the life span.

y contrast, neurons lose all reproductive power at about the time of birth.

Thereafter they are not replaced if destroyed.
Nevertheless, a neuron can repair a reasonable injury.
This is especially true of injuries to cell processes in the peripheral nerves.
A course of degeneration is then followed by gradual restoration (see beyond).
A corresponding regeneration of nerve fibers does not occur in the central system.
A nerve cell can also regulate its deranged internal organization.
Example: recovery from chromatolysis and its related phenomena.
As an adaptive response, a nerve cell can even alter its external form.
This occurs when its environmental relations change and a readjustment is required.
Example: transplanted ganglion cells change shape, develop new processes, etc.; neuro
affected by tissue loss in the central system, alter adaptively.

XII. DEGENERATION AND REGENERATION OF PERIPHERAL NERVES

Cutting or crushing a nerve fiber leads to changes known as *primary degeneration.*
Both of the injured ends (central and peripheral) are involved.
This primary degeneration extends only a short distance from the point of injury.
Within a few days, however, the entire peripheral portion of the fiber is affected.
This is *secondary degeneration,* or 'Wallerian degeneration.'
It is a necessary sequel to a physiological separation of an axon from its cell body.
However, the sheath cells of this portion survive and assist in the regeneration.

1. Changes in Peripheral (Disconnected) Portion.

The axis cylinder swells, fragments within 3 to 5 days, and disappears after 8 to 10 days.
Within a few days after injury, the myelin fragments into oval portions.
The remains of the axon and myelin are then removed by phagocytic absorption.
This is carried out by macrophages which invade the neurolemma tubes.
At the end of one week the neurolemma-sheath cells of each fiber have thickened, a
their nuclei have begun to proliferate.
By the seventeenth day a syncytial cord (*band fiber*) of sheath-cell tissue results.
At this time there is little or no degeneration-debris left.

2. Changes in Cell Body.

Most striking is chromatolysis of the Nissl substance (the *axon reaction*).
This begins one day after the injury and reaches a maximum in 14 days.
Other features are a swelling of the cell and displacement of its nucleus.
Restitution consumes several months, slowly reversing the alterations incurred.

3. Changes in Central Stump.

Primary degeneration proceeds toward the cell over about two internodal segments.
Within a week after injury, the end of the living axon thickens into a growing tip.
Many fine branches sprout from such a tip and grow peripherally.
These regenerating fibers grow 1 to 2 mm. each day.
Growth across the scar tissue at the wound-site is guided by sheath cells.
These cells have outwandered from both cut surfaces of the nerve.
The growing fibers enter the syncytial cords (or band fibers) of sheath-cell origin.
They then follow within these to reach a former site of ending.
Some of the fibers within a cord are inappropriate for the particular part reached.

Many new fibers (up to 50) may enter a single band fiber.
But eventually only one persists in a fiber.
Many others of the new fibers become lost in the scar or elsewhere along the way.
New neurolemma sheaths organize from the band fibers.
Slowly the regenerated axon regains its former diameter.
The total task of cytoplasmic regeneration is formidable.
A single regenerating fiber to the leg may produce axoplasm having a volume 250 times that of the parent cell body.
Myelin sheaths reappear early, but are slow in regaining their former thickness.

Additional Data.
Unmyelinated fibers of the peripheral system undergo a similar regenerative course.
The only difference is the nonparticipation of a myelin sheath.
In the central nervous system of mammals, regeneration is insignificant.
Sheath cells, as such, are lacking; their guiding role may be a crucial need.

XIII. MEMBRANES AND VESSELS OF THE BRAIN AND SPINAL CORD

MENINGES:
The brain and cord are encased within the bony cranium and spinal column.
They are more directly enveloped by fibrous coverings named *meninges*.
The surfaces of these layers are covered with a simple squamous epithelium.
It is a type that has been called mesenchymal epithelium (p. 26).

1. Dura Mater.
This outermost membrane is a separate cylindrical layer about the spinal cord.
In the region of the brain it becomes more or less intimately joined to the internal periosteum of the cranium.
The thick *dura* consists of somewhat vascular, dense fibrous tissue.
The inner surface is covered with a simple squamous epithelium.
It faces upon a thin space located between it and the arachnoid.
This region is known as the *subdural space*.
The outer, free surface in the extent corresponding to the spinal cord is also covered with a similar layer of simple squamous epithelium.
It is separated from vertebral periosteum by the *epidural space*.

2. Arachnoid.
This is a thin layer of nonvascular connective tissue, beneath the subdural space.
The *arachnoid* is covered on both surfaces with simple squamous epithelium.
From the main layer, columns extend inward to join the pia mater.
This cobwebby tissue gives the arachnoid its name.
The labyrinth between the pillars is the *subarachnoid space*.

3. Pia Mater.
The *pia* is a delicate, highly vascular layer of connective tissue.
Its external surface is covered with simple squamous epithelium.
Here also attach the fibrous columns of the arachnoid.
The union is so intimate that the two membranes are often mentioned together.
The single unit is then called the *pia-arachnoid*.

Where it faces the brain and cord, the pia is bound down by astrocytes.
Hence it follows all external contours of these parts faithfully.

B. VESSELS AND NERVES:

Arteries pass from the pia mater into the solid substance of the brain and cord.
Capillary meshworks are denser in the gray substance than in the white.
Returning *veins* reach the pia and then open into the dural sinuses.
These are venous collecting channels located within thicker regions of the dura.
There are no *lymphatic vessels* in the central nervous system.
The dura and pia are richly supplied with *nerves*.
Some are autonomic fibers that innervate blood vessels.
Others are sensory fibers ending in relation to sensory receptors.

C. CHORIOID PLEXUS:

Four regions of the brain have a thin, non-nervous (primitively dorsal) wall.
These regions are the lateral ventricles and the third and fourth ventricles.
Here the brain wall consists of a single layer of cuboidal ependymal cells.
This layer conforms to all the characteristics of a simple epithelium.
Its free surface is supplied with a specialized brush border.
The basal surface of its cells is thrown into complicated infoldings.
Supporting the ependymal sheet is a layer of highly specialized pia mater.
The combined membrane constitutes a *tela chorioidea*.
The pia sends out capillary loops, pushing the ependymal layer into 'fingers.'
The total vascular complex (tela plus local tufts) is a *chorioid plexus*.
The plexuses secrete *cerebro-spinal fluid* into the ventricles.
From the fourth ventricle the fluid escapes into the subarachnoid spaces.
Much, at least, passes into the dural sinuses through *arachnoid villi*.
These are stubby projections of the arachnoid membrane into the dural sinuse
Cerebro-spinal fluid contains proteins (traces), salts and a few leucocytes.
It fills and surrounds the brain and cord, acting like a shock-absorber for them.

Part III. Special Histology (Organology)

FOREWORD ON THE NATURE AND ORIGIN OF ORGANS

he study of organs is designated as *special histology*, or *organology*.

It is the science that deals with organ architecture and tissue adaptations.

is clear that both cytology and histology are fundamentally different from organology.

Cytology and *histology* deal with the nature of actual building materials (cells; tissues).

Organology is concerned largely with how the tissues, as structural units, arrange themselves
to make associated composites with distinctive architectural patterns.

Yet it also deals with the specialization of tissues for particular work to be done.

Organogenesis describes the developmental courses undergone in the creation of organs.

n *organ* is a somewhat independent portion of the body, performing a specific function.

It is an aggregate of tissues, arranged in a characteristic structural plan.

One tissue is primary in functional importance; others are auxiliary and secondary.

Example: the lining epithelium of the stomach (and the glands outgrown from it) is the
primary component; the connective tissue, muscular coat and peritoneal covering are secondary components, or auxiliary features.

A typical organ has a fibrous *framework*, and often an enveloping fibrous *capsule*.

It also has its individual supply of blood, lymph and nerves.

he essential, characteristic, functional cells of an organ are called its *parenchyma*.

By contrast, the internal, auxiliary, supporting tissue is the *stroma*.

Example: the epithelium of a gland is parenchyma; the connective-tissue bed is stroma.

everal types of simple organs have been treated already in the consideration of tissues.

Such are bones, muscles, tendons and nerves.

n *organ system* is a set of organs that collaborate in carrying out related functions.

The component organs sometimes display certain similarities of structure.

Example: nervous system; digestive system; endocrine system.

119

Stating the germ-layer origin of an organ designates the source of the primary tissue only.
A few organs are composites, with important parts differing in origin.
Example: suprarenal gland; hypophysis.
The following list summarizes germ-layer origins for the various organs or organ systems:
Ectoderm gives rise to: epidermis and its derivatives (nails; hairs; cutaneous glands); nervous system; sense organs; external orificial linings (mouth; nose; anus); salivary glands; hypophysis; suprarenal medulla.
Mesoderm gives rise to: circulatory system; lymphoid organs; kidney and ureter; gonads and ducts; suprarenal cortex; muscles; supporting organs (tendons; ligaments; fascia; skeleton); lining of body cavities.
Entoderm gives rise to epithelia of: digestive tube; liver; pancreas; respiratory tract; thyroid; parathyroids; bladder; urethra and associated glands.

Chapter *XIII*. THE CIRCULATORY SYSTEM

The *circulatory system* includes the heart, blood vessels and lymphatics.

The heart and blood vessels, alone, comprise the *cardio-vascular system*.

Blood vessels (and, usually, lymphatics) enter into the composition of all organs.

Because of this role as building units they are often referred to as *vascular tissue*.

Actually they are fairly simple organs that invade other organs and nourish them.

In vertebrates the circulatory system is a complete circuit of closed tubes.

The *heart* is a blood vessel, specialized as a powerful pumping organ.

Arteries conduct blood from the heart to the capillary bed.

The quality of blood is not a factor; it may be either rich or poor in oxygen.

The *capillaries* form a meshwork of the smallest-sized vessels.

Veins return blood from the capillaries to the heart.

The blood may be rich in oxygen (pulmonary vein) or deficient (venae cavae).

Lymphatics are vessels that return fluid (lymph) from tissue spaces to the blood stream.

It is a one-way flow, draining networks and blindly-ending capillary vessels.

The circulatory system conducts nutrients, oxygen and hormones to all parts of the body.

It also collects metabolic wastes from the tissues and transports them to the kidneys.

It is the chief integrator of the various other systems in the body.

The concept of a complete circuit of the blood was enunciated by Harvey (1628).

Yet the actual demonstration of capillaries came somewhat later (Malpighi, 1661).

I. THE BLOOD VESSELS

The clearest approach is to start with the fundamental and simplest vessel, the capillary.

Afterward the addition of accessory coats can be traced progressively in larger vessels.

A. CAPILLARIES:

These are simple, endothelial tubes connecting terminal arterioles and venules.

The name, meaning 'hair-like,' is descriptively appropriate.

Their length in muscle totals some 60,000 miles and presents 1.5 acres of surface.

The total cross-sectional area of the capillary system is 800 times that of the aorta.

Hence the rate of flow is only 0.4 mm. per second; (aorta, 320 mm. per second).

A comparison is a fairly stagnant pond and its swift supplying and draining streams.

Structurally capillaries are the fundamental vascular unit.

They represent blood vessels devoid of all accessory coats.

1. Size.

The average capillary is about 8 μ in diameter.

This bore will allow red blood corpuscles to pass in single file.

The largest-sized capillaries are about 12 μ in diameter.

A resting, collapsed capillary is narrower than when it is functioning.

2. Arrangement.

Capillaries take the form of a network of narrow canals.

The pattern may be that of a flattened net or a spongy meshwork.

This is an adaptation to the character of the region supplied.

Commonly the mesh is isodiametric, as in the lung and mesentery.

In elongate structures, like muscle, the mesh is diamond-shaped.

The intensity of metabolism in a region determines the closeness of the mesh.

There is a close network with narrow interspaces in the lung, mucous membranes, glands, striate muscle, and brain (gray substance).

There is a sparse network in tendon, nerve, smooth muscle and serous membranes.

3. Structure.

The cells are elongate, in the long axis of the vessel.

In most instances the cell margins are wavy and interlocking.

The cell margins usually overlap where they meet.

Cell boundaries (*i.e.,* intercellular cement?) are blackened by silver nitrate.

An endothelial cell is a curving, thin plate, with an ovoid to elongate nucleus.

In some locations plates vary in thickness and are perforated by tiny pores.

Two to three cells line the capillary at any level.

The cells are staggered so that their wide and narrow parts alternate.

The cell base rests upon a very thin basement membrane.

Capillaries course through a supporting bed of connective tissue.

Yet this tissue does not furnish any real wall for the capillary.

Only a delicate, reticular network ensheathes the endothelial tube.

Capillaries are accompanied by fixed macrophages and fibroblasts.

These cells are applied to the wall, but do not control the size of the lumen.

4. Diagnostic Features.

A capillary is a tiny tube, often collapsed and unnoticed in sections.

Its wall is so thin (less than 1 μ) that it appears as a mere line.

The nuclei, however, make local, bead-like bulges.

They resemble fibroblast nuclei, but lack the prominent nucleolus.

The vessel is embedded in connective tissue, yet this is not a part of the wall.

In longitudinal section a capillary takes the form of two parallel, beaded lines.

The lumen (unlike lymphatic capillaries) maintains a rather constant bore.

In transverse section a capillary is a thin ring, with or without a nucleus.

In most instances the caliber has been reduced somewhat by shrinkage.

It is usually not larger than a red blood corpuscle.

The section resembles, in miniature, a sectioned fat cell.

5. Functional Correlations.

Capillaries are functionally the most important of all vessels.

They lie in intimate relation to the various tissue elements.

Hence they can deliver nutrients and oxygen, and receive wastes.

They are the vessels at the scene of action of cellular metabolism.

Their thin wall and sluggish current are favorable for diffusive interchanges.

The endothelium of mammalian capillaries seems to lack any power of contraction.

Its adaptation to the changing blood-flow is a passive stretch and recovery.

Flow through the capillaries of resting tissues is intermittent.

In active tissues both the volume of flow and the area of endothelium bathed by
blood increase greatly.

Capillaries, although completely closed tubes, are quite permeable.

Water, gases, salts, nutrients and certain (introduced) dyes pass through.

Most colloids and all microscopic particulate matter do not pass normally.

Permeability varies regionally; also, under changed conditions, locally.

Blood cells are permitted to pass through endothelium on occasion.

Egress is facilitated by the endothelium first becoming sticky.

Leucocytes then begin to stick to the wall.

They next push a pseudopod through, and the whole cell follows.

Even red corpuscles can escape through badly damaged endothelium.

Endothelium prevents the coagulation of the blood contained within vessels.

True endothelial cells are not normally phagocytic.

Capillary endothelium can proliferate; it does so, for example, in healing wounds.

B. FALSE CAPILLARIES:

Certain tiny channels resemble capillaries in some general respects.

They possess, however, distinctive features not characteristic of capillaries.

1. Sinusoids.

These passages comprise a special set of channels, set between larger vessels.

Some connect arteriole with venule (spleen; suprarenal cortex; bone marrow).

Others connect venule with venule (liver; anterior lobe of hypophysis).

Still others interconnect lymphatic vessels (lymph nodes).

Sinusoids have several unique features that specifically characterize them.

They are relatively broad (up to 30 μ), and not uniform in caliber.

Their lining is an incomplete layer, consisting of scattered cells.

Outlines of the component cells are not demonstrated with silver.

The lining consists of cells that project into the lumen, and of flat cells.

The former cells are fixed macrophages, with pronounced phagocytic ability.

They belong to the so-called *reticulo-endothelial* (or *macrophage*) *system*.

The flat cells are apparently potential macrophages; all transitions exist.

The lining cells lie in close apposition to the surrounding parenchyma.

Only a network of reticular fibrils intervenes.

2. Rete Mirabile.

This is a capillary-like plexus inserted in the course of an arteriole or venule.

It is a 'marvelous network' because an afferent arteriole (or venule) feeds blood to
it and an efferent arteriole (or venule) drains it.

Retia are uncommon in mammals; the only familiar example is the renal glomerulus.

Similar are the sinusoids of the anterior hypophysis (venule—sinusoid—venule)
and of lymph nodes (lymphatic—sinusoid—lymphatic).

3. Diagnostic Features.

Irregular, broad channels and a close relation to parenchyma suggest sinusoids.

These features, however, are shared by some capillaries (*e.g.*, parathyroid).

The lining macrophages are not always easily identifiable as such.

The final proof is physiological—their ingestion of particulate matter.

A rete, by itself, is indistinguishable from capillaries.

It is distinctive merely by not connecting arterioles with venules.

C. PRECAPILLARIES; POSTCAPILLARIES:

These terms designate vessels intermediate between capillaries and arterioles or venules.
They are larger than capillaries and have incomplete accessory coats.

1. Arterial Precapillaries.

These vessels are less than 40 μ in diameter.
The smallest consist of an endothelial tube and smooth muscle fibers.
The muscle cells encircle the tube, but are scattered.
The largest add connective tissue cells and fibers discontinuously.

2. Venous Postcapillaries.

These vessels are less than 200 μ in diameter.
The smallest consist of endothelium and scattered connective-tissue elements.
Larger tubes also add smooth-muscle fibers discontinuously.

3. Diagnostic Features.

Sections that miss the accessory elements resemble oversized, bare capillaries.
Sections that include accessory elements still fail to show complete coats.
(The presence of complete coats in a tiny vessel signifies arteriole or venule.)

4. Functional Correlations.

The concept of pre- and postcapillaries is helpful in understanding the transitions between naked capillaries and vessels with clearly-defined coats.
With the addition of connective tissue, mechanical support is given a vessel.
With the addition of smooth muscle, control of vessel-size becomes possible.
Such *precapillary sphincters* control the flow through capillary beds.
Local beds are even intermittently closed-off in resting tissues.
A main precapillary, feeding a local area, is never completely closed.
It is called a *preferred channel* or a *thoroughfare channel.*

D. STRUCTURAL PLAN OF BLOOD VESSELS:

All blood vessels, above precapillaries, follow a common plan of organization.
Each specific type of vessel merely shows characteristic adaptations.
Certain features of the common plan are emphasized, reduced or omitted.
Certain new features may be introduced to meet local mechanical requirements.
Every typical blood vessel contains three concentric coats (*i.e., tunics*).
1. *Tunica intima* (or interna).
2. *Tunica media.*
3. *Tunica adventitia* (or externa).

1. Tunica Intima.

An *endothelium* (simple squamous epithelium) bounds the *lumen,* or central canal.
A *subendothelial coat* underlies the endothelium.
This is composed of delicate fibro-elastic tissue, mostly longitudinal.
The *internal elastic membrane* is the outermost component of the intima.
It is typically a fenestrated membrane (*i.e.,* a tube with 'windows').
Sometimes it splits into two or more layers.
On the other hand, the 'membrane' may be reduced to a simple network of fibers.
In an empty or contracted vessel the membrane folds.
These longitudinal wrinkles show as a wavy line in cross sections.

2. Tunica Media.

The primary constituent is smooth muscle, circularly arranged.

The fibers are short and often branched.

Elastic fibers are commonly added, but in variable quantities.

They sometimes occur as fibrous networks, circularly disposed.

The highest development is a series of concentric tubes.

Each tube is 'fenestrated' (*i.e.*, it is perforated by openings).

Networks and tubes alternate with muscle in a layered fashion.

3. Tunica Adventitia.

Next to the media, elastic tissue commonly concentrates as an *elastic layer.*

Closest to the media there may be a definite *external elastic membrane.*

Elsewhere the fibers are often preponderatingly longitudinal.

The remainder of the adventitial coat is composed of moderately compact fibro-elastic tissue, whose fibers take a predominantly longitudinal course.

The adventitia grades off into the areolar tissue, nearby.

The latter always accompanies, guys and supports blood vessels.

4. Vasa Vasorum.

Blood vessels more than 1 mm. in diameter have nutrient vessels.

These are *vasa vasorum,* which means 'vessels of vessels.'

In arteries these supply the adventitia and are mostly limited to it.

In veins they may penetrate deeper and extend through the media.

This is correlated with the poor quality of blood flowing in veins.

Some claim that the nutrient veins of veins often drain into the main lumen.

Lymphatics are present in the wall of larger blood vessels.

5. Nerves.

Unmyelinated nerve fibers form networks in the adventitia and terminations on the smooth muscle of the media; they are *vasomotor fibers.*

Myelinated *sensory fibers* arborize in the adventitia, and may even reach the intima.

E. ARTERIES:

Arterial blood vessels can be classified into three groups:

1. Arterioles; the smallest-sized vessels; predominantly muscular vessels.

2. Small to medium-sized arteries; predominantly muscular vessels.

3. Large arteries; predominantly elastic vessels.

These divisions are arbitrary and have no sharp limits.

The transition from the elastic to the muscular type is usually gradual.

Intermediate vessels mingle the features, producing a *mixed type* of artery.

Example: external carotid; axillary; common iliac.

On the other hand, the transition may be rather abrupt.

Example: abdominal aorta and its visceral branches.

Furthermore, size and composition are not always typically correlated.

Vessels of smaller caliber may resemble larger arteries.

Example: popliteal; tibial.

Vessels of rather large size may resemble smaller arteries.

Example: radial; coeliac; external iliac.

1. Arterioles.

These vessels, as a group, are invisible to the naked eye, or nearly so.
> Their diameter lies between about 0.04 mm. and 0.3 mm.

The wall is thicker, relative to the lumen, than in any other blood vessel.

A. TUNICA INTIMA.
> This layer is thin; there is no recognizable subendothelial tissue.
> The internal elastic membrane is really a network of fibers.
>> Yet, in sections, it often looks like a true membrane.

B. TUNICA MEDIA.
> The media is purely muscular and is the thickest and most prominent coat.
>> There are 1 to 5 layers of muscle cells.

C. TUNICA ADVENTITIA.
> This fibro-elastic coat is usually thinner than the media.
> There is no definite external elastic layer or membrane.

2. Small and Medium-sized Arteries.

This group comprises all arteries belonging to the *muscular type*.

Included are most of the arteries that bear names, and all small unnamed ones.
> The smallest are just visible to the naked eye.

A. TUNICA INTIMA.
> A subendothelial layer is represented, but may be very thin.
> The internal elastic membrane is prominent.
>> In older individuals it frequently splits locally into two (or more) layers.

B. TUNICA MEDIA.
> The thick tunica media is predominantly a muscular layer (up to 40 layers).
> The smaller vessels do not have a significant amount of elastic tissue.
> Larger vessels have some elastic tissue arranged in networks.
>> In the largest examples of this group, true elastic membranes occur.
> There is also a small amount of white fibrous tissue scattered about.

C. TUNICA ADVENTITIA.
> Sometimes thick, it is usually thinner than the media.
> Adjacent to the media there is an elastic layer.
>> In arteries not subject to stretching it is weakly represented.
>> Nearest the media there is commonly an actual external elastic membrane.
>>> This is similar to the internal elastic membrane.
> Outside the elastic layer, the adventitia is chiefly collagenous.

3. Large Arteries.

This group comprises all arteries belonging to the *elastic type*.
> The elastic tissue is sufficient to color the freshly cut wall yellow.

It includes the aorta and the largest main branches of the aorta.
>> These are the innominate, common carotid, subclavian (including the vertebral
>>> and internal mammary), and common iliac.

The wall is relatively thin in comparison to the large lumen.

A. TUNICA INTIMA.
> The endothelial cells are polygonal (not elongate, as in smaller vessels).
> The subendothelial layer is rather thick and has many elastic fibers.
> An internal elastic membrane is not a particularly significant feature.
>> Similar membranes are distributed throughout the media.

B. TUNICA MEDIA.

This thickest tunic is composed mainly of elastic and collagenous tissue.

Hence a large part of these main arteries is nonliving substance.

In the aorta there are 40 to 60 elastic membranes about 2.5 μ thick.

Each plate consists of broad bands interspaced by prominent gaps.

Neighboring membranes frequently connect by bands.

Interspaces between the concentric membranes contain fibroblasts, an amorphous ground substance, fibro-elastic tissue and sparse muscle cells.

C. TUNICA ADVENTITIA.

This layer is relatively thin and not highly organized.

There is no distinctive external elastic layer or membrane.

The outermost fenestrated membrane could be said to serve this purpose.

(A similar relation exists for the innermost membrane and the intima.)

The collagenous fibers take longitudinally spiral courses.

The adventitia restrains the expansile media and intima.

It acts much like the casing of a tire to an inner tube.

4. Specialized Arteries.

Some arteries deviate considerably from the generalized plan, already described.

These reflect adaptations to special locations and functional demands.

The intima may contain longitudinal muscle.

Example: occipital; uterine; palmar.

The media may contain muscle in two layers (inner, longitudinal; outer, circular).

Example: superior mesenteric; splenic; renal.

In general, arteries subjected to bending are reinforced by longitudinal and oblique muscle in the media; sometimes also by longitudinal muscle in the intima.

Example: common carotid; axillary; common iliac; popliteal.

The adventitia may contain longitudinal muscle.

Example: lingual; renal; splenic.

The wall may be relatively thin, with a reduction of some components.

In the pulmonary arteries this is correlated with lower blood pressure.

Arteries protected within the skull have the adventitia reduced, whereas elastic tissue is almost restricted to a thick internal elastic membrane.

Elastic tissue is highly developed in the renal arteries.

By contrast, it is practically lacking in the umbilical arteries.

Cardiac muscle extends into the roots of the aorta and pulmonary artery.

Some small arteries contain longitudinal thickenings of the tunica intima.

Example: penile; prostatic; renal; thyroid; umbilical; nipple; nasal mucosa.

These are produced by prominent local concentrations of smooth muscle.

Such intimal cushions control blood flow by occluding the lumen.

Some specializations are associated with arrival at sexual maturity.

The deep penile arteries have longitudinal muscle in the intima.

Uterine arteries vary with the menstrual cycle and alter irreversibly in pregnancy.

5. Age Changes.

Some arteries, such as the aorta, do not complete their differentiation until late.

In the aorta this is well into the third decade of life.

Aging is a physiologic process that passes insensibly into arteriosclerosis.

Each artery has its characteristic pattern and schedule of change.

Example: the coronary artery shows alterations at 20 years; other arteries ma[?]
have changed little at 40 years.
In elastic arteries the effect of wear is expressed chiefly in the intima.
There are irregular thickenings of elastic tissue.
In muscular arteries the response is mainly a calcification of the media.

6. Diagnostic Features.

The following entries summarize the general characteristics of the arterial wall.
A. TUNICA INTIMA.
This ranges from very thin (arterioles) to fairly thick (elastic arteries).
An internal elastic membrane is always present, even in small arterioles.
B. TUNICA MEDIA.
This middle coat is almost always the thickest of the three.
In arterioles and small to medium-sized arteries it is dominantly muscular.
In larger arteries the media becomes increasingly elastic.
Elastic membranes and muscle layers then tend to alternate.
The largest arteries are dominantly elastic, having many elastic membranes.
C. TUNICA ADVENTITIA.
The external tunic is thinner than the media in arterioles and small arteries.
It equals, or nearly equals, the media-thickness in medium-sized arteries.
It is much thinner than the media in the largest arteries.
An elastic layer and external elastic membrane are present in most examples.
Exceptions are arterioles, some muscular arteries and aorta types.
D. OTHER FEATURES.
The wall is a robust tube, but its relative thickness varies.
The smaller an artery, the thicker is its wall (compared to the lumen).
Rigor mortis contractions tend to empty blood from the arterial lumen.
Hence sections of the arteries usually do not show much blood.
Thick elastic membranes are easily seen, even when unstained.
Fine networks are demonstrable only with special stains.

7. Functional Correlations.

The heart delivers blood to the aorta in spurts and under considerable pressure.
The aorta and its elastic branches have two functions.
One is to absorb some of the pulse beat by the expansion of its elastic tissue.
This intermittent resistance stores latent energy.
The second is to relax the stretched walls while the heart is filling again.
This passive return to unstretched elastic tissue releases kinetic energy.
It maintains a more constant pressure and smoother flow of blood.
The elastic arteries are often termed *conducting arteries*.
This term emphasizes their conducting or 'piping' function.
The muscular arteries are able to regulate the amount of blood delivered to any part o[?]
the body, according to its changing needs.
This is done through nervous control of the muscular tunic.
Hence these arteries are also called *distributing arteries*.
The arterioles have relatively thick walls and narrow lumina.
They are the prime controllers of systemic blood pressure and of local flow.
Hence only a gentle stream escapes into the delicate capillary beds.
Most of the fall in pressure occurs within the arterioles.

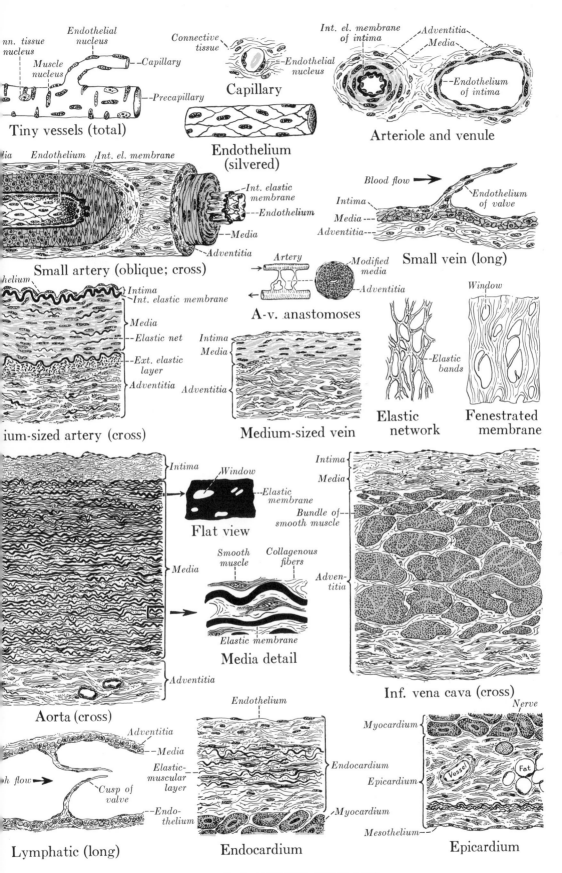

Tiny vessels (total)

nn. tissue nucleus
Endothelial nucleus
Muscle nucleus
Capillary
Precapillary

Capillary

Connective tissue
Endothelial nucleus

Capillary

Endothelium (silvered)

Arteriole and venule

Int. el. membrane of intima
Adventitia
Media
Endothelium of intima

Small artery (oblique; cross)

Endothelium
Int. el. membrane
Int. elastic membrane
Endothelium
Media
Adventitia

Small vein (long)

Blood flow
Endothelium of valve
Intima
Media
Adventitia

A-v. anastomoses

Artery
Modified media
Adventitia

ium-sized artery (cross)

helium
Intima
Int. elastic membrane
Media
Elastic net
Ext. elastic layer
Adventitia

Medium-sized vein

Intima
Media
Adventitia

Elastic network

Elastic bands

Fenestrated membrane

Window

Aorta (cross)

Intima
Window
Elastic membrane

Flat view

Media

Smooth muscle
Collagenous fibers

Media detail

Elastic membrane

Adventitia

Inf. vena cava (cross)

Intima
Media
Bundle of smooth muscle
Adventitia

Lymphatic (long)

Adventitia
Media
Cusp of valve
h flow

Endocardium

Endothelium
Elastic-muscular layer
Endothelium
Endocardium

Epicardium

Nerve
Myocardium
Epicardium
Myocardium
Mesothelium
Vessel
Fat

THE CIRCULATORY ORGANS

8. Carotid Body.

Each is a small mass located at the bifurcation of a common carotid artery.

It contains epithelioid cells, dilated capillaries and many nerve fibers.

It is a sensory chemo-receptor in relation to the adjoining carotid sinus.

A similar mass, the *aortic body*, lies within the arch of the aorta.

These organs are responsive to a reduction in the oxygen tension of the blood.

They play the important role of initiating respiratory reflexes.

VEINS:

Venous blood vessels are usually grouped into three classes:

1. *Venules.*

2. *Small to medium-sized veins.*

3. *Large veins.*

These divisions are often unsatisfactory as rigid categories.

Size and structure are not always well correlated.

There is more individual variation within a size-group than occurs in arteries.

Also the same vein may change structurally along its course.

Hence detailed generalizations are not so practical as with arteries.

1. Venules.

The diameter of these vessels lies between 0.2 and 1 mm.

A. TUNICA INTIMA.

The internal tunic is nothing more than an endothelium.

(A subendothelial layer and internal elastic membrane are lacking.)

B. TUNICA MEDIA.

This is a very thin tunic, composed almost exclusively of smooth muscle.

Muscle cells are only 1 to 3 layers deep; elastic fibers are scanty or lacking.

C. TUNICA ADVENTITIA.

It is relatively thick in comparison to the very thin total wall.

This layer consists almost wholly of collagenous fibers, largely longitudinal.

2. Small and Medium-sized Veins.

The diameter ranges from 1 mm. to 9 mm.

Included are: cutaneous branches; deeper veins of the forearm and leg; veins of the head, trunk and viscera (except main vessels and their tributaries).

A. TUNICA INTIMA.

The subendothelial layer is delicate and often lacking.

Bundles of longitudinal smooth muscle fibers occur in some vessels.

Elastic fibers vary from absence to a dense, net-like membrane.

Frequently this tunic is not clearly demarcated from the media.

B. TUNICA MEDIA.

Usually this is a weak layer; smooth muscle often occurs in plate-like bundles.

These muscle-masses are separated by collagenous fibers and elastic nets.

The media is best developed in the veins of the lower limbs.

C. TUNICA ADVENTITIA.

This well developed, fibro-elastic coat forms the bulk of the wall.

Its inner region often contains some longitudinal smooth muscle.

There is no tendency to develop an external elastic layer or membrane.

3. Large Veins.

This type includes: superior and inferior vena cava; portal vein.

Also the main tributaries to these trunks (including the upper arm and thigh).

A. TUNICA INTIMA.

The subendothelial layer is thicker than in smaller vessels.

It may contain scattered bundles of longitudinal muscle.

An internal elastic membrane is sometimes present, but is relatively delicate.

B. TUNICA MEDIA.

The smooth muscle is much reduced and may even be lacking.

At best this tunic is a relatively thin and feeble coat.

C. TUNICA ADVENTITIA.

This is by far the thickest of the three coats.

In it occur usually prominent bundles of smooth muscle, longitudinally arranged

This muscle may occupy almost all of an extremely broad tunic.

There is no external elastic layer or membrane.

4. Valves.

Many small and medium-sized veins are provided with pocket-like valves.

They are especially well represented in the limbs.

They are absent in the cranium, and sparse in the thorax and abdomen.

Valves usually occur in pairs, facing each other on opposite sides of the lumen.

They are commonly located just distal to the entry of a tributary vein.

This position is favorable to prevent backflow (away from the heart).

Also they aid in moving blood toward the heart when veins become squeezed.

This occurs in many locations where veins lie between contracting muscles.

Structurally a valve is produced by a local folding of the intima.

Internally it bears a network of elastic fibers on the side facing the current.

It is covered with endothelium on both surfaces.

5. Specialized Veins.

Some veins lack smooth muscle, and so are without a media.

Example: cerebral; meningeal; dural sinuses; veins of the retina, bones, spleni

trabeculae and maternal placenta.

Some veins are rich in muscle.

Example: suprarenal; umbilical; uterine (of pregnancy); limbs (especially lower)

Some veins have muscle in all three coats.

Example: uterine (of pregnancy).

Longitudinal muscle bundles occur in the intima of some veins.

Example: limbs (some); mesenteric; uterine (of pregnancy); internal jugular.

Longitudinal muscle may occur in the internal layers of the media.

Example: limbs (some); umbilical.

Longitudinal muscle may constitute the bulk of the adventitia.

Example: veins of the belly cavity.

Longitudinal muscle may constitute all of the muscle content.

Example: inferior vena cava (in part).

Cardiac muscle extends for a distance into the adventitia.

Example: venae cavae; pulmonary.

6. Arterio-venous Anastomoses.

In certain regions, arterioles and venules connect directly by cross connections.

In such a bridge, endothelium lies directly on a specialized tunica media.
Modified smooth-muscle cells have become short and thick, forming a sphincter.
In section they resemble a stratified cuboidal epithelium.
One type of location for these is the skin of exposed parts of the body.
Example: palm; sole; terminal phalanges; lips; nose; eyelids.
A second site is in tissues where metabolic activity is intermittent.
Example: mucous membrane of the gastro-intestinal tract; thyroid gland.
When the shunt is closed, arterial blood passes through the regular capillary bed.
When open, much of the blood by-passes directly across to the venule.
It is held that they are mechanisms for regulating circulation and blood pressure.
In exposed parts they can serve as protective devices.
They can increase the heat-loss and also prevent excessive local chilling.

COCCYGEAL BODY
This is a small mass, 2.5 mm. wide, located at the tip of the coccyx.
It consists of a group of arterio-venous anastomoses, with epithelioid muscle.
They are embedded in connective tissue representing adventitial coats.
No special function is attributable to the coccygeal body.

7. Diagnostic Features.

The following entries summarize the general characteristics of the venous wall.

A. TUNICA INTIMA.
In general, this tunic is thin.
Bundles of longitudinal muscle are present in some vessels.
This is especially true in large vessels.
An internal elastic membrane is an inconstant feature, never present in venules.

B. TUNICA MEDIA.
Smooth muscle and elastic tissue are relatively deficient.
The smooth muscle occurs mostly in flat bundles, circularly disposed.

C. TUNICA ADVENTITIA.
This is the thickest layer of a vein.
It commonly contains longitudinal bundles of smooth muscle.
An external limiting membrane is lacking in all examples.

D. OTHER FEATURES.
The three tunics are frequently without clear boundaries.
The media, in particular, may not be distinguishable as such.
Some have urged that the media and intima be considered as one tunic.
Collagenous tissue occurs in excess of all others.
The wall tends to be thin as compared with the size of the lumen.
It is loosely organized and flabby.
Hence a vein tends to collapse after death.
However, veins are often held open by accumulated blood.
(Venules packed with blood are sometimes mistaken for nerve fascicles.)
The characteristics of veins are correlated with low pressure of their blood.

8. Functional Correlations.

Blood in the venous system is under a pressure one-tenth of that in the aorta.
Hence it travels slowly, yet must replace the blood pumped out of the heart.
This is accomplished by using relatively large vessels.
Since the venous pressure is low, thin walls are adequate.
Since the flow is constant, elastic tissue (for pulse absorption) is little needed.

Since a control of distribution against fluid pressure is not necessary, circular muscle
not needed in large quantity.
Longitudinal muscle is featured undoubtedly as a useful functional adaptation.
The proper interpretation of its specific local role is not always clear.
Raising blood against gravity is aided by the presence of valves.
Valves are more commonly present in vessels subject to external pressure or in
fluenced by muscular movements.
Thin, weak walls correlate with the compression of veins by neighboring muscles.
This compressibility is a factor in promoting the venous circulation.
Also veins are easily distended; sometimes they act as reservoirs for blood.

G. REGENERATIVE ABILITY:

Blood vessels repair local injuries and also participate in wound healing.
Vessels send solid endothelial sprouts into regenerating areas.
The sprouts hollow out; fibroblasts are at hand and myoblasts soon differentiate.
Accessory coats are laid down about the endothelial tubes, as needed.
Transplanted segments of vessels, not from the same individual, are replaced slowly.
Endothelium grows in from both ends, and serves as a temporary bridge.
Fibrous tissue then replaces the muscular and adventitial coats of the transplant.

H. COMPARISON OF AN ARTERY AND VEIN OF THE SAME SIZE:

Paired vessels, encountered in sections, are usually identified easily as artery or vein.
Direct comparisons are then facilitated, especially in transverse sections.
But when a vessel is cut lengthwise, its mate often is not included.
Moreover, some structural features show to poor advantage in this plane.
The lumen of an artery is always smaller than that of its companion vein.
(Or the combined lumen of the companion veins, if there are two of these.)
The arterial wall is thicker and more rigid.
It holds its shape better and is less likely to collapse.
An artery is better supplied with elastic and muscular tissues.
Hence the media of an artery is usually the thickest coat.
Stronger postmortem contraction tends to force blood from the lumen.
Even the smallest arteries (arterioles) have a distinct internal elastic membrane.
Only some veins, larger than venules, are so supplied.
A vein is more loosely constructed than an artery and varies more from type.
The three tunics often lack clear boundaries.
Especially is the media inconspicuous or even absent.
The wall of a vein is relatively thin and its lumen relatively large.
A vein has collagenous tissue in excess of muscle and elastic tissue.
Hence the adventitia is usually the thickest coat.
Weaker postmortem contraction leaves blood in the lumen of a vein.
If blood has been drained away, veins collapse.
The lumen then becomes an irregular slit.
Veins are sometimes supplied with valves; arteries never have them.
However, valves are infrequently encountered in random sections of veins.

II. THE HEART

The heart is a highly specialized blood vessel that pumps 4000 gallons of blood daily.
There are the usual three coats of a blood vessel, but a distinctive name is given to each.

1. Endocardium.

The internal coat is homologous to a tunica intima.
Endothelium lies next to the central cavity of the heart.
The subendothelial layer is a thin sheet of fine white fibers.
With endothelium, it continues into the intima of vessels connecting with the heart.
Still deeper is a thick layer of fibro-elastic tissue and some smooth muscle fibers.
Farthest from the lumen is a loose connective-tissue layer.
This *subendocardial layer* binds the endocardium proper to the myocardium.
In the ventricles it contains the modified muscle of the impulse-conducting system.

2. Myocardium.

This is a middle coat that corresponds to the tunica media.
It is composed of cardiac muscle, much thicker in the ventricles than in the atria.
The *trabeculae carneae* are the only remnants of an embryonic spongy condition.
The cardiac muscle is arranged in sheets which wind around the atria and ventricles in
complex, spiraling courses.
The spaces between muscle fibers contain reticular, collagenous and elastic fibers.
This endomysial tissue also carries vessels and nerves.

3. Epicardium.

The external coat (also called *visceral pericardium*) is a serous membrane.
It is surfaced with mesothelium and supported by a thin fibro-elastic layer.
It affords a smooth, wet, slippery surface that minimizes friction.
Elastic fibers pass into the adventitia of vessels entering and leaving the heart.
A *subepicardial layer*, composed of areolar tissue, contains vessels, nerves and fat.
It attaches the epicardium to the myocardium.

4. Cardiac Skeleton.

The central support of the heart is dense fibrous tissue, the *cardiac skeleton*.
It is a continuous 'fibrous base' on which cardiac muscle inserts and valves attach.
The system consists of two sets of *fibrous rings* related to two *fibrous triangles*.
One pair of rings surrounds the origin of the aorta and pulmonary artery.
Another pair surrounds the atrio-ventricular canals and joins the ventricular septum.
In old age the cardiac skeleton may calcify locally; it may even ossify.

5. Valves.

There are reduplications of endocardium about the cardiac orifices.
Each valve-fold is supported by an internal plate of dense fibro-elastic tissue.
At the base of a fold this fibrous tissue is continuous with a fibrous ring.
The ring is a component of the cardiac skeleton, already described.
The *bicuspid* and *tricuspid valves* connect with papillary muscles by fibrous cords.
These *chordae tendinae* attach to the free borders of the cusps.
Such guys restrain the cusps from everting when the ventricles contract.
The *semilunar valves* of the aorta and pulmonary artery have three cusps each.
The central, fibrous plate forms a thickening (*nodule*) at the free border of a cusp.

6. Impulse-conducting System.

Mammals possess a system of cardiac muscle fibers, specialized for conduction.
This system has the function of co-ordinating the heart beat.

Its modified fibers lie in the subendocardium, close to the myocardium.
Two parts of this integrated, neuroid system are usually described separately.
The *sino-atrial node* lies at the superior vena cava–right atrium junction.
This is the site of the embryonic sinus venosus.
A plexus extends from this node under the myocardium of the right atrium.
The *atrio-ventricular node* is located in the median wall of the right atrium.
Its position is just below the orifice of the coronary sinus.
A common stem from this node begins the so-called *atrio-ventricular bundle*.
This stem gives off a branching trunk to each ventricle.
The constituent muscle fibers of the system are known as *Purkinje fibers*.
They are large, rich in sarcoplasm and poor in myofibrils.
The bundles of fibers are more or less encapsulated by connective tissue.

7. Vessels and Nerves.

The *coronary arteries* supply the heart, and cardiac veins drain it.
The myocardium is profusely furnished with capillaries.
This supply is about twice as rich as in skeletal muscle.
Lymphatics are abundant and intimately associated with muscle fibers.
The *nerve supply* is from the vagus and the autonomic system.
Their functions are antagonistic: vagus, inhibiting; sympathetic, accelerating.
Both sensory and motor fibers are represented.
Small autonomic ganglia occur in the heart substance.

8. Regenerative Ability.

The heart repairs injuries that are incurred by wounding or disease.
This is done by filling-in the defect with fibrous tissue.
The regenerative capacity of cardiac muscle itself is negligible.

9. Diagnostic Features.

The heart does not lend itself easily to simple diagnostic characterization.
This is partly because of its wide regional differences in organization.
Also the large size of the organ does not permit inclusive sections to be made.
The myocardium is unmistakable because of its massive content of cardiac muscle.
Any trace of it makes the diagnosis of epicardium or endocardium much easier.
Endocardium or epicardium alone are not especially distinctive, respectively, over the tunica intima of large vessels or some serosal membranes elsewhere.
Fat, sometimes abundant in the epicardium, helps to distinguish it from endocardium.
Smooth muscle and absence of fat indicate endocardium rather than epicardium.

III. THE LYMPHATIC VESSELS

These are closed tubes that collect some of the tissue fluid and conduct it as *lymph*.
So-called stomata, connecting lymphatics with tissue spaces, are artefacts.
Distally, lymphatics form networks, whose capillaries end blindly or in loops.
Centrally the converging lymphatic vessels empty into the great veins, near the heart.
Lymph drainage is a one-way flow, not a circulation.
Only a few organs lack a lymphatic supply.
Example: brain; spinal cord; eyeball; internal ear; bone marrow.

Capillaries.

Lymph capillaries are somewhat broader than blood capillaries.

They are not uniform in caliber but bear dilatations and constrictions.

The capillaries form dense networks, roughly co-extensive with blood capillaries.

They often run in company with blood capillaries.

Near surfaces they frequently begin as loops or as blind, swollen tubules.

Such surfaces are the skin and internal membranes.

The wall is composed of endothelium alone, even though embedded in connective tissue.

The endothelial cells are large, thin and delicate.

Lymph capillaries permeate nearly all parts of the body (see above).

Collecting Vessels.

Lymphatics larger than capillaries have the endothelium reinforced by auxiliary tissue.

These are connective tissue and scanty smooth muscle.

Vessels of about 0.3 mm. begin to have three tunics, and then resemble a vein.

However, these coats are indistinct and poorly demarcated.

Also, their walls tend to be thinner than a vein of equal size.

The largest of these collecting vessels are usually less than 1 mm. in diameter.

A. TUNICA INTIMA.

An endothelium lies upon a delicate network of longitudinal elastic fibers.

B. TUNICA MEDIA.

Smooth muscle occurs in a thin layer, mostly circularly arranged.

A few elastic fibers lie between muscle bundles.

C. TUNICA ADVENTITIA.

This thickest coat consists of interlacing collagenous and elastic fibers.

At the periphery, fibers continue into the adjacent areolar tissue.

Longitudinal bundles of smooth muscle occur in the adventitia.

D. VALVES.

Lymphatic valves are much more closely spaced (up to 2 mm. apart) than in veins.

Between the valves the vessels are swollen, giving a beaded appearance.

They occur in opposed pairs, their free edges directed with the current flow.

A valve is a pocket, formed by a local fold of endothelium alone.

Main Lymphatic Trunks.

These are the thoracic and the right lymphatic ducts, and their tributaries.

The structure is much like that of a vein of equal size.

But the three coats are even less distinctly demarcated.

Also, they vary more, at different levels, in thickness and internal organization.

The structure of the *thoracic duct* (4 to 6 mm. wide) is best known for details.

The *intima* has some longitudinal muscle and a thin, inconstant, elastic membrane.

It is well provided with valves; fibrous tissue supports the endothelial fold.

The *media* is the thickest coat; it has more muscle than a vein of equal size.

The muscle is grouped in bundles which have a circular arrangement.

In the best organized media-coats inner and outer longitudinal layers occur also.

The *adventitia* is not well defined and blends into the adjacent areolar tissue.

It contains a few bundles of longitudinal muscle.

Blood Vessels and Nerves.

Blood vessels supply the wall of the thoracic duct, much as they do in veins.

Nerve fibers, both motor and sensory, are found in the wall of larger vessels.

5. Regenerative Ability.

Injuries to lymphatics can be replaced by outgrowths from existing capillary vessels.

The process is similar to that in blood vessels, but slower.

6. Diagnostic Features.

Capillaries are large and irregularly swollen, in contrast to blood capillaries.

Collecting vessels are thinner-walled than blood vessels of the same size.

Their tunics are less well defined; they are more subject to collapse.

Valves are encountered more frequently than in veins.

The vessel is commonly bulbous in the intervals between two sets of valves.

This feature is apparent in longitudinal sections only.

Collecting lymphatic vessels often accompany an artery and vein.

There are often several in close association with a vein.

This makes comparison and diagnosis easier.

The main trunks (*e.g.*, thoracic duct) resemble a vein of equal size.

But they have more muscle in the media than do comparable veins.

It is mostly circular, but is broken into well-spaced bundles.

The typical content in the lumen is a granular or fibrinous coagulum.

Lymphocytes occur sparingly; other leucocytes rarely; red corpuscles, almost never.

In clotted lymph the leucocytes tend to lie at the periphery of the clot.

7. Functional Correlations.

Material, escaped from blood capillaries, must be returned to the blood stream.

Among these transudates in the tissue spaces there is some protein.

If left, such colloid would bind increasing amounts of water and produce edema.

Only lymphatic capillaries are able to recapture this colloid material.

Lymphatic capillaries also convey a larger part of the fat absorbed from the intestine.

Flow is promoted by compression from adjoining muscles and pulsating blood vessels.

Among other possible factors, muscular propulsion by the vessel wall is uncertain.

The valves seem to be the dominant feature in controlling the direction of flow.

Valves also occur at the junction of the main trunks with systemic veins.

These act to prevent a backflow of blood into lymphatic trunks.

Injected dyes appear in the thoracic duct promptly (in 10 sec. from the foot of a dog).

Discharge from the human thoracic duct averages 1 ml. per min., but is variable.

The pressure is quite low in comparison to the blood pressure in veins.

Lymph, in its onward passage beyond capillaries, encounters interposed lymph glands.

It percolates through these organs, thereby being filtered but gaining lymphocytes.

Lymphatic endothelium is not normally phagocytic.

Chapter XIV. THE LYMPHOID ORGANS

everal organs and parts of the body consist largely of a material named *lymphoid tissue.*
These can be arranged in a series based on increasing complexity of organization.

I. LYMPHOID TISSUE

ymphoid tissue also bears an older name, *adenoid tissue.*
consists of two primary tissue-elements, intermingled in intimate association:
   (1) *Reticular tissue;* (2) *cells*, chiefly lymphocytes, in the reticular interstices.
he crowded lymphocytes tend to conceal the reticular-tissue components.
his common association of cells and reticulum makes a sort of elementary building material.
   Since it occurs in various organs, it is for convenience spoken of as a tissue.
   When it is dominant in an organ, such is called a *lymphoid organ.*
   Lymphoid tissue, as a whole, constitutes one of the largest organ-masses of the body.
      Some believe it exceeds the liver in bulk, or is at least one per cent of body weight.
he reticular tissue component has the structural features already described (p. 44).
   The *reticular cells* are arranged in an apparent syncytium.
      Some have little cytoplasm and are relatively undifferentiated, like mesenchymal cells.
         These are the *primitive reticular cells.*
      Others have acquired more cytoplasm and have gained phagocytic abilities.
         These are *fixed macrophages* which, on detachment, become *free macrophages.*
         Both the fixed and free macrophages can increase by cell division.
   The *argyrophil fibers* are ensheathed, at least in part, by reticular-cell cytoplasm.
he *free cells* are of several types.
   Commonest are the small lymphocytes.
      Medium-sized lymphocytes and large lymphocytes are much less abundant.
      Also all intergrades in size can be found between these three types.
   Large lymphocytes divide into medium-sized, and medium-sized into small lymphocytes.
      Small lymphocytes can then grow into larger forms, but this is uncommon.
   Free macrophages occur, especially in the sinuses of lymph glands and in splenic pulp.
   Plasma cells and granulocytes are also found at times.

DIFFUSE LYMPHOID TISSUE:
   This is the simplest manifestation of lymphoid tissue.
   It occurs as an infiltration into the lamina propria of a mucous membrane.
      The chief locations are the alimentary and respiratory tracts.
      In the intestine the composite is not a pure lymphoid tissue.
         Collagenous and elastic fibers may be present also.
         Other cells, not typically associated (plasma cells; eosinophils), may occur.
   There is no special organization beyond a fairly homogeneous distribution.
      Proliferation occurs, essentially in the manner to be described for the nodule.

B. LYMPH NODULES:

Other names sometimes given are *lymph follicle* and *primary nodule*.

Nodules are dense aggregations of lymphoid tissue arranged in rounded masses.

Such a mass (up to 2 to 3 mm. in diameter) is easily visible to the unaided eye.

Many occur as *solitary nodules*, most commonly embedded in diffuse lymphoid tissue.

Example: in the intestinal tract there are some 30,000 of these in the mucosa.

Others occur as components of specific lymphoid organs (tonsil; lymph node; spleen).

Here they constitute a kind of structural building unit.

1. General Features.

A nodule may be homogeneous throughout, the small lymphocyte predominating.

But often there is a darker *cortex* and a lighter *germinal center*.

The cortex consists of small lymphocytes, at times in concentric zones.

The center contains paler, larger cells.

The reticulum is denser in the cortex and is concentrically arranged there.

This is due to cells being crowded away from the center by growth.

At the periphery the reticulum continues into that of adjacent diffuse tissue.

Lymph nodules are not constant features, either in structure or in position.

They appear, remain for a time, and then disappear.

New nodules may arise at any time or place in diffuse lymphatic tissue.

2. Germinal Centers.

The lighter-staining *centers* (also called *secondary nodules*) are inconstant features.

They are absent in the fetus and in old age.

They also appear and disappear periodically.

A typical center is sharply demarcated from the more peripherally located cortex.

Its measures up to 1 mm. in diameter.

The component cells are larger, with more cytoplasm and paler nuclei.

Hence, the whole central area appears lighter in stained sections.

Most of the cells are medium-sized lymphocytes.

These are the most actively dividing elements.

Some large lymphocytes and a few small lymphocytes are also seen.

Reticular-tissue cells are found here (and elsewhere) in the nodule.

Their nuclei are pale, oval and wrinkled; the cytoplasm is not well defined.

Occasionally these cells divide also.

3. Proliferative Cycle.

Lymph nodules, at relative rest, do not possess germinal centers.

Such a nodule consists mainly of small lymphocytes.

But periodically the central cells may begin a phase of mitotic activity.

The dominant central cells are proliferating, medium-sized lymphocytes.

Some of them transform into large lymphocytes.

Primitive reticular cells give rise to some medium-sized lymphocytes.

This activity is in addition to their production of macrophages.

Thus the *center* organizes and acquires its characteristics.

During an active phase, small lymphocytes are the most abundant product.

They are mostly the daughter cells of the medium-sized lymphocytes.

To a lesser degree they are derived from large lymphocytes.

Also some trace origin indirectly to primitive reticular cells.

This is through the latter elements giving rise to medium-sized **lymphocy**

These activities at the expanding center create pressure in a peripheral direction.

    The small lymphocytes, adjoining the center, are crowded into a peripheral zone.

    This compact region comes to be the *cortex*, sharply demarcated from the center.

    The cortex is also augmented by newly-formed small lymphocytes from the center.

After a time the center approaches a new period of inactivity.

    Mitotic divisions decrease in frequency.

    The last mitoses of the stem cells give rise to small lymphocytes.

    Such an inactive center contains reticular cells, macrophages and a few lymphocytes.

As the center becomes inactive, the former growth pressure subsides.

    This removes the sharp boundary between germinal center and cortex.

    New small lymphocytes then mingle with older ones.

    Thus the nodule may return to its homogeneous, resting appearance.

The formation of lymphocytes is not wholly confined to the center.

    It occurs in the cortex and in diffuse lymphoid tissue as well.

4. Reaction Centers.

    In certain inflammatory states, nodules have central areas of a different kind.

        The cells are free macrophages and reticular cells.

        In such pale areas new lymphocytes are not being produced.

        These areas are called *reaction centers* to toxic and other stimuli.

            They function in destroying toxic agents and producing antibodies.

    Reaction centers are frequently observed in the tonsil and appendix.

5. Vessels and Nerves.

    An *arteriole* and a *venule* supply the nodule, forming a peripheral plexus.

        Another plexus supplies the germinal center, when this region is present.

    Lymph capillaries envelop the exterior of the nodule, but do not invade it.

    Nerve fibers are apparently all vasomotor.

6. Diagnostic Features.

    The darkly stained, basophilic mounds are prominent even to the naked eye.

    Sections, outside the midplane, may fail to include the pale germinal center.

        Such a section is unreliable evidence for or against the presence of a center.

        Any rounded, sizable mass of lymphocytes is, however, recognizable as a nodule.

    Reticular cells have pale, wrinkled nuclei; the cytoplasm is indistinct.

        Indistinct cytoplasm is explained by its ensheathing relation to reticular fibers.

    Medium-sized and large lymphocytes have nuclei with somewhat more chromatin.

        Cytoplasm and its limits are plainer because these cells are free.

    Small lymphocytes have checkered, dark nuclei and show little or no cytoplasm.

7. Functional Correlations.

    An obvious function of lymphoid tissue is the production of new lymphocytes.

        Some of these cells migrate into blood capillaries; others enter the sinuses of lymph nodes and of the spleen in large quantities.

        (Under various abnormal conditions, lymphoid tissue can also produce granulocytes.)

    Also plain are the phagocytic potentialities of free and fixed macrophages.

        This activity is directed against bacteria, spent blood cells and foreign matter.

The macrophage system of lymphoid tissue filters tissue fluid, lymph or blood.

The particular fluid, so treated, depends on where the filtering is done.

Lymphoid tissue is believed to be associated with the production of immunity.

Lymphocytes are rich in specific antibodies.

Yet the source and significance of these have not been established surely.

The immature plasma cell is suspect as the chief producer of antibodies.

II. THE AGGREGATE NODULES

1. Structural Plan.

These aggregations have attained a small degree of organization.

Each is a closely grouped mass of lymph nodules that has definable limits.

Its appreciable size and its response to growth pressure have produced a visible bulge in the intestinal lining.

These masses are also called *agminate nodules* and *Peyer's patches*.

Their location is in the lamina propria, and mainly in the ileum.

Some occur in the jejunum and even in the duodenum.

A Peyer's patch is an oval group of closely associated, pear-shaped nodules.

It is always located in the lining, opposite to the attachment of the mesentery.

The long axis of a patch runs lengthwise of the intestine.

The total number of patches larger than 25 sq. mm. is 25 to 50.

They vary in size; a large patch measures several centimeters in length.

The lymph nodules of a fairly large patch will total into the hundreds.

They lie close together and commonly show germinal centers.

The broad bases of the expanded nodules have burst through the muscularis mucosae.

They thus encroach on the submucosa and compress it.

There is, however, no definite encapsulation of the massed nodules.

The nodules commonly merge, except at their apices, thus becoming confluent.

The surface facing the lumen is covered with intestinal epithelium.

Emigrating lymphocytes infiltrate the epithelium profusely.

Some cells pass through the epithelial lining and enter the intestinal lumen.

Intestinal villi and glands are largely obliterated locally where a nodule occurs.

The patches are seemingly rather permanent until senile involution overtakes them.

2. Diagnostic Features.

An aggregate of lymph nodules bounds a minor portion only of the intestinal lumen.

The superficial surface is bordered by a simple columnar epithelium.

The deep surface encroaches on the submucosa of the intestine.

The adjoining tissue (villi; glands) identifies the small intestine.

Where nodules occur, the villi and glands tend to be suppressed through pressure.

3. Functional Correlations.

All lymphoid tissue that is supplied by efferent lymphatics only, and lacks specialized sinuses, serves as a filterer of local tissue fluids.

This group includes diffuse tissue, solitary nodules, aggregate nodules and tonsils.

No specific function can be ascribed to aggregate nodules.

It is commonly said that they act in some way protectively against bacteria.

Yet they are the chief seats of ulceration in typhoid fever.

Neither can their choice of the ileum as a preferred location be explained adequately.

III. THE TONSILS

hree tonsillar groups form a lymphoid ring about the entrance of the throat.
    There is structural similarity in all three types.
me advances in organization have been made over the simpler aggregate nodules.
    These are: epithelial inpocketings; encapsulation; and a coarse internal framework.

. PALATINE TONSIL:
    Faucial tonsils is a less common name applied to these paired organs.
    Their location is at the entrance to the throat, one on each side.
        Each tonsil lies between two arching folds of the pharynx.
        This relation gave the fanciful name of tonsilla, 'a mooring stake.'
    A tonsil is ovoid, with its long axis directed vertically.
        Each measures about 1 x 0.5 in.
    The medial surface is freely exposed and sometimes bulging.
        This surface is studded with pits, which are mouths of distinctive pockets (*crypts*).

1. Structural Plan.

    A tonsil is a dense mass of diffuse and nodular lymphoid tissue.
        It is a specialized region of the pharyngeal mucous membrane.
    It is loosely *encapsulated* and is subdivided by *septa*.
    The free surface is covered with *epithelium*, continuous with that of the pharynx.
    Invaginated, epithelial pockets (called *crypts*) invade the tonsillar substance.

2. Detailed Structure.

    A. FRAMEWORK.
        Fibrous tissue, adjacent to the deepest portions of the tonsil, is compacted.
            This came about through pressure from the expanding organ on the sub-
                mucosa.
            Such compressed tissue produces a poorly organized, thin *capsule*.
            The capsule covers the base and sides of the tonsil.
        Continuations of the capsule extend, as *septa*, into the interior of the tonsil.
            These plates separate incompletely some 10 to 20 territories.
                Such territories, or *lobules*, are centered about individual crypts.
            The fibrous septa bind the capsule firmly to the tonsil proper.
                As a result, the tonsil can be removed surgically as a unit.
            Various cell types are found in the septa: lymphocytes; mast cells; plasma cells;
                neutrophils (indicative of inflammation).
        Reticular fibers are continuous with the capsule and septa.
            They permeate the parenchyma everywhere as a delicate support.
    B. EPITHELIUM AND CRYPTS.
        The free surface is covered with a stratified squamous *epithelium*.
            This is continuous with the lining of the mouth and pharynx.
                The epithelium rests upon a *basement membrane*, under which is often some
                    loose connective tissue.
        About 40 epithelial *crypts* penetrate into the interior of the tonsil.
            Some are simple tubules, but many branch complexly and extend far inward.
                Only the larger ones open on the surface as easily noticeable pits.
            The lumen of a crypt contains material that may even form cheesy plugs.

Included are: lymphocytes and plasma cells (living and dead); desqu
mated epithelial cells; micro-organisms; cellular debris.

The surface area of the crypt systems of both tonsils is some 90 sq. in.

This is twelve times the exposed surface-area of the entire pharynx.

c. LYMPHOID TISSUE.

The general *lymphoid tissue* is a fairly dense cellular mass.

It borders the surface epithelium in a layer 1 to 2 mm. thick.

This layer also follows the epithelium wherever it dips inward as crypts.

Hence a fold of lymphoid tissue is bordered by epithelium on the cry
side and by a connective-tissue septum on its deeper side.

Lymph nodules occur abundantly in the general sheet of lymphoid tissue.

They usually lie in a single layer, paralleling the epithelium.

Germinal centers are unusually large; see *reaction centers* (p. 139).

(Slanting sections exaggerate locally the thickness of the lymphoid layer.)

d. LEUCOCYTIC INFILTRATION.

Emigrating lymphocytes are seen in the surface epithelium and especially with
the epithelial lining of the crypts.

In addition, plasma cells and polymorphonuclear leucocytes may participa
The invasion of the epithelium may involve only a scattering of lymphocytes.

By contrast, the infiltration is frequently so intense that many pockets form.

In this instance the epithelium is largely destroyed locally.

Usually, however, a few layers of cells remain at the original surface.

Also, the basement membrane is usually still recognizable.

Highly eroded and nearly intact areas of epithelium often exist side by side.

Many migrant-lymphocytes escape and appear in the saliva.

They are added to cells occurring there, known as *salivary corpuscles*.

e. ASSOCIATED STRUCTURES.

Mucous glands lie in the submucosa, beneath the tonsil and its capsule.

Their ducts empty into the cavity of the pharynx.

These openings are on the surface of a tonsil, or near its periphery.

Only rarely does a duct open into a crypt, and then near its mouth.

Skeletal muscle underlies the capsule and mucous glands.

A little of it is often encountered in sections of an excised tonsil.

Sometimes small islands of cartilage (or even bone) lie near the tonsils.

These are probably inconstant derivatives of the embryonic branchial arch

B. LINGUAL TONSIL:

This organ is located on the root of the tongue, behind the vallate papillae.

It is an aggregation of epithelial pits, each surrounded by lymphoid tissue.

In all, there are between 35 and 100 of these units.

In surface view, each unit is a low mound with a central crater.

The pit is a simple *crypt* which, however, sometimes bifurcates.

It is lined with a continuation of the surface *epithelium* (stratified squamous).

Leucocytic infiltration is usually less severe than in the palatine tonsils.

The mound-like elevation is due to a mass of *lymphoid tissue* 1 to 5 mm. in diameter.

This surrounds the crypt and is ovoid to inverted-conical in shape.

It contains usually a single layer of *lymph nodules* with germinal centers.

Bordering each unit is a thin connective-tissue *capsule*.

Ducts of underlying *mucous glands* open into the crypts or onto the surface.

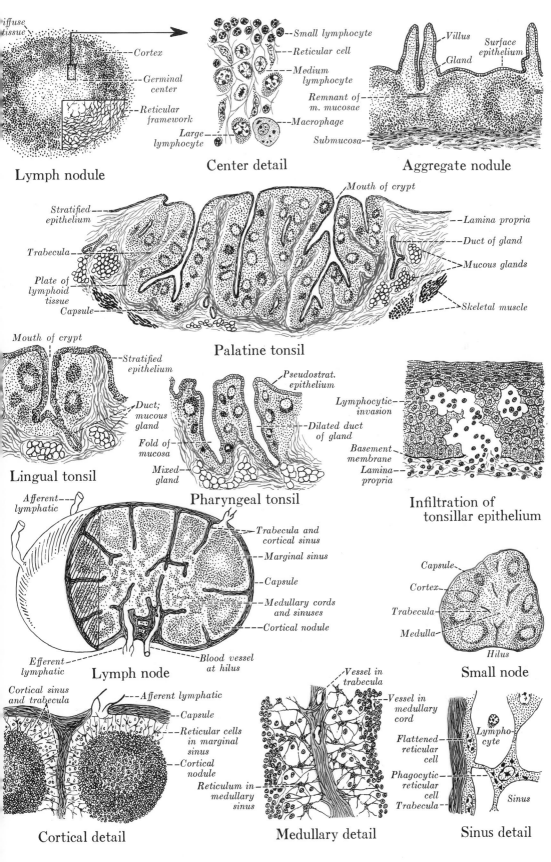

Lymph nodule

Center detail

Aggregate nodule

diffuse tissue
Cortex
Germinal center
Reticular framework

Small lymphocyte
Reticular cell
Medium lymphocyte
Macrophage
Large lymphocyte

Villus
Gland
Surface epithelium
Remnant of m. mucosae
Submucosa

Palatine tonsil

Stratified epithelium
Trabecula
Plate of lymphoid tissue
Capsule
Mouth of crypt
Lamina propria
Duct of gland
Mucous glands
Skeletal muscle

Lingual tonsil

Mouth of crypt
Stratified epithelium
Duct; mucous gland
Fold of mucosa
Mixed gland

Pharyngeal tonsil

Pseudostrat. epithelium
Dilated duct of gland

Infiltration of tonsillar epithelium

Lymphocytic invasion
Basement membrane
Lamina propria

Lymph node

Afferent lymphatic
Trabecula and cortical sinus
Marginal sinus
Capsule
Medullary cords and sinuses
Cortical nodule
Efferent lymphatic
Blood vessel at hilus

Small node

Capsule
Cortex
Trabecula
Medulla
Hilus

Cortical detail

Cortical sinus and trabecula
Afferent lymphatic
Capsule
Reticular cells in marginal sinus
Cortical nodule
Reticulum in medullary sinus

Medullary detail

Vessel in trabecula
Vessel in medullary cord
Flattened reticular cell
Phagocytic reticular cell
Trabecula

Sinus detail

Lympho- cyte
Sinus

SMALL LYMPHOID ORGANS

C. PHARYNGEAL TONSIL:

The clinical name is *adenoids*, especially when overgrowth occurs.
This organ comprises an accumulation of lymphoid tissue, about 3 cm. long.
 It is located in the median dorsal wall of the nasopharynx.
At the tonsillar site, the pharyngeal lining makes a series of longitudinal *folds*.
 Sections cut across them look like longitudinal sections of a series of crypts.
 However, this is a deception and true, pocket-like crypts are lacking.
The *epithelium* is pseudostratified, with cilia and goblet cells.
 There are some islands of stratified epithelium, especially in the adult.
 Infiltration of epithelium by migratory leucocytes occurs and can be extensive.
The *lymphoid tissue* occupies a layer about 2 mm. thick.
 It contains *lymph nodules* with germinal centers.
A thin *capsule* underlies the tonsil and sends *septa* outward into the folds.
Mixed *sero-mucous glands* are plentiful beneath the capsule.
 Their *ducts* open into the trough-like downfoldings and onto the alternating crests.
 Most of these ducts widen surfaceward into prominent, long funnels.
 They resemble unbranched crypts and seem to serve the same purpose.

D. VESSELS AND NERVES:

Blood vessels course in the capsule and septa, and supply the lymphoid tissue.
Lymphatic vessels form plexuses about the lymphoid mass, but do not invade it.
Nerves follow the blood vessels into the septa and parenchyma.

E. INVOLUTION:

Tonsils, in general, reach their maximal development in childhood.
The *pharyngeal tonsil* begins to decline at about the time of puberty.
 In the adult it is usually atrophic to a marked degree.
  The pseudostratified epithelium has been replaced largely by stratified squamous.
When *palatine tonsils* enter involution is not generally agreed upon.
 Different observers favor middle childhood, puberty and adulthood.
 This divergence of opinion probably reflects an inherent variability in the onset.
 In advanced age tonsils become replaced to a large degree by fibrous tissue.
The *lingual tonsils* mature slowly, and involution begins later than in other tonsils.

F. REGENERATIVE ABILITY:

Both the palatine and pharyngeal tonsils have marked regenerative capacity.
 Incomplete removal may be followed by extensive regrowth.

G. DIAGNOSTIC FEATURES:

Dense lymphoid tissue, with nodules, is bordered on one surface with epithelium.
 Lingual and *palatine tonsils*, stratified; *pharyngeal tonsil*, pseudostratified.
 Lymphocytic infiltration is characteristic, but variable in extent and intensity.
The surface epithelium dips into pockets; these are surrounded with lymphoid tissue.
 In the *lingual tonsil* the crypt is single, and each tonsil unit is small.
 In the *pharyngeal tonsil* a series of folds, when cut across, resembles crypts.
  These do not feature branching, as do true crypts of the palatine tonsil.
  Still more crypt-like are dilated ducts from glands located beneath the tonsil.
 In the *palatine tonsil* many of the crypts are long and branched.
  Numerous branches are cut so as to appear isolated in the lymphoid tissue.

Glands and skeletal muscle underlie all three types.
Only the pharyngeal tonsil has mixed muco-serous (rather than pure mucous) glands
Only the lingual tonsil has its associated muscle interlaced in three planes.

H. FUNCTIONAL CORRELATIONS:

The several tonsils constitute a discontinuous lymphoid ring about the pharynx.
They are situated favorably so as to guard the entrance to the pharynx.
Lymphocyte production, however, is the only certain function known.
Such activity is generally held to be a defense maneuver against bacteria.
Yet epithelial erosion would seem to enhance an invasion by micro-organisms.
At least, the tonsils are frequent portals of infection.
Possibly entering bacteria are made less virulent and vaccines are produced.
Glands opening into the crypts of the lingual tonsil presumably flush them clean.
Perhaps this is why this organ is rarely diseased.

IV. THE LYMPH NODES (OR LYMPH GLANDS)

These lymphoid organs show four distinct advances over those previously considered.
There is a supporting framework consisting of a complete *capsule* and beam-like *trabeculae*.
The lymphoid tissue exhibits two different regions, a *cortex* and a *medulla*.
Lymphatic vessels open freely into the organ; other lymphatics drain it.
There is a system of internal *lymph sinuses*, adapted for filtering lymph.
Lymph nodes are so named because they resemble knots at intervals on lymphatic vessels.
They are also called *lymph glands* because they generate cells, as do some other glands.
Lymph nodes, interposed in the lymph stream, are restricted to mammals.
They usually occur in chains or groups, and in definite regions.
Example: prevertebral region; mesentery; vicinity of large joints; along large arteries.
The stated total of some 500 lymph nodes in the body is believed to be too low.

A. STRUCTURAL PLAN:

A *lymph node* is an ovoid or bean-shaped body, ranging from 1 to 25 mm. in diameter.
It has a convex contour except at an indented region named the *hilus* (or hilum).
A fibrous *capsule* encloses the entire gland and gives it shape.
It is continuous with an internal trestlework of *trabeculae*.
These, in turn, connect with a much finer spongework of *reticular tissue*.
The *parenchyma* (lymphoid tissue) is specialized into two regions.
Beneath the capsule there is a solider *cortex*, characterized by *lymph nodules*.
At the hilus the cortex is lacking.
The interior of the gland is the *medulla*, characterized by *medullary cords*.
Cortex and medulla are not sharply demarcated, but blend irregularly.
Extensive *lymph sinuses* bound the parenchyma and also penetrate it.
They constitute a communicating system of cortical and medullary channels.
Afferent lymphatic vessels open into the sinus system at multiple points.
They are located on the convex surface of the node, opposite the hilus.
Efferent lymphatics drain the sinuses in a restricted area at the hilus of the node.
Blood vessels and *nerves* enter and leave at the hilus.
Neither arteries nor veins communicate with the sinus system.

B. DETAILED STRUCTURE:

1. Framework.

A. CAPSULE.

There is a firm external envelope, convex except at the indented hilus.

At the hilus this *capsule* is thick and, in a sense, intrudes into the organ.

It is composed mostly of densely packed collagenous fibers.

Scattering elastic fibers and some smooth-muscle fibers are present also.

Muscle fibers are located noticeably around the orifices of lymphatic vessels.

On its external surface, the capsule is uneven or rough.

This is because fibers pass from it to the surrounding connective tissue.

B. TRABECULAE.

At intervals, fibrous *trabeculae* project vertically inward from the capsule.

They stake off the cortex into many incomplete compartments, about 1 mm. wide.

Each space is bluntly pyramidal in shape and contains a lymphoid mass.

Such trabeculae are broad interrupted bands, rather than complete partitions.

In the medulla, trabeculae lose even these membranous tendencies.

Here they become truly beam-like, and are irregular and branching.

They converge toward the hilus and connect with the thickened capsule there.

Each trabecula is completely surrounded by a space belonging to the sinus-system.

All trabeculae resemble the capsule structurally.

C. RETICULUM.

This tissue extends as a delicate, spidery meshwork throughout the node.

Its fibers blend with the collagenous fibers of the capsule and trabeculae.

Many of the reticular-tissue cells are fixed phagocytes (macrophages).

These cells belong to the category called the reticulo-endothelial system.

Some are primitive reticular cells, relatively undifferentiated (p. 44).

2. Cortical Parenchyma.

In glands rich in trabeculae, each *cortical nodule* (and the diffuse lymphoid tissue about it) is marked off by a set of cortical trabeculae.

The nodules underlie the capsule and cause it to bulge locally.

Each nodular mass is attached to the nearby capsule and trabeculae by reticulum.

It is, in a sense, suspended in the sinuses that border it intimately.

If there are fewer trabeculae, the nodular masses are more irregular in shape.

Several then unite by their lateral surfaces and occupy a larger compartment.

Each cortical nodule is about 0.5 mm. in diameter.

Nodules usually show *germinal centers,* but these features are impermanent (p. 138).

In glands of the inguinal region, centers are never well developed.

It is also said that the whole nodule may disappear as such, and reform.

3. Medullary Parenchyma.

In the medulla the lymphoid tissue takes the form of dense lymphoid strands.

These *medullary cords* branch and anastomose, thereby making a loose spongework.

Some are continuous with the deep surface of the cortical lymphoid masses.

Other cords end blindly near the hilus.

Still others form loops by joining with neighboring (otherwise loose) ends.

Medullary cords are entirely surrounded by medullary sinuses.

Reticulum, bridging the sinuses, attaches each cord to adjacent trabeculae.

The cellular components of cords are like those in a cortical nodule.
However, germinal centers never occur.

4. Lymphatic Vessels and Sinuses.

A. LYMPHATIC VESSELS.

No other organ is similarly inserted into the course of lymphatic vessels.
That is, none other is supplied with afferent and efferent lymphatics.
Afferent vessels pierce the half of the convex capsule, opposite the hilus.
They enter slantingly at various points, encircled by a little smooth muscle.
Efferent vessels are fewer, but larger, and are restricted to the hilus-region.
They penetrate the thickened capsule and emerge; smooth muscle occurs here.
Valves restrict the flow of lymph to an onward direction, as in all lymphatics.

B. LYMPH SINUSES.

Every node contains a tortuous system of irregular channels, named *sinuses*.
They are a looser sort of lymphoid tissue.
Such labyrinthine channels widen and slow the lymphatic stream.
Lymph sinuses differ from lymphatic vessels in structure.
They are not lined with endothelium; on the contrary, they are *sinusoids*.
They are merely washed-out spaces in lymphoid tissue, probably impermanent.
Their 'lining' is furnished by flattened reticular cells.
These cells make an incomplete layer.
Hence lymph seeps into the parenchyma.
The sinus is criss-crossed by a meshwork of typical reticular tissue.
Some of the cells stretched along the fibers are *primitive reticular cells*.
Others are fixed macrophages (reticulo-endothelium).
A varying number of transient cells occur in the spaces of this spongework.
These cells are mostly lymphocytes.
There are also some free macrophages.
In addition, a few granulocytes and red corpuscles may be seen at times.
One border of the sinus-system underlies the capsule and follows all trabeculae.
The other border bounds all cortical nodules and medullary cords.
Hence all trabeculae and lymphoid masses are anchored in a lymph stream.
Thus three parts of the sinus system are distinguished.
The *marginal sinus* (or subcapsular sinus) underlies the capsule.
It separates the capsule from the cortical parenchyma.
Cortical sinuses lie between cortical trabeculae and cortical nodules.
Medullary sinuses lie between medullary trabeculae and medullary cords.

5. Blood Vessels and Nerves.

Arteries enter the lymph node at the hilus and tunnel within trabeculae.
Some branches continue to run in trabeculae, and ultimately reach the capsule.
Other branches leave the trabeculae, enter the medullary cords, course axially in them, and finally reach and supply each cortical nodule.
Dense capillary plexuses enclose the medullary cords and cortical nodules.
Here also they gather into venules.
Veins return blood to the hilus over the same general route taken by arteries.
Nerves, which are at least mostly vasomotor, follow the blood vessels.

6. Structural Variations.

Lymph nodes are highly variable, depending on their locations within the body.
A node may be much simpler than the ordinary type.
  This is especially true of the very small ones.
On the other hand, any of the structural constituents may be reduced or exaggerated.
  Example: hilus; trabeculae; sinus extent; cortical parenchyma; medullary cords.
The relative amount of cortex and medulla, and their inter-relations vary widely.
  The cortical nodules may be several layers deep.
  The cortex may surround the medulla completely or only partially.
  The cortical and medullary components may even lie at opposite poles of the node.
  Either the cortex or medulla may be lacking, or unrecognizable as such.
  Nodes of the peritoneal cavity are rich in medullary cords and sinuses.

C. INVOLUTION:

After puberty the cortex of lymph nodes tends to decrease steadily.
  With this decline goes a regression of the germinal centers.
  Eventually the medulla may reach to the marginal sinus, in places.
In some nodes these changes are relatively slight.

D. REGENERATIVE ABILITY:

Young animals may replace excised glands from local tissue.
  This capacity is lost rapidly as age advances.
Local injuries to nodes are usually healed by the differentiation of scar tissue.

E. DIAGNOSTIC FEATURES:

The encapsulated organ possesses a cortex and medulla, not sharply demarcated.
  The cortex consists of lymph nodules, usually with germinal centers.
    (A single section naturally misses some of the centers.)
  The medulla consists of lymphoid strands, appearing like a network.
Lymph sinuses border the cortical nodules and medullary cords.
  They are variable in abundance, but usually are more numerous in the medulla.
The lymph node is the only organ in the body that contains lymph sinuses.
  The free cells are mostly small lymphocytes.
  The sinuses do not contain red blood corpuscles in significant numbers.

F. FUNCTIONAL CORRELATIONS:

For its size, a lymph node is the most active hemopoietic organ in the body.
  Lymphocytes enter the sinuses partly by amebism and partly by crowding pressure.
    Some lymphocytes enter directly into blood capillaries of the lymphoid tissue.
    In doing this they bypass the ordinary lymphatic route.
  Lymph is not cellular to any extent until it passes through lymph nodes.
    Many more lymphocytes leave a node than enter it.
  In some abnormal conditions, lymph nodes may produce myeloid elements.
A lymph node is the only organ in the body acting as a filterer of lymph.
  Favoring this is the reticular tissue, crossing the system of sinus-channels.
  Also favorable is the slow trickle of lymph percolating through these passages.
  It is estimated that all of the returning lymph of the body passes through at least
    one node before entering the blood stream.
Filtration depends on the phagocytic ability of fixed and detached reticular cells.
  Fixed cells are fixed macrophages; detached cells are ordinary free macrophages.

Cells located in sinuses are especially active because of their favorable position.
Dust, carbon, bacteria and degenerating cells are ingested by the phagocytes.
Bronchial lymph nodes are even blackened by carbon storage.
Lymphatic vessels provide paths for the spread of cancerous cells from a primary focus.
Within lymph nodes their proliferation leads to the setting up of secondary centers.
This is abetted by the slowness of passage through the sinus-labyrinth.
Antibodies are presumably elaborated, and the node is important in producing immunity.
The complete functions of a node, in this and other regards, are not known.

V. THE HEMAL NODES

The term *hemolymph node* is also used, but this is not generally appropriate.
Hemal nodes are poorly understood, and there are many conflicting opinions concerning them.
They are characterized by a rich content of red blood corpuscles within sinuses.
Accordingly, the organ is red, or dark, in color.
True hemal nodes occur along the ventral side of the vertebrae of some animals.
They are distinct entities in ruminants, such as the sheep and ox.
On the other hand, their presence, in man, is doubtful.
Alleged nodes have also been interpreted as abnormal lymph nodes and accessory
spleens.

1. Structure.

The size ranges up to that of a pea.
The general organization is much like a lymph node.
However, the *sinuses* are purely blood sinuses; there is no lymphatic supply.
Trabeculae are so reduced as to be almost completely lacking.
Typical *lymph nodules*, with or without germinal centers, do not occur.
The blood vessels are not known definitely to communicate directly with sinuses.
Some claim that perforations exist in the vessel wall, but others deny this.
Yet red corpuscles must emerge in some way and gain entrance into the sinuses.
The problem is much like that in the spleen (p. 152).
In structure a hemal node approaches the relations existing in the spleen.
The hog has a type midway between a lymph node and an ordinary hemal node.
The contents both of blood vessels and of lymphatics mingle in the sinuses.
In this instance, the term 'hemolymph node' is appropriate.
A structural series would then run: ordinary lymph node; hemolymph node (of
hog); hemal node; spleen.

2. Diagnostic Features.

Trabeculae, cortical nodules and germinal centers are lacking.
The presence of red blood corpuscles in the sinuses is positively diagnostic.
Yet inflamed, hemorrhagic lymph nodes also show sinus blood.
Also the sinuses of normal lymph nodes contain a few red corpuscles.

3. Functional Correlations.

Activities resemble those of the spleen, on a small scale.
A hemal node is lymphopoietic and a filterer of the blood.
It destroys many red blood corpuscles; these are probably nearing death.

VI. THE SPLEEN

his largest of all lymphoid organs is ovoid in shape and about the size of the fist.
  After death it expels blood and loses up to three-fourths of its live weight.
he spleen is much like a huge, congested hemal node, interposed in a blood stream.
  But it has developed a peculiar kind of storage-sinus for blood.
  It is the only human organ that is unquestionably specialized for filtering blood.
  The spleen is located between the stomach, left kidney and diaphragm.

. STRUCTURAL PLAN:

The soft spleen is surrounded by a fibrous *capsule*, surfaced with peritoneum.
Many *trabeculae* pass from the capsule to the interior.
There is a long, deep *hilus* where blood vessels enter and leave the large trabeculae.
The parenchyma (*splenic pulp*) is of two distinct types.
  These masses are distributed throughout the spleen as fairly discrete entities.
    White pulp surrounds and follows the arteries, like a sheath.
      At intervals it thickens into ovoid masses, the *splenic nodules*.
    Red pulp is more abundant and takes the form of plates, known as *pulp cords*.
Splenic sinuses are sausage-shaped channels that intervene between arteries and veins.
  Sinuses and terminal blood vessels are embedded in a common mass of red pulp.

LOBULATION:

Primary trabeculae mark out the spleen into many pyramidal compartments.
  Each of these *lobules* is about 1 mm. in diameter and is bounded by several trabeculae.
    It receives a terminal arterial branch, with a splenic nodule on it.
    It is drained by veins that leave the lobule within the trabeculae that bound it.
  Such lobulation is indicated on the surface by a faint mottling.
This *primary lobule* is subdivided (actually imperfectly demarcated) by smaller trabeculae.
  About ten *secondary lobules* are created in this manner.
  Terminal arterial twigs vascularize each of these ultimate 'compartments.'
Splenic lobulation is imperfect and is demonstrable only in favorably cut sections.
  It is of academic, rather than practical, value.
  Yet it is interesting that a semblance of orderly, unit organization can be found.

. DETAILED STRUCTURE:

1. Framework.

  A. CAPSULE.

    This is tough, but elastic, and is firmly anchored by trabeculae.
    In man the *capsule* is relatively thin (0.1 to 0.15 mm.), except at the hilus.
      It is heaviest at the hilus, where it supports the large splenic vessels.
    The capsule contains dense fibro-elastic tissue and scanty smooth-muscle fibers.
      Some mammals possess a rich content of smooth muscle, even in layers.
    Superficially the capsule is covered with reflected peritoneum.
      Hence there is a layer of mesothelium at the actual free surface.

  B. TRABECULAE.

    Heavy *trabeculae* radiate inward from the hilus and subdivide repeatedly.
      Other trabeculae extend perpendicularly inward from the capsule.
    Branching and anastomosis produce a complex trestlework throughout the interior.
      On the whole, the splenic trabeculae are notably robust.
      The largest are easily visible to the naked eye.

Trabeculae are similar to the capsule in composition.

Elastic fibers are even more numerous than in the capsule.

c. RETICULUM.

Splenic pulp is supported throughout by a fine spongework of *reticular fibers*.

Both the red and white pulp are permeated with them.

The reticulum blends insensibly into the trabeculae, vessels and capsule.

Some *reticular cells*, as elsewhere, are like primitive, multipotent mesenchyme.

Others are fixed macrophages that can detach and become free macrophage

2. White Pulp.

On a cut surface, *white pulp* appears as scattered gray areas of compact tissue.

The pulp actually occurs as elongate, branched strands, 0.2 to 0.8 mm. wide.

White pulp always is associated with arteries coursing free in the parenchyma.

The adventitia of these vessels is largely replaced by reticular tissue.

This modified meshwork is infiltrated with lymphocytes, most of which are sma

These lymphocytes constitute the great majority of free cells in white pulp.

Less frequent types include monocytes, plasma cells and macrophages.

The amount of white pulp decreases in old age and, perhaps, with starvation.

Splenic nodules, also called 'Malpighian corpuscles,' occur at intervals.

Each is a thicker accumulation along the strands of white pulp.

They are interconnected by more slender cylinders of ordinary white pulp.

Splenic nodules are spindle-shaped, but become spheroidal where arterioles branch.

They are spaced quite evenly along those arterioles that have left trabeculae.

Their diameter averages about 0.5 mm.; hence they are visible to the naked eye.

They are typical lymph nodules that enclose an unusually prominent arteriole.

From this vessel nutrient twigs pass to the tissue of the nodule.

The number and size of splenic nodules diminish with increasing age.

They are also said to disappear and organize anew from time to time.

A *germinal center* is an inconstant feature.

It disappears and reappears at irregular intervals.

Centers are numerous in the young, few in the adult and absent in the age

The *central artery* is really an eccentric arteriole; it avoids the germinal center.

Frequently a splenic nodule is located in the crotch of a branching vessel.

In such instances two (or more) 'central arterioles' pierce the nodule.

The supporting *reticulum* makes a denser basket-work peripherally in the nodule.

3. Red Pulp.

This is a pasty, dark-red mass that can be scraped from a freshly-cut surface.

Its density and firmness vary with the amount of blood contained.

Structurally, red pulp is a modification of white pulp and blends into it.

It is looser in texture, owing to an abundant tissue-fluid.

It is infiltrated with all elements of the circulating blood.

The support of pulp is a typical *reticulum* and its associated reticular cells.

Red pulp occupies all space not utilized by sinuses, white pulp and trabeculae.

Its tissue is tunneled by innumerable venous sinuses.

On section, the intervening pulp gives the appearance of cellular cords.

These *pulp cords* are actually a continuous system of joined plates and mass

Red pulp shows variations in composition among different mammalian groups.

Its density and erythrocyte content vary widely.

Many mammals have some marrow cells in their red pulp, as did the human fetus.
Among the free cells of red pulp the nongranular leucocytes are commonest.

A. LYMPHOCYTES.

All sizes intermingle; they are relatively less numerous than in white pulp.

Many came from white pulp by amebism; others were brought by the blood stream.

Once in the red pulp the larger ones continue to multiply there.

Numerous modified lymphocytes occur as *plasma cells.*

B. MONOCYTES.

These abundant elements are often called *splenic cells.*

Some are brought by the blood stream; others arise locally from hemocytoblasts.

All are capable of self-proliferation.

Monocytes have phagocytic potentialities, and may become vigorous scavengers.

Such enlarged phagocytes become indistinguishable from other macrophages.

C. FREE MACROPHAGES.

These ameboid elements are descended from primitive reticular cells.

They are similar to the fixed macrophages still attached to the reticulum.

Evidences of phagocytosis are often seen within their cytoplasm.

Pigment granules are stored; red corpuscles are digested.

D. GRANULOCYTES.

Neutrophils, eosinophils and, rarely, basophils are all represented.

They are blood cells that have taken temporary residence in the red pulp.

E. ERYTHROCYTES.

These are abundant in red pulp and give it a characteristic, red color.

Normally neither red cells nor granulocytes arise in the pulp.

4. Blood Vessels.

The vascular arrangement is of great importance in the spleen.

It determines the distribution and inter-relation of both red and white pulp.

It also determines the structural plan of the spleen as a whole.

The terminal vessels are peculiar in structure and in their inter-relations.

A. ARTERIES.

These vessels are especially associated with white pulp.

They enter at the hilus and follow the larger trabeculae for a short distance.

As the trabeculae branch, the arteries subdivide also.

They are distinguished from veins by their muscular coat and small lumen.

When reduced to a diameter of 0.2 mm., they leave the trabeculae as arterioles.

Passing into the splenic parenchyma, the adventitia changes in character.

It loosens and becomes a mesh, composed largely of reticular tissue.

Infiltration by lymphocytes produces the ensheathing white pulp.

These *central arterioles* supply capillaries to all of the white pulp.

Arterioles about 50 μ in diameter lose their investment of white pulp.

In so doing, they necessarily enter the red pulp.

Here each subdivides into several branches that diverge like a fan.

This cluster is named a *penicillus (i.e.,* brush).

Each branch of a penicillus shows three successive segments:

First is the *pulp arteriole,* which rapidly narrows to 15 μ.

It still retains a thin layer of smooth muscle.

Next is the *sheathed arteriole* (30 μ), with a markedly thickened wall.

This spindle-shaped *ellipsoid* is composed of cellular reticulum.

Finally is the *terminal capillary,* whose manner of ending is disputed.

Each set of arterioles within the splenic pulp is a functional 'end artery.'

That is, if such a vessel is blocked, the tissues served by it suffer.

The impairment results from lack of an adequate collateral supply of blood

B. VENOUS SINUSES.

The so-called *sinuses* constitute a system of tunnels through the red pulp.

They occupy more space than do the 'pulp cords' between them.

Actually the 'sinuses' are specialized sinusoids of the pulp.

The sinus lumen has a fluted outline; it is highly distensible (12 to 100 μ).

The appearance of a sinus after death is one of relative collapse.

The sinus wall is not endothelium, but specialized reticular cells.

They are fixed macrophages (reticulo-endothelium), greatly elongated.

Normally they are less actively phagocytic than those of the red pulp.

The construction of the wall is peculiar and difficult to interpret.

It contains longitudinal, rod-like cells, seemingly separated by slits.

The long, slender cell-body bulges into the lumen of the sinus.

Especially is this pronounced in the region of the nucleus.

A transverse section shows the cells to be spaced loosely in a circle.

The appearance is somewhat like the minute-markings on a clock dia

The outer cell-region consists of condensed, dark-staining cytoplasm.

Branching reticular fibers encircle the wall externally and support it.

The fibers occupy grooves on the external surface of the sinus-cells.

The main dispute turns on whether actual slits separate the lining cells.

Many believe that such permanent openings do occur.

Some claim to have seen them in the living spleen.

Others think a thin, structureless membrane extends between cells.

(This 'membrane,' however, could be flanged extensions of the cells.

Regardless of the interpretation, blood does pass through the wall.

C. VEINS.

The venous sinuses connect with the so-called *pulp veins*.

These are true endothelial tubes that are much like precapillary venules.

They are supported by condensed reticulum and some elastic fibers.

Leaving the parenchyma, the veins unite and continue within trabeculae.

Here they consist of bare endothelium, buried in trabecular tissue.

Veins run longer distances in trabeculae than do most arteries.

Hence they are the only vessels present within the smaller trabeculae.

The *trabecular veins*, on reaching the hilus, drain into the splenic vein.

D. THE ARTERIO-VENOUS JUNCTION.

The manner of junction or union has long been a subject of dispute.

Some claim that arterial capillaries open freely into the splenic pulp.

Blood then enters the sinuses indirectly; it is an *open circulation*.

Others hold for a primarily continuous system, or *closed circulation*.

That is, arterial capillaries communicate directly with venous sinuses.

Still others think that both types of circulation (open and closed) exist.

Majority-opinion has wavered as new observations continue to be added.

A final decision still awaits crucial evidence, generally acceptable.

In any event, cellular interchange between red pulp and sinuses occurs.

With this basic concept in mind, the exact routing of blood is, in a sens

a technical detail.

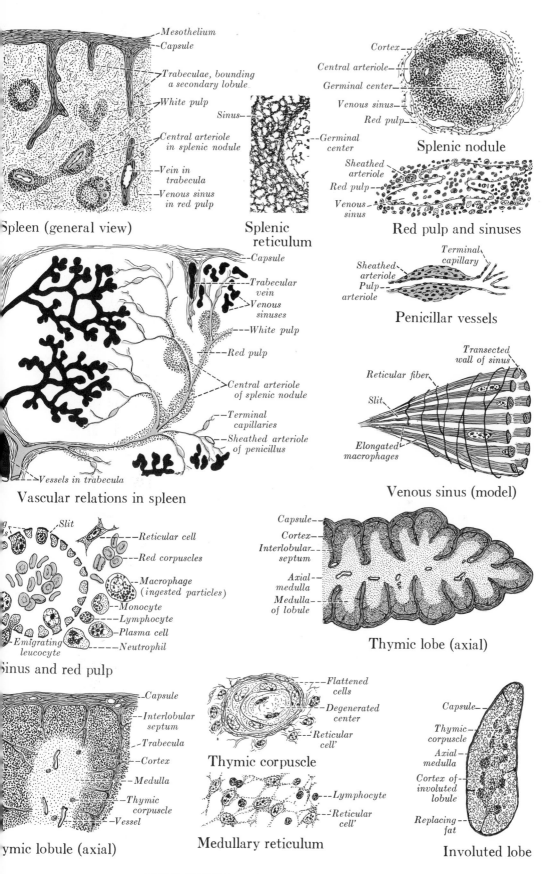

Mesothelium
Capsule
Trabeculae, bounding a secondary lobule
White pulp
Sinus
Central arteriole in splenic nodule
Vein in trabecula
Venous sinus in red pulp
Germinal center

Spleen (general view)

Splenic reticulum

Cortex
Central arteriole
Germinal center
Venous sinus
Red pulp

Splenic nodule

Sheathed arteriole
Red pulp
Venous sinus

Red pulp and sinuses

Capsule
Trabecular vein
Venous sinuses
White pulp
Red pulp
Central arteriole of splenic nodule
Terminal capillaries
Sheathed arteriole of penicillus
Vessels in trabecula

Vascular relations in spleen

Terminal capillary
Sheathed arteriole
Pulp arteriole

Penicillar vessels

Transected wall of sinus
Reticular fiber
Slit
Elongated macrophages

Venous sinus (model)

Slit
Reticular cell
Red corpuscles
Macrophage (ingested particles)
Monocyte
Lymphocyte
Plasma cell
Neutrophil
Emigrating leucocyte

Sinus and red pulp

Capsule
Cortex
Interlobular septum
Axial medulla
Medulla of lobule

Thymic lobe (axial)

Capsule
Interlobular septum
Trabecula
Cortex
Medulla
Thymic corpuscle
Vessel

Thymic lobule (axial)

Flattened cells
Degenerated center
Reticular cell

Thymic corpuscle

Lymphocyte
Reticular cell

Medullary reticulum

Capsule
Thymic corpuscle
Axial medulla
Cortex of involuted lobule
Replacing fat

Involuted lobe

THE SPLEEN AND THYMUS

5. Lymphatics.

Contrary to earlier belief, vessels are demonstrable in white (but not red) pulp.

These efferents accompany pulp arterioles and conduct lymph to trabeculae.

Efferent vessels are present in the capsule and larger trabeculae.

6. Nerves.

Unmyelinated nerve fibers follow the arteries and end in their smooth muscle.

Sparse myelinated fibers occur; they are probably sensory in function.

Some fibers enter both the red and white pulp, but their endings are unknown.

REGENERATIVE ABILITY:

The spleen is able to heal local injuries.

This it does through the formation of scar tissue at the site of the wound.

DIAGNOSTIC FEATURES:

The spleen has lymph nodules scattered widely in a pulp containing many red corpuscles.

It is characterized negatively by the lack of a cortex and medulla.

The smooth capsule is surfaced with peritoneum (and hence mesothelium).

The trabeculae are conspicuously robust; more so than in any other lymphoid organ.

Splenic nodules, with prominent eccentric arterioles, are specifically diagnostic.

The venous sinuses, interspersed with red pulp, are exclusively characteristic.

Blood sinuses do not exist surely in any other human lymphoid organ.

FUNCTIONAL CORRELATIONS:

Splenic activities are incompletely understood.

The spleen is not essential to life; the body withstands its extirpation successfully.

Readjustment is made through the compensatory growth of lymphoid tissue elsewhere.

Phagocytic functions are then carried out by the macrophages of other organs.

The spleen is an elastic, controllable reservoir that is important in adjusting the volume of the circulating blood to changing needs.

In life the spleen undergoes both rhythmic and passive contractions.

In part this activity is attributed to the smooth muscle in its framework.

But the major control of size is regulated through changes in its blood-volume.

The spleen is expansible because of its abundant elastic tissue.

Especially does it store, temporarily, red corpuscles in the sinuses and red pulp.

The spleen is an important hemopoietic organ, generating both lymphocytes and monocytes.

Lymphocytes are formed in both types of pulp, but chiefly in the white pulp.

Thence they pass to the red pulp, and so into the sinuses and splenic vein.

Monocytes differentiate from hemocytoblasts in the red pulp and splenic sinuses.

Pathologically the spleen may come to resemble bone marrow and imitate its functions.

It can then generate all types of blood cells (as in early fetal life).

It is a filterer of the blood; phagocytosis is actively engaged in by the free and fixed macrophages of the red pulp and by the lining cells of the sinuses.

Red corpuscles, leucocytes, bacteria, pigment, and other particles are ingested.

They are then digested, destroyed or stored.

Iron, obtained from disintegrating red corpuscles, is stored in macrophages.

It is then given up as needed and re-utilized in forming hemoglobin.

The method of transfer to developing red cells of the bone marrow is not known.

The spleen is probably the most important organ in the production of antibodies.

Evidence indicates that plasma cells, derived from reticular cells, are the source.

It is also active in defense against air-borne infections.

It produces the most macrophages, and the most active ones in any filtering organ.

Its macrophage system is surpassed in size by the liver alone.

Endocrine functions, such as depressing marrow activity, remain unaccepted.

The spleen has no cellular element that is not shared by other lymphoid organs.

Hence the cellular basis for the elaboration of a distinctive hormone is lacking.

VII. THE THYMUS

The *thymus* is a broad, flat, bilobed mass of lymphoid tissue.

Its location is beneath the upper sternum, in the anterior mediastinum.

A. STRUCTURAL PLAN:

The *thymus* consists of two halves, thus retaining its bilateral origin.

The halves are *lobes*, closely applied and united by connective tissue.

A lobe contains thousands of *lobules*, each with a cortex and medulla.

A lobule, however, is an incompletely isolated unit.

The *medulla* is a central core that sends a lateral projection into each lobule.

Thymic corpuscles (of Hassall) are a characteristic constituent of the medulla.

The *cortex* surrounds the lateral extensions of the medulla as so many local caps.

There is a rather sharp demarcation between cortex and medulla.

A *capsule* encloses each lobe, and extensions of it (*septa*) mark off the lobules.

Trabeculae pass vertically from the capsule through the cortex, and end there.

B. LOBULATION:

Each *lobe* is subdivided into thousands of *lobules*, each 0.5 to 2 mm. in diameter.

A *lobule* is a representative sample of both the cortex and medulla.

It is encapsulated by connective tissue except on its central side.

Here the medulla of the lobule becomes continuous with the main medullary axis.

This axial strand, or medulla proper is not a part of the system of lobules.

The main medulla forms a continuous central axis, or core, within each lobe.

It sends a bud-like, lateral offshoot into each lobule.

Hence the lobules radiate about the central medullary axis.

Each lateral bud of medullary tissue is covered, except at its base, by a thimble-shap-
cap of cortical tissue.

Between adjoining lobules the axial medulla may lack any associated cortex.

In sections, many lobules are cut across and appear like closed compartments.

That is, the encapsulated cortex surrounds completely the medullary bud.

(Only sections cut through the axis of a lobule show its complete relations.)

C. DETAILED STRUCTURE:

1. Framework.

The thin *capsule* is composed of collagenous and some elastic fibers.

It surrounds the lobe, and extensions from it continue as far as the medulla.

In doing so, these interlobular *septa* separate the lobules from each other.

Intralobular *trabeculae* extend perpendicularly from the capsule through the cortex.

They end abruptly at the junction of cortex and medulla.

The '*reticular cells*,' which support the parenchyma, are peculiar branching cells.

They take form by a loosening-up of the cells constituting the embryonic thym

(The original, paired primordia were solid masses of entodermal epitheliur

The resulting stellate cells are completely lacking in associated fibrils.

Also they do not store dyes, like true reticular cells (of mesenchymal origin).

Their nuclei are larger, paler and more ovoid than those of lymphocytes.

The only typical reticular tissue present came in with invading blood vessels.

2. Cortex.

The parenchyma consists of lymphocytes (mostly small), densely and uniformly packed.

They occupy the spaces in the sparse reticular meshwork and obscure it.

Some have believed them to be a specific cell (*thymocyte*) of entodermal origin.

On the contrary, these small thymic cells show all the characteristics, normal behavior and experimental reactions of true lymphocytes.

They originate from mesenchyme and wander into the developing thymus.

The invasion of the epithelium is similar to that occurring in the tonsils.

But in the thymus the process is far more extensive.

Lymph nodules are lacking in both the cortex and medulla of the normal thymus.

3. Medulla.

This region is much lighter staining and less compact than the cortex.

In children it is sharply demarcated from the cortex; in adults, less so.

Lymphocytes are not so numerous as in the cortex.

Consequently, the 'reticular cells' are predominant and prominent.

These constitute an apparent syncytium, with large pale nuclei.

Some plasma cells and eosinophilic myelocytes are additional constituents.

Thymic corpuscles (of Hassall) are characteristic and diagnostic features.

During childhood these total about 1,500,000.

Each is a nest of epithelioid cells, arranged like a layered ball.

Their size is large; almost all lie within the range of 20 to 150 μ.

A thymic corpuscle is in direct continuity with nearby 'reticular cells.'

The component cells are acidophilic, and often strongly so.

The central cells are larger and form a core to the total mass.

They are surrounded by flattened and compacted cells, arranged concentrically.

There is much hyalinization and degeneration, especially at the center.

The origin of corpuscles is from enlarged, entodermal 'reticular cells.'

4. Vessels and Nerves.

Arteries enter along the medullary core and distribute largely to the cortex.

Interlobular *veins* drain the cortex; medullary veins drain the medulla.

Lymphatics lie mainly in the interlobular connective tissue.

Afferent vessels and lymph sinuses are wholly absent.

Nerves are furnished by the vagus and sympathetics.

They are, at least mainly, vasomotor.

. INVOLUTION:

The thymus reaches its maximum size at puberty, and then begins to wane.

Wasting, or involution, continues even into old age.

It is more severe than that occurring in other lymphoid organs.

The cortex loses density; the cortico-medullary boundary thereby becomes less sharp.

The medulla also declines progressively in the postpuberal years.

Fat replaces the degenerated lymphocytes and 'reticular cells.'
The thymic corpuscles are spared longest; their remains are identifiable in the aged.

E. REGENERATIVE ABILITY:

The regenerative capacity of the thymus has not been studied adequately.
The normal decline of the organ reflects an early inability to maintain itself.

F. DIAGNOSTIC FEATURES:

The thymus is a highly lobulated organ; it is the only lobulated lymphoid organ.
> The medulla is continuous from lobule to lobule by way of a common axial strand.
There is a fairly sharp and even demarcation of cortex from medulla in each lobule.
> After childhood this clear-cut boundary is progressively lost.
Fibrous tissue (including intralobular trabeculae) is confined to the cortex.
There are neither lymph nodules nor sinuses; it is the only lymphoid organ lacking both.
The thymic corpuscle is specifically diagnostic.
> (Small blood vessels, full of blood, resemble them at low magnifications.)

G. FUNCTIONAL CORRELATIONS:

Lymphopoiesis is a known thymic activity; it is vigorous in infants.
> Plasma cells and eosinophilic myelocytes are also formed in small numbers.
The thymus is not essential to life in experimental adult animals.
Thymus removal at birth results in lymphocyte deficiency and immunity lack.
> Such animals become incapable of repelling invading microorganisms.
> Apparently the thymus creates migrant, antibody-making cells.
> These cells colonize the spleen and other lymphocytic organs.
The involution curve is suggestive of prepuberal rather than postpuberal function.
> Gonadal hormone is known to induce involution, and this might explain the timing.
A relation to growth and sex differentiation is claimed for the thymus.
> This or other hormonal function has never been established surely.
There is little anatomical basis for an endocrine secretory activity.
> Yet the reticular meshwork is an altered epithelial tissue.
> > It is not fibril-forming, and might conceivably be secretory.
> The vascular and nerve supply, however, do not suggest endocrine function.
The thymic corpuscle is a degenerating mass, at least centrally.
> There is no reason to suspect it of furthering any significant function.

Chapter *XV.* MOIST MEMBRANES AND GLANDS

ertain structural and functional units enter into the composition of many organs.

Chief among these are the moist, *internal membranes* and various kinds of *glands*.

is advantageous to introduce these topics before describing the remaining organs.

After this is done, in subsequent chapters only the special features of the membranes and glands in any particular region will need to be brought to attention.

That is, by presenting the fundamental information now, later repetitions can be avoided.

I. THE MOIST MEMBRANES

hese membranes are the joint product of an epithelium and its underlying connective tissue.

They are kept moist either by a watery exudate or by a slimy secretion.

On this basis they are named *serous membranes* and *mucous membranes*, respectively.

. SEROUS MEMBRANES:

1. Occurrence.

Each of the closed body cavities is bounded by a membranous sheet, or *tunica serosa*.

These membranes are specifically named the *pericardium, pleura* and *peritoneum*.

A *parietal portion* lines the external wall of each of the body cavities.

A *visceral portion* is reflected over the exposed surfaces of protruding organs.

It also envelops and provides mesenterial supports for some organs.

2. Structure.

A *serous membrane* consists of mesothelium lying upon a connective-tissue layer.

The *mesothelium* consists of simple, squamous, cellular plates.

Their serrated edges interlock and their surface bears short microvilli.

Minute apertures (*stomata*) can be found between some cells of the omentum.

They are apparently temporary openings caused by outwandering cells.

(A *basement membrane*, said to be present, is not an obvious feature.)

A layer of delicate connective tissue underlies mesothelium and gives it support.

The thickness and density of this *lamina propria* vary regionally.

In some regions (visceral pleura; mesenteries) it is quite elastic.

It contains abundant blood vessels and lymphatics, but no glands.

The cellular population includes a considerable range of cell types.

The *milky spots* of the omentum and lungs feature massed macrophages.

A *mesentery* (including omenta) is a double membrane whose laminae propriae fuse.

Hence there is mesothelium on each free surface, and connective tissue between.

Such double structures contain fat, and some of them enclose lymph nodes.

Beneath freely movable regions of serous membranes there is lax areolar tissue.

This constitutes a *subserous layer* (tela subserosa).

The serous cavities contain a small amount of watery fluid.

This *serous transudate* suspends various kinds of free cells.

Included are detached mesothelial cells, macrophages and lymphocytes.

3. Regenerative Ability.

Denuded areas are resurfaced by spreading and proliferation of mesothelial cells.
The omentum, when excised, does not regenerate to any significant degree.

4. Diagnostic Features.

A serous membrane is a thin layer in vertical section.
Its surface epithelium appears as scarcely more than a bordering line.
Occasionally flattened nuclei make bead-like bulges along it.
The lamina propria is not distinctive, except negatively for the lack of glands.
A lax subserosa is a feature present only in some locations.
Identifying the exact location of a serous membrane, by itself, is impossible.
It can be done only when clues are furnished by associated organs or parts.

5. Functional Correlations.

Serous membranes cover all surfaces that face upon the coelom in any way.
Mesenterial and 'ligamentous' extensions of the parietal layer pass to some organs
These provide obvious support and permit some freedom of movement.
They also provide thoroughfares for the passages of vessels and nerves.
Mobility of a membrane is correlated with its composition in any local region.
Conducive to mobility is an increased elastic content.
Additionally important is the presence of a stretchable subserosa.
The lymph-like transudate moistens and lubricates the free surfaces of serosae.
This facilitates free play between the individual visceral organs.
It also permits the viscera to glide against the body wall; both are slippery.
The serous transudate, though normally small in amount, undergoes rapid turn-over
Pathologically the amount may become very large.
In conditions of inflammation it then contains many neutrophils.
The omentum, in particular, is an efficient absorptive organ.
It is the direct avenue from the peritoneal cavity to the blood stream.
The macrophages, especially in 'milky spots,' are important in defense activities.
They take care of inert particles and of bacteria in infections.

B. MUCOUS MEMBRANES:

These membranes (*tunicae mucosae*) are mucus-secreting sheets in the interior of the body.
All are in communication, mostly indirect, with the exterior of the body.
Mucous membranes constitute the lining of various hollow organs, including small tubes.
Subject to distention in most locations, they tend to fold when relaxed.
A few membranes in this category do not secrete mucus, but are otherwise typical.
Example: bladder; vagina; ductus deferens.
Membranes, in general, use several methods of increasing their effective free surface:
Folds. Rather extensive wrinkling of the sheet (stomach rugae; intestinal plicae).
Evaginations. Local elevations above the general surface (various villi).
In this outpocketed fold the bases of opposed epithelial cells face each other.
Invaginations. Local inpocketings into the subjacent connective tissue (glands, varying
from simple tubes to complex, tree-like branchings).
In this type of local fold the tops of opposed epithelial cells face each other.

1. Occurrence.

Alimentary tract (and large glandular ducts opening into it).
Respiratory tract (and associated accessory sinuses).

Auditory tube; tympanic cavity.

Urinary and genital tracts.

Conjunctiva.

2. Structure.

The *mucous membrane,* or tunica mucosa, consists typically of four layers.

A. EPITHELIUM.

This layer may be simple, pseudostratified or stratified.

In man, even the stratified type is never truly cornified.

The epithelium is moistened and lubricated by a mucous secretion.

This may be produced by ordinary surface cells or specialized *goblet cells.*

Or it may be produced by multicellular glands beneath the epithelium.

B. BASEMENT MEMBRANE (MEMBRANA PROPRIA).

It is composed of an amorphous ground substance and some reticular fibers.

The thickness of the membrane varies within wide limits.

Example: trachea, thick; intestine, thin.

In some instances a basement membrane is unrecognizable, or lacking.

Example: urinary passages.

C. LAMINA PROPRIA MUCOSAE.

Attached to the basement membrane is a bed of connective tissue.

Areolar tissue is commonest, but reticular tissue is utilized also.

The name of this sheet is commonly shortened to *lamina propria.*

Glands, frequently located in this layer, open onto the surface epithelium.

The lamina propria may become variably infiltrated with lymphocytes.

D. LAMINA MUSCULARIS MUCOSAE.

Sometimes smooth muscle marks exactly the deep boundary of the lamina propria.

The name of this sheet of muscle is commonly shortened to *muscularis mucosae.*

It may be arranged longitudinally, or circularly and longitudinally.

When both layers are present, the one nearer the epithelium is circular.

TELA SUBMUCOSA.

The mucous membrane commonly rests upon a deeper, fibrous layer.

This *submucosa* consists of loose areolar tissue, and is rich in vessels.

It may contain glands (that drain to the free surface) and fat cells.

A demarcation from the lamina propria is distinct only when a muscularis mucosae

is present to delimit the latter.

In some regions a submucosa is unrecognizable as a definite entity.

The submucosa commonly is more lax than the mucosa, and affords it mobility.

It also serves to bind the mucosa to deeper, firmer structures.

This connection may be to a muscular wall, cartilage or bone.

3. Regenerative Ability.

The epithelium restores the continuous, normal loss of covering and gland cells.

Local destruction of the membrane can be followed by complete regeneration.

Even glands differentiate from the still unspecialized, replacing epithelium.

4. Diagnostic Features.

A mucous membrane lines all internal, hollow organs that connect with the exterior.

Its surface epithelium may be simple columnar, pseudostratified or stratified.

The epithelium is soft and moist; it is almost always slimy.

Typically the epithelium has either gland cells in it or glands beneath it.
Both conditions may exist in the same membrane.
A basement membrane may or may not be recognizable.
A lamina propria is always present and usually has considerable thickness.
But its composition and special features are subject to local adaptations.
Glands and lymphoid infiltration are commonly present.
The deep surface of the muscularis mucosae establishes the limit of the membrane.
In its absence, the junction of the mucosa and submucosa is usually ill defined.
In some instances the submucosa is considered to be lacking.
This, however, can be a matter of individual opinion, since a looser texture a**
richer content of vessels are quantitative features.

5. Functional Correlations.

A mucous membrane is secretory and self-lubricating; it may be highly absorptive.
Slimy mucus protects surfaces against mechanical irritation and drying.
It entangles foreign particles, and is possibly bactericidal.
Increased mucus-flow, following irritations, tends to clean surfaces.
Ordinary mucus is inert chemically, but is a good lubricant for chafing surfaces.
The mucus discharged on the epithelial surface varies in amount.
There is more mucus where mechanical irritation is greatest.
Example: gastro-intestinal tract; respiratory tract.
Mucus may even be lacking in some locations.
Example: urinary tract (moistened by passing urine).
A mucous membrane may also elaborate a secretion of a more watery nature.
These serous secretions typically contain chemically active enzymes.
Example: enzymic juices of gastric and intestinal glands.
Absorption is a primary function of the gastro-intestinal mucosa.
Intestinal epithelium even elaborates a specialized border for this purpose.

II. THE GLANDS

Certain cells create and expel materials not related to their ordinary metabolic needs.
Such cells are specialized in the direction of glandular activity.
It is customary to distinguish glandular products as secretions or excretions.
Secretion involves constructive metabolism and synthesis.
The raw materials in the blood are elaborated into nonliving substances of a new sort.
These manufactured products are of use to the organism (or to its young).
Example: digestive enzymes; hormones; mucus; milk (useful to young).
Certain glands produce whole cells as their product.
Example: lymphocytes; sex cells (useful, not to the organism, but to the race).
Excretion sifts waste products from the circulation and eliminates them.
Example: bile pigments; urea; carbon dioxide.
Excess useful materials are also eliminated as excretions.
Example: water; salts; glucose; female sex hormone (a synthesized secretion).
Secretory activity is a function displayed most commonly by epithelium.
Cells of nervous- and connective-tissue origin are more rarely concerned.
Some epithelial sheets not only are protective but they also secrete and absorb.
The body, however, requires more secretory products than simple sheets can supply.
Also, specialization for complex secretion necessarily ignores protective requirements.

Hence the surface epithelia developed downgrowths that became specialized as glands. These lodged in the underlying connective tissue which then gave them support. *gland* is an aggregation of cells, specialized as an organ of secretion or excretion. Some single cells act as independent glandular units, but they are not organs.

1. Bases of Classification

lands can be classified in several different ways:

1. By Cell Numbers.

A. Unicellular. Single cells within epithelial sheets act as complete glandular units. Example: goblet mucous cell; surface cells of stomach lining.

B. Multicellular. Many cells co-operate in producing a gland-complex. This type commonly organizes as tubes or sacs, opening onto the parent surface. Example: uterine glands; sweat glands; salivary glands; mammary glands. (Endocrine glands, however, do not maintain this relation to a parent surface.)

2. By Kind of Secretion.

A. Mucous. Slimy, chemically inert mucus (palate; colon; uterine cervix).

B. Serous. Watery, albuminous discharge; commonly containing enzymes (parotid; pancreas), but not necessarily so (lacrimal glands; olfactory glands).

C. Sero-mucous. Mixed discharge, owing to the presence of both cell types in the same or different alveoli (labial gland; submaxillary gland).

D. Cellular. Blood cells (hemopoietic organs) and sex cells (gonads).

E. Miscellaneous. The secretion differs from the common types already listed. The product may be watery (sweat; urine; most hormones); viscid (seminal vesicle); greasy (sebum); waxy (cerumen); etc.

3. By Manner of Release.

A. With Respect to the Place of Discharge.

1. exocrine. Onto the epithelial surface from which the gland developed. In general, the secretion reaches the outside of the body directly (skin glands) or indirectly (digestive, respiratory, and urogenital glands).

2. endocrine. Into the blood or lymph streams (hormones).

3. acrine. No discharge of the elaborated product from the cells that synthesize it. Example: granular leucocytes.

B. With Respect to the Method of Initial Transport.

1. through a duct. 'Duct-glands' (all ordinary multicellular glands).

2. by diffusive transfer. 'Ductless glands' (hormone-secreting glands).

C. With Respect to Gland-cell Participation.

1. merocrine. The cell remains essentially intact. Release is accomplished by the secretory materials diffusing through the cell membrane or rupturing it. Example: most of the common glands.

2. apocrine. Some of the apical cytoplasm of the gland cell detaches, along with secretory products that collect there. Example: mammary gland; some specialized sweat glands.

3. holocrine. The entire cell is discharged during secretion. The cell may be discharged intact; such glands are also called *cytogenic*. Example: hemopoietic organs; sex glands.

The cell may disintegrate and thereby liberate the secretion.
Example: sebaceous glands, which undergo fatty degeneration.

2. THE EXOCRINE GLANDS

i. *Unicellular Glands*

Single secretory cells may be scattered throughout an epithelial sheet.
Example: intestine; uterine tube.
The commonest type is the *goblet mucous cell* of the respiratory and intestinal tracts.
In the resting condition it is an ordinary-looking columnar cell.
On resuming activity, droplets of *mucigen* (*i.e.*, premucin) appear in the cytoplasm.
They collect in the upper part of the cell and distend it progressively.
(For the characteristics of mucigen and its end-product, *mucin*, see p. 165.)
The upper, swollen end of the cell finally contains a huge vacuole filled with mucigen.
By contrast, the basal end is slender; the whole cell takes on a goblet shape.
In the base is found the main mass of unaltered cytoplasm.
Here also is the nucleus, sometimes pressed downward and flattened against the base.
As discharge begins, the cell membrane ruptures at the free surface.
Mucin is often seen, in sections, protruding through, like a plug.
The evacuation of a goblet cell may be explosive or gradual.
If sudden, the cell collapses and is compressed by its neighbors.
After a time, refilling begins and the cycle is repeated.
Sometimes, however, gradual discharge and replacement go on simultaneously.
In this instance the goblet shape is retained for some time.
Goblet cells are seemingly long-lived and repeat the secretory cycle several times, at least.
Finally, however, a cell dies and is cast off.
Replacement comes from a neighboring cell which takes on specialization.
The goblet-cell shape occurs only when mucous cells are interspersed in an epithelium.
The goblet shape is assumed as neighboring, ordinary cells become crowded and distorted
When every cell in an epithelium is mucous-secreting, then no goblet cells occur.
This is the case in the surface lining of the stomach and of the uterine cervix.

DIAGNOSTIC FEATURES.
The goblet cell occurs in either a simple columnar or pseudostratified epithelium.
The goblet to barrel shape of this bloated cell is distinctive.
If mucigen is preserved, it stains fairly well with basic dyes in general.
If mucigen fails to stain, then three possibilities exist.
The cell may have discharged recently, and is now temporarily empty.
The mucigen may have been dissolved by an improper fixing method.
The stain may be inappropriate to demonstrate mucigen.
In ordinary preparations, inactive and early-regenerating stages are not conspicuous.

ii. *Multicellular Glands*

All the cells of an epithelium may become secretory units.
This arrangement can be called a secretory epithelial sheet.
Example: surface layer of the stomach, uterus and chorioid plexus.

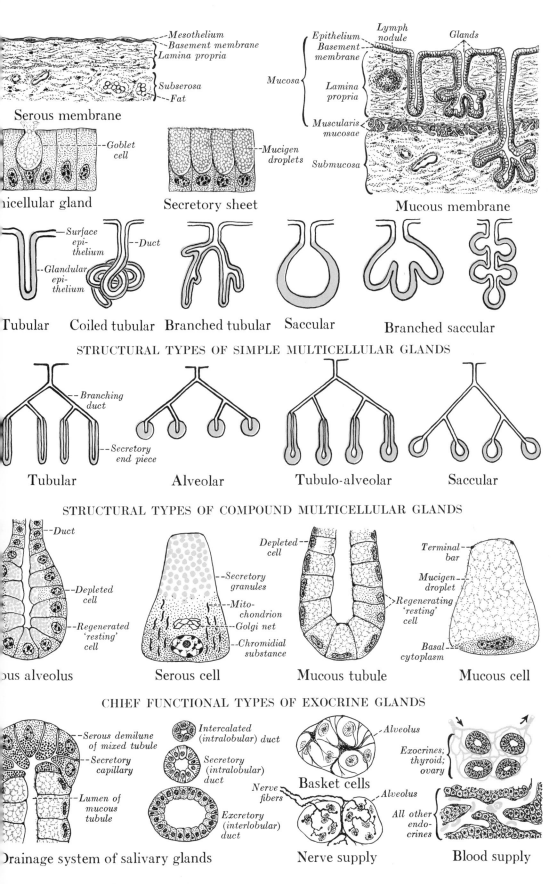

Mesothelium
Basement membrane
Lamina propria
Subserosa
Fat

Serous membrane

Epithelium
Basement membrane
Lymph nodule
Glands
Mucosa
Lamina propria
Muscularis mucosae
Submucosa

Goblet cell

nicellular gland

Mucigen droplets

Secretory sheet

Mucous membrane

Surface epithelium
Duct
Glandular epithelium

Tubular   Coiled tubular   Branched tubular   Saccular   Branched saccular

STRUCTURAL TYPES OF SIMPLE MULTICELLULAR GLANDS

Branching duct
Secretory end piece

Tubular   Alveolar   Tubulo-alveolar   Saccular

STRUCTURAL TYPES OF COMPOUND MULTICELLULAR GLANDS

Duct
Depleted cell
Regenerated 'resting' cell

ous alveolus

Depleted cell
Secretory granules
Mito-chondrion
Golgi net
Chromidial substance

Serous cell

Depleted cell

Mucous tubule

Terminal bar
Mucigen droplet
Regenerating 'resting' cell
Basal cytoplasm

Mucous cell

CHIEF FUNCTIONAL TYPES OF EXOCRINE GLANDS

Serous demilune of mixed tubule
Secretory capillary
Lumen of mucous tubule

Intercalated (intralobular) duct
Secretory (intralobular) duct
Nerve fibers
Excretory (interlobular) duct

Alveolus
Basket cells
Alveolus

Exocrines; thyroid; ovary
All other endo-crines

Drainage system of salivary glands   Nerve supply   Blood supply

MOIST MEMBRANES AND EXOCRINE GLANDS

intermediate between unicellular and multicellular glands are the pit-like, intra-epithelial glands
that lie wholly within a generalized epithelial layer.
Example: nasal mucosa; urethra; efferent ductules.
In general, multicellular glands arise as invaginations into vascularized connective tissue.
Most of them have an *excretory duct*, which is a nonsecretory drainage tube.
The functionally active portion of the gland consists of secretory *end pieces*.
The simplest glandular invaginations have a secretory portion, but lack a separate duct.
Example: intestinal 'crypt.'
More complex glands have a single, unbranched excretory duct.
Example: duodenal gland.
The most complex glands have a branched, tree-like system of ducts.
The branching may be slight (labial gland) or extensive (kidney; parotid).
The secretory end pieces of a gland are named according to their shapes.
Tubular refers to a blindly ending, hollow cylinder.
Alveolar (or *acinar*) refers to a globular to pear-shaped ending, with a small lumen.
Tubulo-alveolar refers to a secretory unit that combines the tubular and alveolar types.
An alveolus occurs at the end of a tubule, and others are set into its side wall.
Saccular refers to a pouch-like ending, with a large lumen.

A. ANATOMICAL CLASSIFICATION:
1. Simple Glands.
The excretory duct, if present, is single and unbranched.
A. TUBULAR.
1. Straight tubular (*e.g.*, intestinal crypts).
2. Coiled tubular (*e.g.*, ordinary sweat glands).
3. Branched tubular.
a. Without an excretory duct (*e.g.*, stomach; uterus; axilla).
b. With an excretory duct (*e.g.*, small glands of mouth and esophagus; deep
glands of the duodenum).
B. SACCULAR.
1. Unbranched saccular (*e.g.*, seminal vesicle).
2. Branched saccular (*e.g.*, sebaceous glands).

2. Compound Glands.
Such a gland consists of several to many component *lobules*.
Each lobule is a unit that is the equivalent of a simple, branched gland.
The several lobular ducts join and finally unite into one main excretory duct.
Four subtypes are based on the shape of the secretory end-pieces.
A. TUBULAR.
Example: kidney (blind tubules); testis (anastomosing tubules).
B. ALVEOLAR.
Example: some of the simpler glands of the respiratory tract.
C. TUBULO-ALVEOLAR.
Example: large salivary glands; pancreas; large glands of the esophagus and
respiratory tract.
D. SACCULAR.
Example: mammary gland.

B. CHARACTERISTICS OF SECRETORY CELL-TYPES:
Most of the exocrine glands are composed of serous cells, mucous cells, or both types.

1. Serous Cells.

This type is also called *albuminous*, because a clear, watery albuminous secretion is elaborated from a granular precursor substance.

Secretions related to digestion contain salts, proteins, and pro-enzymes.

The parent cells could well be designated as *sero-zymogenic*.

The serous cells occur in typical rounded to pear-shaped alveoli.

The component, pyramidal cells are arranged about a notably small lumen.

A narrow lumen is correlated with the watery character of the secretion.

At the margins, between cell-tops, there is a system of terminal bars.

Secretory capillaries pass from the lumen between the lateral surfaces of cells.

These may branch, but they never extend as far as the basement membrane.

They are merely grooves between abutting cell surfaces.

Rarely the tiny canals extend to the cell interior (*e.g.*, gastric glands).

The Golgi silver-technique demonstrates these canaliculi well.

When full of secretion, the so-called resting serous cells are distended.

Cell boundaries are then indistinct and the lumen is of minimal size.

The cytoplasm contains highly refractile, spheroidal *secretion granules*.

These are actually semifluid droplets; they are secretion-precursors.

In digestive glands they are enzyme-precursors, called *zymogen granules*.

Aqueous fixatives (and especially formol) preserve the secretion granules.

Basic stains, such as iron hematoxylin or neutral gentian, stain them well.

The cytoplasm of the cell-base contains *chromidial* (or *chromophil*) *substance* (p. 13).

This material contains ribonucleic acid and stains with basic dyes.

It appears usually as vertical striations, the *basal lamellae*.

Its presence is correlated with active protein synthesis by these cells.

The nucleus is rounded, basally located (or nearly so) and not flattened.

During active secretion, the 'secretion granules' transform into watery droplets.

The fluid secretion is discharged into the lumen, the secretory vacuoles perhaps carrying portions of the cell membrane with them.

As secretion continues, the cells shrink and the lumen enlarges somewhat.

At the close of normal emptying, the remaining granules are few.

The cytoplasm straightway enters upon a new constructive period.

A depleted cell is small, with dark-staining cytoplasm.

Secretion granules then increase in number in the cytoplasm above the nucleus.

As they enlarge, the cytoplasm between them is reduced to a spongework.

The nucleus may even be forced to the base of the cell.

Nevertheless, it does not flatten like that of a mucous cell.

During a cycle there is a waxing and waning of certain cell-components.

Before the protein secretion-granules are elaborated, the nucleolus is large.

Also the Golgi net and basal chromidial substance are both abundant.

During the formation of the secretion-product these several components decline.

The Golgi net is associated with the formation of secretion granules.

Granules first make their appearance in the Golgi territory.

After enlarging, they migrate toward the free surface (apex) of the cell (p. 14).

2. Mucous Cells.

Mucous tubules have a fairly large lumen, usually filled with secretion.

A wide lumen facilitates the flow of the viscid, mucous fluid.

The wedge-shaped cells about the lumen are arranged as a simple epithelium.

Cell membranes show as well-defined boundaries.

Along the margins at the tops of the cells is a system of *terminal bars*.
Secretory capillaries, such as occur in serous cells, are lacking.
A peculiar protein, *mucigen*, is elaborated by the cytoplasm of mucous cells.
When discharged, it imbibes water and is known as *mucin*.
This is a thick, viscid, glairy secretion.
Having acquired inorganic salts and other additions, it is often called *mucus*.
It is chemically inactive, but is important protectively and as a lubricant.
The quality of the secretion apparently varies greatly in different glands.
This may be true of different tubules of the same gland; staining differs.
It may even occur in different regions of the same tubule.
In living cells many large droplets of mucigen hide the nucleus.
This secretion-mass is hard to preserve satisfactorily.
The mucigen droplets are destroyed and dissolved by aqueous fixation.
The cell body then contains a honeycomb that stains like mucin.
This consists of cytoplasm, with mucigen precipitated on it.
Mucigen is preserved better by alcoholic fixatives.
Mucigens are glycoproteins that vary in composition but commonly are acidic.
Such acidic products stain with basic dyes, such as alum-hematoxylin or thionine.
They stain specifically with mucicarmine and muchematin.
It is claimed that the droplets originate in relation to the Golgi net.
The secretion droplets collect first near the free end of a cell.
They then progressively invade deeper parts of the cell.
Accumulating secretion pushes the nucleus progressively downward.
The nucleus is finally flattened against the cell base.
Thin partitions of cytoplasm separate the mucigen droplets.
The basal cytoplasm is poor or lacking in chromidial substance.
When the cell is ripe, the surface membrane ruptures.
This permits the escape of the secretion-mass.
If all the secretion is emptied at once, the cell reverts to a slender shape.
The nucleus rises higher in the cell and becomes rounded.
The cytoplasm then regenerates and fills out the cell.
The cell resembles somewhat the serous type until secretory activity resumes.
If discharge is but partial, the events of restoration are less dramatic.

3. Mixed Sero-mucous Tubules.

Some serous cells also stain slightly with mucicarmine.
They are sometimes designated as sero-mucous cells.
Quite different are glands that have both cell types in at least some tubules.
If the mucous cells dominate a tubule, the serous cells occur in groups.
They may occupy the blind end of a mucous tubule or overlap it.
More rarely the serous group outpockets from the side of a tubule.
These oval-shaped, serous patches are called *demilunes* or *crescents*.
The serous cells of a demilune are smaller than the mucous cells of the tubule.
Intercellular secretory capillaries connect the serous cells with the lumen.

4. Diagnostic Features.

Secretory *end pieces* appear as circular to elongate groups of epithelial cells.
When the lumen is cut across, the cells are wedge-shaped and radially arranged.
When the lumen is cut axially, the cells are cuboidal to columnar in shape.
(Most of the end pieces become cut across somewhat obliquely.)

Serous cells usually stain fairly well with ordinary dyes.

The cytoplasm is distinctly granular; cell boundaries are not clear.

Specific zymogen granules may show distinctly in ordinary preparations.

As a whole, they stain with some acid dyes and some basic dyes.

Nuclei may lie at the cell base, but they are not flattened.

The alveolar lumen is small, or even not noticeable.

Mucous cells commonly remain pale after ordinary fixation and staining.

If the mucigen is partially preserved, a reticulum can be seen.

It stains moderately well with basic dyes.

Nuclei are basal in position and tend to be definitely flattened.

The alveolar lumen is conspicuous; cell boundaries are sharply defined.

C. STRUCTURAL PLAN:

1. Secretory End-pieces.

The secretory epithelium of a gland is arranged as specialized *end-pieces.*

These attach to the terminal ducts.

Their shape may be that of a tube, berry, long-necked flask or sac.

The lumen is variable in size, depending on the type of gland.

The component cells of an end-piece are usually but one layer deep.

They are most commonly shaped like truncated pyramids.

A *basement membrane* almost always separates epithelium from connective tissue.

Basket (or *basal*) *cells* frequently occur about secretory end-pieces.

These are scattered, stellate, flat cells.

They lie between the gland cells and the basement membrane.

In section they appear thin, with dark flat nuclei.

They are clasping elements, supposedly contractile but possibly only supporting.

In some glands (sweat; mammary) they are prominent as *myo-epithelial cells.*

2. Ducts.

The ducts are primarily drainage tubes of different sizes.

The duct systems of small and large glands compare as does a shrub to a tree.

In a large gland the ducts outside of lobules alone may number 1500.

A duct is lined with a very regular epithelium, showing distinct cell boundaries.

The epithelium is frequently clasped by basket cells.

The duct system reaches its highest specialization in salivary glands.

An *intercalated* (or *intermediate*) *duct* attaches to the alveolus.

Its cells are of a low, cuboidal type.

Secretory ducts, next in order, are peculiar to the salivary glands.

Their columnar cells bear vertical basal-striations.

This appearance is produced in part by parallel rows of mitochondria.

Also many infoldings of the basal plasma membrane pass into the cytoplasm

Such ducts are said to secrete water and salts.

Excretory ducts are the largest branches and the main trunk of the duct-system.

In general, they are lined with a high columnar epithelium.

The main trunk of some of them has a pseudostratified epithelium.

In some locations the region of the outlet changes to a stratified epithelium.

The several ducts are sometimes designated as being *interlobular* and *intralobular.*

These terms refer merely to a location between or within lobules, respectively.

Excretory ducts are preponderantly interlobular in position.

Intercalated ducts are wholly intralobular, and secretory ducts almost always so

3. Framework.

A fibro-elastic *capsule* surrounds many of the larger glands.

Fibrous *septa* divide large, compact glands into *lobules* (and sometimes into *lobes*).

Each lobule is arranged about a branch of the duct-system and its twigs.

It represents a somewhat independent unit of glandular organization.

The septa contain the larger ducts; also blood vessels, lymphatics and nerves.

Fat cells may occur in the septa, and even within the lobule.

Delicate connective tissue within a lobule forms a *stroma* that embeds the alveoli.

4. Vessels and Nerves.

Blood vessels follow the ducts and form rich capillary networks about secretory end-pieces and terminal ducts.

Lymphatics are said to be scarce in many glands.

Secretory *nerve fibers* form plexuses of bare filaments beneath the epithelium.

Extensions penetrate between the cells and make simple or branched endings.

D. REGENERATIVE ABILITY:

Mucous cells show mitoses rarely, and there are few signs of degeneration.

Serous cells, under normal conditions, undergo mitoses occasionally.

In general, replacements come from cells recruited from the adjoining ducts.

Some glands regenerate rather well after incurring considerable gross loss.

E. DIAGNOSTIC FEATURES:

All but the simplest glands appear as multiple, closely-packed, epithelial islands.

These are set in a small amount of delicate, connective-tissue stroma.

The continuity and unity of the system is not apparent in a random, single section.

The larger glands are subdivided into lobules by coarse connective tissue.

This interlobular tissue often is subject to marked shrinkage.

The epithelial *end-pieces* are circular, ovoid or tubular in section.

A lumen may or may not be seen; it varies greatly in size.

The variation is correlated with the type of gland and its functional state.

For the characteristic features of mucous and serous alveoli, see pp. 164, 165.

Other types of glands will be considered under the several organ systems.

Intercalated ducts are much smaller than alveoli, and hence are rather inconspicuous.

They are easiest seen when traceable to alveoli as small tubules.

Their epithelium is scarcely thicker than the contained nuclei.

Secretory ducts, when present, are the most conspicuous structures within a lobule.

This is because of their fair size, bright acidophilic coloration, precisely regular proportions and prominent lumen.

The lumen is somewhat the same thickness as the epithelial wall of the duct.

The component columnar cells show vertical basal-striations.

The epithelium frequently shrinks away from its basement membrane.

Excretory ducts course in the connective tissue between lobules.

This location and their large size readily identify them.

The epithelium is usually tall columnar or pseudostratified; it is not striated.

The lumen tends to be definitely wider than the wall.

3. The Endocrine Glands

This is a group of glands, some of which are composed of atypical epithelium.
> Detached epithelial masses have lost connection with the parent epithelium.
> Embedded in connective tissue, they lack a free surface in most instances.
There are no ducts of any kind; secretion is released directly into the blood stream.
> Hence these glands are designated as *ductless* or *endocrine* (internally secreting).
> It follows that the vascular supply to these organs must be both rich and intimate.
>> The thyroid and suprarenal are among the best vascularized organs of the body.
>> The final, intimate vessels are either sinusoids or capillaries.
Most of the endocrine glands are separate entities, recognizable as distinct organs.
> Example: thyroid; suprarenal.
> Some, however, occur as scattered masses within an exocrine gland.
>> Example: pancreatic islands; interstitial cells of testis; corpora lutea of ovary.
>> These combined exocrine-endocrine organs are sometimes spoken of as *mixed organs*.
> The endocrine tissue may be distributed so diffusely that it is not regarded as an 'organ.'
>> Example: cells in the lining of the duodenum that produce 'secretin.'
Endocrine glands, as a group, have a simpler organization than exocrine glands.
> This is largely because they lack the organization imposed by a duct system.
>> As a result, the gland cells must abut directly against vascular channels.
> Most of this group of glands are arranged in cords or plates of atypical epithelium.
>> The cords are separated by sinusoids or broad capillaries.
>>> Example: suprarenal; parathyroid; pancreatic islands; hypophysis; corpus luteum.
> A few glands consist of typical epithelial sacs, surrounded by a vascular plexus.
>> Example: thyroid; ovarian follicles.
The secretion-products of endocrine glands are named *hormones*.
> A hormone is capable of eliciting a response from a target organ at some distance.
>> The response is usually an arousal or activation, but it may depress action.
>> The responsive part may be a tissue, an organ or the body as a whole.
> Only a minute quantity of a hormone is required to produce an effect.
>> Its action is essentially like that of a chemical catalyst.
> Some glands produce only one hormone; others elaborate from two to eight.
Secretion granules (hormone precursors) are visible in most endocrines, but not in all.
All endocrine organs store their secretory products to some extent.
> Storage is usually within the cells of origin; notably so in the pancreatic islands.
>> Yet in the suprarenal cortex, secretion is released almost as fast as it is formed.
> By contrast, storage may be in a pool enclosed by the glandular cells.
>> In this instance the epithelium takes the form of sacs (*e.g.*, thyroid).
The group of endocrine glands constitutes an organ system.
> Their mode of secretion and target effectiveness are characteristics shared in common.
> These organs not only integrate other parts but interact to regulate themselves.
The individual endocrine glands will be described in the following chapter.

Chapter XVI. THE ENDOCRINE GLANDS

n introduction to the endocrine organs has been presented in the preceding chapter.
he present accounts will discuss in detail those glands that are separate organs.
everal other endocrines are contained within organs of a wholly different type.
 Such include pancreatic islands, gonadal tissue and gastro-intestinal epithelium.
 These will be described with the major organs of which they are a part.

I. THE THYROID GLAND

he meaning is 'shield-shaped,' in reference to its relation to the upper trachea.
he main bulk of the organ consists of a *lateral lobe*, on each side of the trachea.
 These two lobes are connected by a narrow *isthmus* in front of the trachea.
 In addition, a median *pyramidal lobe* frequently extends upward.
ach main lobe is roughly the size of half of a golf ball.

. STRUCTURAL PLAN:
 An enveloping *capsule* is continuous externally with the deep cervical fascia.
  This outer, looser fascia separates easily from the thinner capsule proper.
 Capsular tissue continues inward as *septa* to ensheath *lobules*.
  The manner of lobulation, however, is peculiar.
  Groups of follicles form large, irregular plates or bars, incompletely ensheathed.
  Such lobules interconnect at intervals to produce a complex total-mass.
   Hence, no lobule is surrounded completely with connective tissue.
 The gland consists of enormous numbers of closed epithelial sacs, or *follicles*.
  Each lies separately in a common, connective-tissue *stroma*.
  Each contains little to much stored secretion, known as *colloid*.

. DETAILED STRUCTURE:
1. Framework.
 A fibro-elastic *capsule* is continued into delicate *septa* and *trabeculae*.
  These septa delimit the *lobules* which, however, are not completely separate.
 Areolar and reticular tissue provide a thin, highly vascular *stroma*.
  In this bed lie myriads of individual *thyroid follicles*.

2. Follicles.
 The structural unit is a closed, single-layered epithelial sac, the *follicle*.
 The size of a normal follicle in the adult varies from 50 to 500 μ in diameter.
  This range depends on the degree of distention by secretion.
 Normally the smaller follicles are more numerous than the larger ones.
  The total number of follicles is, perhaps, 20 millions.
 The shape of a follicle is spheroidal, or sometimes elongate.
  Occasionally there are constricted, twisted or bizarre shapes.

169

A. EPITHELIUM.

The shape of the component cells varies about a mean, which is cuboidal.

The cells are low when the gland is underactive (much stored colloid).

The cells are high when the gland is overactive (little stored colloid).

However, cell height also varies with age, sex, diet, season, etc.

The epithelium is underlaid by a mesh of reticular fibers (in ground substance).

In older individuals this meshwork is denser, making a *basement membrane*.

This membrane, however, is so delicate that its presence is often denied.

Cell height in any follicle is quite uniform and the arrangement is regular.

The large, vesicular nuclei lie centrally to somewhat basally, in an even row

The cytoplasm is finely granular and palely basophilic.

Its free border bears microvilli, visible only with the electron microscope.

All the cells appear to be of one kind in man.

Different 'types,' sometimes claimed, are probably variants that are re
lated to age and functional activity (secretory cycle, etc.).

So-called *colloid cells* are slender elements, with pyknotic nuclei.

The cytoplasm is strongly acidophilic and often contains colloid droplet

Doubtless these are old and dying cells.

The cell *organoids* show definite, polarized positions.

The Golgi apparatus and centrioles are located above the nucleus.

The Golgi net enlarges during the formation of secretion.

Certain cytoplasmic *inclusions*, apparently related to secretion, are found.

These include colloid droplets, granules, fat globules and vacuoles.

Terminal bars encircle the margins of cells, near their free surfaces.

B. COLLOID.

The thyroid is a gland that is notable for its storage of reserve secretion.

This reserve is the semifluid *colloid* that fills the follicular lumen.

Fresh colloid is homogeneous, clear and viscous.

The amount of colloid varies normally between wide limits.

A large amount indicates glandular inactivity; such colloid is a stiff jelly.

An active gland contains a small amount of thin, more fluid colloid.

Regional differences in this regard reflect local phases in the cyclic events.

Colloid does not stain identically in all follicles.

It may even stain differently in local regions of the same follicle.

In active follicles the colloid is definitely basophilic.

This may be owing to the presence of ribonucleic acid.

Inactive follicles have acidophilic (or very weakly basophilic) colloid.

Colloid sometimes contains cast-off follicular cells and vacuoles.

Peripheral *vacuoles*, in active glands, are indicative of colloid resorption.

Colloid is rich in nucleoproteins, and contains *thyroglobulin* and *enzymes*.

3. Interfollicular Cells.

Groups of epithelial cells can be found in the stroma between sectioned follicles.

Most of them are merely slices from the sides of true follicles.

Others are clusters that may represent unused embryonic tissue.

Fibroblasts, lymphocytes, macrophages and mast cells occur in the stroma.

4. Secretion and Storage.

Secretion is difficult to follow, and it is complicated by temporary storage.

Thyroid cells remove iodine rapidly from the blood stream and concentrate it.

It is then slowly transformed into a protein-bound iodide, the hormone substance.
This iodine-complex is segregated in the cytoplasm as stainable *colloid droplets*.
The normal direction of secretion is first into the follicular lumen.
Here the secreted droplets join the colloid-pool and are stored.
The storage-form is *thyroglobulin* (thyroxin conjugated with a globulin).
The uptake of radioactive iodine by the thyroid and its incorporation into the epithelium and colloid can be followed by properly timed experiments.
For release, viscid thyroglobulin is split into a smaller, more diffusible molecule.
It is presumably done by a proteolytic enzyme known to be present in the colloid.
The main split-product is *thyroxin*, the chief active principle of the hormone.
This substance has been isolated in pure crystalline form.
It is taken up into the cells and then resecreted into adjoining capillaries.
The resorption gives rise to border vacuoles in the colloid-pool.
Thus secretion is reversible, and it can proceed in both directions simultaneously.
Under excess stimulation, secretion is chiefly direct—into the blood.

5. Vessels and Nerves.

Blood vessels and *lymphatics* form intimate plexuses about follicles.
Arterio-venous anastomoses are common.
The thyroid is about the best vascularized organ of the body.
Thyroxin is demonstrable in both veins and lymphatics, but chiefly in veins.
Most of the *nerve fibers* are vasomotor in function.
A few fibers end about follicles, but their secretory function is not proved.
(Transplants to another region function in the absence of such innervation.)

C. REGENERATIVE ABILITY:

There is normal loss and replacement of thyroid cells, but the details are disputed.
A thyroid can repair its loss, after partial removal, if the diet lacks iodine.

D. DIAGNOSTIC FEATURES:

Sections show crowded epithelial rings, set in a scanty stroma.
These rings (follicles) are of assorted sizes, the largest macroscopic.
What seem to be small follicles may be only border slices off larger ones.
Solid, epithelial masses can be assumed to be tangential shavings from follicles.
The lining epithelium of a follicle is a simple layer, usually of cuboidal cells.
Homogeneous, eosinophilic colloid fills the follicles.
With some compound stains, colloid colors variously in different follicles.
Colloid commonly is shrunken and has a spiny border.

E. FUNCTIONAL CORRELATIONS:

The thyroid is an important gland, but not essential to life.
One-fifth of the gland suffices to maintain its normal functioning.
The thyroid regulates the metabolic rate; thyroxin increases cell metabolism.
It also is concerned with development, differentiation and growth.
A congenital thyroid deficiency leads to a condition known as *cretinism*.
This is a complex that includes dwarfism and impaired mentality.
Thyroid secretion affects variously certain other endocrine glands.
Interaction with the hypophysis maintains balanced functional responses in both.
An hypophyseal hormone (*thyrotropin*) stimulates the release of thyroxin.
But thyroxin in the blood exerts a restraint on thyrotropic production.

The thyroid is a notably labile gland that varies greatly in size and structure.

Undersecretion, after childhood, leads to simple *colloid goiter* and *myxedema*.

Colloid collects in excess, but there is a lack of iodinated protein in it.

Hence there is a deficiency in available hormone.

Oversecretion is associated with overgrowth of the follicular epithelium.

Follicles are large, folded and the cells are tall and active.

The secretion is in excess, yet it may or may not be rich in thyroxin.

II. THE PARATHYROID GLAND

There are typically four brownish, *parathyroid glands*.

Two are attached to the back of the capsule of each lateral thyroid lobe.

Other, accessory, glands occur frequently (30 per cent of individuals).

The glands are ovoid in shape; each is about the size of an apple seed.

A. STRUCTURAL PLAN:

Each gland has a thin *capsule*, from which delicate *septa* extend inward.

The *parenchyma* takes the form of solid masses and irregular cords of cells.

The general appearance is one of compact epithelial tissue, without a free surface.

Between the cell groups there are broad capillaries.

Some clumps of *acidophilic cells* usually occur among the preponderant, *pale cells*.

B. DETAILED STRUCTURE:

1. Framework.

The fibro-elastic *capsule* is a delicate layer.

Thin *septa* penetrate into the gland and divide it incompletely into *lobules*.

This invasion begins some time after birth and continues as age advances.

In this way the parenchyma increasingly is reduced to cord-like strands.

A basketwork of reticular tissue supports the cell groups as a delicate *stroma*.

2. Parenchyma.

The *epithelium* is a type that has secondarily lost its free surface.

It was originally a part of the pharyngeal lining, but became detached and buried

The masses and cords, as seen in sections, commonly appear to be relatively thick.

Yet it is claimed that each cell abuts against a capillary.

(When uninjected, capillaries are inconspicuous and tend to escape notice.)

There is probably no true basement membrane in relation to these cells.

Two main cell types, each with two subtypes, are recognized.

They seem to represent stages in the life cycle of a single kind of gland-cell.

A. CHIEF CELL.

This is the most abundant, and probably the fundamental, type.

They are the only cells seen until about the tenth year.

These cells are arranged in masses and cords.

The *clear chief cells* stain palely, but have prominent cell boundaries.

The cytoplasm is usually clear and nongranular, yet it is rich in glycogen.

The nucleus is relatively large and vesicular.

So-called *dark chief cells* differ from the clear chief cells quantitatively.

They have smaller nuclei and finely granular cytoplasm.

B. OXYPHIL CELL.

This type first appears in late childhood and becomes more abundant in adults.

It is characteristic of man, but is absent in most mammals.
The arrangement of these cells is in small and large groups.
Oxyphil cells are larger than the chief cells.
The cytoplasm is much more abundant and granular; it is acidophilic.
The ordinary dark oxyphil is deeply acidophilic.
Its nucleus is small and dark staining.
There are also pale oxyphil cells with lighter staining nuclei and cytoplasm.

3. Miscellaneous Features.

The several cell types are usually interpreted as representing stages in the life cycle of a single kind of secretory cell.
These stages would be, in order: (1) pale chief cell; (2) dark chief cell; (3) pale oxyphil cell; (4) dark oxyphil cell.
The dark, pyknotic oxyphils have all the appearances of senile cells.
Yet it is possible that oxyphils constitute a separate secretory element.
Precursor substances of the secretion have not been established with certainty.
Yet there is evidence (mitochondria; Golgi; vacuoles) of cyclic activity.
Only a minority of the parenchymal cells are active at the same time.
Small colloid-containing follicles are seen occasionally.
These are especially noticeable after thyroid removal and in old age.
This material has no functional relation to the colloid of the thyroid.
Fat cells collect in the connective-tissue stroma, especially with advancing age.
Parathyroid cells resist postmortem autolysis better than any other epithelium.

4. Vessels and Nerves.

The *blood supply* is fairly rich, the larger vessels following the septa.
The parenchyma is channeled by broad, irregular capillaries.
The presence of *lymphatics* is asserted, but details are few.
Nerve fibers, probably vasomotor, are scanty.

. REGENERATIVE ABILITY:

The chief cells are seemingly the only ones that proliferate, and they do so rarely.
The parathyroid transplants readily, but fails to regenerate significantly.

. DIAGNOSTIC FEATURES:

The general picture is of a densely cellular organ, arranged in masses and cords.
Both capsule and septa are subordinated, and are often a minor feature.
The parenchyma consists of closely packed epithelial cells.
These fit together in a mosaic of polyhedrons.
Interspersed are capillaries (many of which are collapsed and inconspicuous).
Most numerous are pale cells, with a small amount of clear cytoplasm.
Their closely spaced nuclei give an appearance somewhat like lymphoid tissue.
Conspicuous are groups of larger cells (except in children).
Their cytoplasm is abundant, granular and acidophilic.
The cell nucleus is relatively small, shrunken and dark.
There is no regularity in the distribution of these acidophilic cell-aggregates.

. FUNCTIONAL CORRELATIONS:

Evidence of secretion is almost wholly experimental, not cytological.

The parathyroid hormone has been isolated in pure chemical form.
Its normal effect is to withdraw calcium from bones (the calcium bank).
The liberated calcium then accumulates in the blood plasma.
An increasing calcium level in the plasma depresses parathyroid activity.
These balanced effects maintain blood calcium at a nearly constant level.
Atrophy or removal of the parathyroids is followed by a fall in blood calcium.
This is accompanied by nervous hyperexcitability and muscular spasms.
This condition, known as *tetany*, will lead to death unless intervention occurs.
The administration of calcium or parathyroid extract affords relief.
Overactivity of the glands occurs when there is calcium deficiency, as in rickets.
The glands enlarge and their cells proliferate in attempting to compensate.
Overactivity can also result from tumorous growth of parathyroid tissue.
This may lead to extensive resorption of bone, and hence to elevated blood-calcium.

III. THE HYPOPHYSIS

The meaning is 'a sprout beneath' (the brain); an older name is the *pituitary body*.
It is a compound gland, made up of two wholly unlike parts.
An *epithelial portion* originates from a sac pinched off from the primitive mouth.
A *neural portion* is a downgrowth from the floor of the brain.
The hypophysis is largely buried in a fossa of the sphenoid bone.
An accessory nodule, the *pharyngeal hypophysis*, lies beneath the lining of the naso-pharynx.
It is a developmental remnant of the epithelial portion and resembles it in structure.

A. STRUCTURAL PLAN:

The *hypophysis* is about the size of a small, somewhat flattened grape.
A pinkish portion can be designated as the *adenohypophysis*, or epithelial hypophysis.
It consists of glandular tissue, derived from the oral epithelium.
This portion is subdivided by the *residual lumen* into very unequal parts.
The lumen represents remnants of the cavity of the embryonic sacculation.
The larger part is in front of these clefts; it is the *pars distalis*.
An extension that surrounds the neural stalk is the *pars tuberalis*.
Both are composed of epithelial cords and sinusoids.
The smaller part, behind the clefts, is very thin; it is the *pars intermedia*.
A second, whitish, fibrous portion can be designated as the *neurohypophysis*.
It consists of three component parts:
One is the *pars nervosa*, fused to the epithelial portion of the total gland.
The second and third parts are, respectively, the *infundibular stalk* (which extends
upward from the pars nervosa) and the *median eminence* of the brain.
Often the terms 'anterior lobe' and 'posterior lobe' are used, for convenience.
Anterior lobe refers to the portion anterior to the residual lumen.
This is the pars distalis (and tuberalis), foremost in functional importance.
Posterior lobe refers to the substance posterior to the residual lumen.
It includes the pars intermedia (epithelial) and pars nervosa (neural).
But only the neural portion is of functional significance in mammals.

B. DETAILED STRUCTURE:
1. Framework.
The fibro-elastic *capsule* is merely an innermost part of the neighboring dura mater.
It is thickest where it encloses the anterior lobe.

Trabeculae, bearing blood vessels, radiate from one region into the anterior lobe.

A meshwork of *reticular tissue* supports the epithelial cords and sinusoids.

A homogeneous *basement membrane* separates the cords from the reticulum proper.

2. Pars Distalis.

This portion constitutes about three-fourths of the organ (exclusive of its stalk).

Its epithelium is arranged in anastomosing cords and masses; it is *parenchyma*.

Epithelial vesicles, filled with a colloid substance, occur occasionally.

The epithelial parenchyma is supported by a network of reticular fibers.

Between the cords are dilated *sinusoids*, lined with fixed macrophages.

The component epithelial cells are of two main types, unequal in number.

However, their distribution varies regionally, and locally within a region.

Also cell ratios are modified by pregnancy, castration and other conditions.

The cell shape is ovoid to polyhedral; nuclei vary somewhat in the cell types.

But the cytoplasm is the differential feature that distinguishes types.

One group responds feebly to stains, and is named *chromophobes*.

The other group has strong staining affinities, and is called *chromophils*.

A. Chromophobe Cells.

These faintly staining cells are also known as *reserve cells*.

They seem to be inactive stages of the other main group (chromophils).

They tend to be located more axially within the cell cords.

That is, they do not border on sinusoids, as active cells do.

The chromophobe cell is smaller than the chromophil.

Its cytoplasm is scanty, stains lightly and lacks specific granules.

Cell boundaries are not seen in ordinary preparations.

During pregnancy many cells fill with small, weakly acidophilic granules.

Such elements are termed *pregnancy cells*.

B. Chromophil Cells.

These cells are larger than chromophobes, and their cell boundaries are distinct.

The cytoplasm is definitely granular and stainable.

This quality makes chromophils more conspicuous than chromophobes.

Chromophils tend to lie at the surface of cell cords, next to the sinusoids.

It is believed that the granules are actual precursors of the secretion.

The degree of granularity varies with the functional state of a cell.

There are two cell types: acidophils and basophils.

The *acidophil cells* are nearly three times more abundant than basophils.

Hence they are the most conspicuous of all the cell types.

The specific granules are spherical and fairly uniform in size.

They take on acid dyes, but also stain with certain basic dyes (safranin).

For this reason some prefer to call them, noncommittally, *alpha cells*.

Staining responses demark two subtypes (orangeophils; carminophils).

Acidophils are more numerous in the central region of the lobe.

The *basophil cells* tend to be appreciably larger than acidophils.

Their granules are smaller and not uniform in size.

At comparable stages the granules are fewer than those of acidophils.

They stain less readily than acidophils, yet take methylene blue strongly.

But the granules also stain with aniline blue, an acid dye.

Hence some prefer to call these elements *beta cells*.

Staining responses distinguish at least two subtypes (gamma; delta).

c. SECRETORY CYCLE.

Mitoses are rare; therefore, the cells must pass through repeated cycles.

The relations between the cell-types have seemingly been solved (in the rat).

The chromophobes are inactive resting cells, of two distinguishable types.

As they approach a new phase of activity, granules appear in them.

The granules are of two different kinds, and two cell-types differentiate.

One type becomes acidophils; the other type becomes basophils.

Engorged cells then secrete and return to their chromophobic, inactive state

3. Pars Tuberalis.

There are cell groups and short cords, set in a well vascularized reticulum.

Some of the cells are finely granular and faintly basophilic.

There is a tendency toward the formation of cysts with 'colloid' in them.

4. Residual Lumen.

The *lumen* is typically an epithelial-lined cleft.

It is well represented in most mammals, including young children.

In adult man it may be entirely obliterated or may persist as remnants.

Such cystic cavities frequently possess a ciliated lining.

5. Pars Intermedia.

In most mammals this portion is a narrow, but definite, layer.

It is located behind the residual lumen and is several cells deep.

Its polyhedral cells stain with basic dyes.

Secretory granules have been described in them.

Cysts are common, filled with a colloid or hyaline material.

In man and apes, the pars intermedia is usually an ill-defined region.

This is because the residual lumen is virtually obliterated as a cleft.

The pars intermedia is probably the most variable organ of the body.

A thin layer of *cells* and *colloid cysts* occurs next to the neural lobe.

Portions of this tissue project backward into the neural lobe.

Some cells are pale staining; others are granular and basophilic.

The basophils are prone to invade the neural lobe by migration.

6. Neurohypophysis.

The extension of the brain cavity into the pars nervosa is obliterated in man.

It is now recognized that the solid *pars nervosa* belongs to a larger entity.

This is a complex that can be named the *neurohypophysis*.

Besides the pars nervosa it also includes the *infundibular stalk* and *media eminence* of the diencephalon.

All three portions have the same characteristic cells, a common blood and ner supply, and contain the same active hormonal principle.

Some 100,000 unmyelinated nerve fibers pass into the neurohypophysis.

These constitute the *hypothalamico-hypophyseal tract*.

The great majority end in the neurohypophysis (mostly in the pars nervosa).

The distinctive cell type, the *pituicyte*, resembles neuroglia cells elsewhere.

Four subtypes are recognized; many contain fatty droplets, granules and pigmer

It is unproved, however, that these cells have secretory significance.

A homogeneous, intercellular substance is characteristic of the neurohypophysis.

On fixation it precipitates into masses known as *Herring's bodies*.

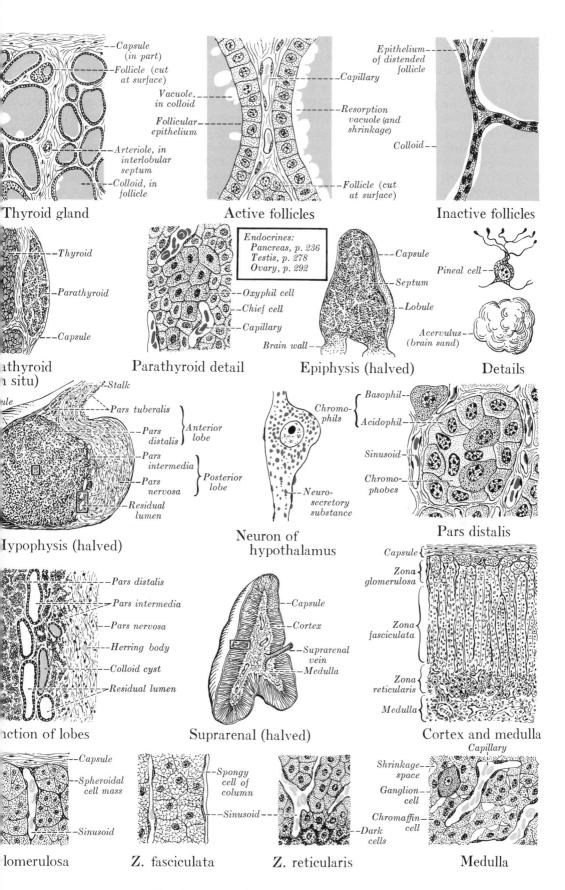

Capsule (in part)
Follicle (cut at surface)
Vacuole, in colloid
Follicular epithelium
Arteriole, in interlobular septum
Colloid, in follicle

Capillary
Resorption vacuole (and shrinkage)
Follicle (cut at surface)

Epithelium of distended follicle
Colloid

Thyroid gland   **Active follicles**   **Inactive follicles**

Thyroid
Parathyroid
Capsule

Endocrines:
Pancreas, p. 236
Testis, p. 278
Ovary, p. 292

Oxyphil cell
Chief cell
Capillary

Capsule
Septum
Lobule
Brain wall

Pineal cell
Acervulus (brain sand)

Parathyroid (in situ)   **Parathyroid detail**   **Epiphysis (halved)**   **Details**

Stalk
Pars tuberalis
Pars distalis — Anterior lobe
Pars intermedia
Pars nervosa — Posterior lobe
Residual lumen

Chromo-phils {
Basophil
Acidophil
Neuro-secretory substance
Sinusoid
Chromo-phobes

Hypophysis (halved)   **Neuron of hypothalamus**   **Pars distalis**

Pars distalis
Pars intermedia
Pars nervosa
Herring body
Colloid cyst
Residual lumen

Capsule
Cortex
Suprarenal vein
Medulla

Capsule
Zona glomerulosa
Zona fasciculata
Zona reticularis
Medulla

Junction of lobes   **Suprarenal (halved)**   **Cortex and medulla**

Capsule
Spheroidal cell mass
Sinusoid

Spongy cell of column
Sinusoid

Dark cells

Capillary
Shrinkage space
Ganglion cell
Chromaffin cell

Z. glomerulosa   **Z. fasciculata**   **Z. reticularis**   **Medulla**

THE ENDOCRINE GLANDS

The same substance is probably responsible for swellings that occur on nerve
fibers and at nerve terminations in the neurohypophysis.
Some interpret this material as the actual hormonal substance of the regions.
They hold that it is elaborated in the nerve cells of the tract, travels down the
fibers, and accumulates near their ends.

7. Vessels and Nerves.

The plan and richness of *vascularization* are not constant throughout the organ.
The pars distalis and tuberalis have a very rich sinusoidal supply from arterioles.
A venous supply also comes from a capillary bed in the infundibulum.
This is a true portal system, like that supplying the liver.
The pars intermedia has very few vessels of its own.
The pars nervosa has an independent vascular supply and drainage.
Its vascularity is good, but much poorer than that of the anterior lobe.
Lymphatics have never been demonstrated in relation to the gland.
There is a thick *nerve bundle* that descends into the pars nervosa (see above).
Some of its fibers enter the anterior lobe and terminate close to gland cells.
Stimulation of the tract in the rabbit is effective (inducing ovulation, etc.).
This is not true of mammals in general, which ovulate spontaneously.
Other fibers end in the pars intermedia, but the great majority terminate within
the neurohypophysis, and especially in the pars nervosa.
Autonomic fibers supply the vessels of the anterior and posterior lobes.

8. REGENERATIVE ABILITY:

The anterior lobe can replace completely losses incurred by fairly extensive injuries.
The posterior lobe heals injuries by scar-like tissue, as do other parts of the brain.

9. DIAGNOSTIC FEATURES:

A section through a total gland displays two quite different regions.
There is a larger, highly cellular part, that represents the anterior lobe.
A smaller, fibrous-looking part is the pars nervosa of the posterior lobe.
The one stains well (preponderantly acidophilic); the other is relatively pale.
Epithelial-lined clefts tend to separate the two regions.
The *pars distalis* consists of short cords, interspersed with sinusoids.
Acidophilic cells are prominent, and are the most abundant elements seen.
They are most numerous in the center of each half lobe, and posteriorly.
Basophils tend to stain much deeper than acidophils.
They may take a purplish-pink tone with hematoxylin and eosin.
They are most numerous in the midplane and at the antero-lateral margin.
Chromophobes are easily identified as groups of closely spaced, nearly naked nuclei.
They lie within cords, and their cytoplasm is not well seen.
The region of the residual lumen and *pars intermedia* is distinctive.
It is dominated by cyst-like spaces and cells with basophilic coloration.
The *pars nervosa*, with ordinary stains, has a fibrous appearance.
It resembles the texture of unmyelinated-nerve tissue.
Only with special silver stains are the distinctive pituicytes made clear.

10. FUNCTIONAL CORRELATIONS:

The hypophysis is the master endocrine organ, controlling various other endocrines.
Seven hormones have already been obtained from it in rather pure form.

The physiological effects of an endocrine organ can be ascertained by experiment.

A gland can be removed and the resulting functional loss noted.

Administering an extract of the gland then should promote functional recovery

The cell type responsible for a particular effect may also become known.

Removal of a target organ may lead to an increase in the number of those cells re
sponsible for elaborating the associated hormone.

Pathology of a cell-type may accompany abnormal functioning of an organ.

Regional abundance or lack of a cell-type may correlate with hormone assays there

1. Anterior Lobe.

A. Pars Distalis.

The *growth hormone* stimulates general body growth, and especially at epiphyses.

Undersecretion leads to *dwarfism* of the midget type.

Oversecretion prolongs growth and produces *gigantism*.

Evidence implicates a particular type of acidophil (orangeophil) as the source

Three hormones influence the gonads, and are hence called *gonadotrophic*.

The γ-basophil elaborates FSH and LH; an acidophil (carminophil) form
LTH.

The *follicle-stimulating hormone* (FSH) promotes growth of ovarian follicles.

In the male it activates the testis to produce spermatozoa.

The *luteinizing hormone* (LH) is the decisive factor in producing ovulation.

It also converts the ruptured follicle into a corpus luteum.

In the male it incites the interstitial cells of the testis into function.

The *luteotrophic hormone* (LTH) makes the corpus luteum secrete progesterone

It has also been called the *lactogenic hormone* (or prolactin).

It activates the secretion of milk by the properly developed breast.

The *thyrotrophic hormone* (TSH) maintains and stimulates the thyroid epithelium.

Evidence points toward the β-basophil as the cell of origin.

The *adrenocorticotrophic hormone* (ACTH) causes growth of the suprarenal cortex an
the secretion of its hormone.

The evidence as to the cell of origin is indecisive; basophils are suspected.

Chromophobes are believed not to be active hormone producers.

Tumors occur that feature these cells, with a loss of the other cell types.

Such excessive growths do not produce any specific symptoms.

This leaves acidophils and basophils as the sources of seven important hormone

Three or more hormones are attributed to the basophils.

Yet the problem of more products than known cell-types is not unique.

Other examples are multiple enzymes of the stomach, intestine and pancrea

B. Pars Tuberalis.

No specific hormonal function has been assigned to its cells.

2. Pars Intermedia.

A hormone, *intermedin*, expands the pigment cells of lower vertebrates.

This hormone is said to be produced by the mammalian pars intermedia, as wel
An influence, if exerted, is not known.

3. Neurohypophysis.

Two active factors have been extracted from all three parts of this organ.

It is not settled yet whether more than one hormonal entity is secreted.

There is adequate evidence that these products are *neurosecretions*.

That is, the source is granular nerve cells in the hypothalamus of the brain.
The secretion travels down their axons to the pars nervosa.
One factor (*vasopressin*) is satisfactorily hormonal in character.
It exerts an antidiuretic effect on the kidney tubules.
They are influenced to reabsorb water from the provisional urine.
This salvage prevents the voiding of large quantities of dilute urine.
Another effect is raising blood pressure (by constricting arterioles).
The second factor (*oxytocin*) contracts the smooth muscle of the uterus.
It also ejects milk, following a nervous response through suckling.

IV. THE SUPRARENAL GLAND

An older name, the *adrenal gland,* is unofficial but often used.
Each gland has the shape of a flattened, triangular cocked-hat; its size is 5 x 3 x 1 cm.
Each perches upon the cranial pole of a kidney and adapts itself to that contour.
A sectioned, fresh gland presents two different regions (three, by color).
The *cortex* is firm; it is yellow externally and reddish-brown internally.
The *medulla* is thinner, softer and dark gray.
Development proves that these regions are separate components, united secondarily.
The cortex grows from peritoneal mesothelium.
The medulla differentiates from primitive autonomic-ganglion tissue.
Comparative anatomy also shows their historical individuality as separate organs.
In placental mammals alone is the medullary tissue concentrated into a central mass.
It is wholly separate from the mesodermal cortex, rather than intermingling with it.
Accessory suprarenal tissue (usually cortex) may occur nearby or at a distance.

A. STRUCTURAL PLAN:

A robust *capsule* sends delicate, radial *trabeculae* inward toward the medulla.
The *cortex* consists of epithelial columns, arranged radially like a palisade.
Three concentric *zones* (but not separate layers) can be recognized in it.
These are based on three different patterns of cell arrangement.
The thinner *medulla* is spongy and more irregularly arranged.
Its epithelium takes the form of cords and masses, separated by vascular channels.
There is a *hilus* where a large vein leaves the gland.

B. DETAILED STRUCTURE:

1. Framework.

The *capsule* is a rather thick, fibro-elastic covering.
Its inner zone is looser and more vascular.
Slender *trabeculae* extend from this inner capsule radially through the cortex.
They consist mainly of reticular fibers; sinusoidal vessels accompany them.
Through their influence the cortex is divided into cell cords or columns.
The *medullary reticulum* forms coarser baskets about the parenchymal masses there.

2. Cortex.

The radial, cellular *cords* are relatively long, slender and distinct.
Thin trabeculae and elongate sinusoids separate them from each other.
For the most part the cords are two cells thick.
There are three poorly demarcated layers in the cortical parenchyma.
These strata are arranged concentrically and blend without sharp boundaries.

A. ZONA GLOMERULOSA.

This is a thin layer, located just beneath the capsule.

It consists of ovoid groups of cells, continuous with the zone beneath.

Some groups are shaped like an inverted U or J.

The component cells of a cluster are arranged about a focal center.

Nevertheless, no central lumen occurs normally.

The cells are columnar in shape, with deeply staining nuclei.

The lightly basophilic cytoplasm contains a few lipid droplets.

B. ZONA FASCICULATA.

The middle cortical layer is much the thickest of all.

Its parenchyma is arranged in long, parallel columns, usually two cells wide.

The component cells are irregularly cuboidal in shape.

They are larger than those of the zona glomerulosa.

The nucleus (frequently two) is vesicular; the cytoplasm is basophilic.

In the outer two-thirds of the zone the cytoplasm contains many lipid droplets.

They are composed of cholesterol, fatty acids and neutral fat.

Lipid extraction leaves extremely thin-walled, cytoplasmic compartments.

Hence these vacuolated cells are sometimes called *spongiocytes*.

These cords course obliquely, rather than regularly parallel.

The inner third of the zone is poor in lipids and is more basophilic.

C. ZONA RETICULARIS.

The parenchyma takes the form of anastomosing cords, mostly one cell wide.

Near the zona fasciculata, the component cells are much like those of that zone.

Yet, as a detail, they contain still fewer lipid droplets.

Near the medulla there is an intermixture of '*dark cells*.'

These have deeper staining, acidophilic cytoplasm and shrunken nuclei.

The cytoplasm contains large lipid droplets.

After puberty, it also acquires a yellow-brown pigment.

Both the light and dark cells are perhaps senescent elements.

They differ only in degree from dying cells, also seen here.

The demarcation between cortex and medulla is quite sharp.

D. HISTOLOGICAL ZONES.

The three zones just considered are based on different arrangements of cells.

From the standpoint of similarity of cell structure there are four zones:

1. Zona glomerulosa (and a transitional region of the z. fasciculata).
2. Outer two-thirds of the z. fasciculata; a region of marked spongiocytes.
3. Inner third of the z. fasciculata and outer half of the z. reticularis.

   A region poor in lipids and less basophilic.
4. Inner half of the z. reticularis (juxtamedullary portion).

   A region characterized by pigment and senescent, dark cells.

3. Medulla.

In man this region is thin; it comprises only 5 to 10 per cent of the whole organ.

In the wing-like expansions of the gland, laterally, medullary tissue fails.

Here connective tissue and vessels may occur alone.

Medullary cells assemble in rounded groups or short, anastomosing cords.

Venules and capillaries intervene between these parenchymal masses.

The component cells are ovoid to polyhedral, with large, vesicular nuclei.

In sections they often shrink into stellate shapes.

The cytoplasm contains variable numbers of specific secretory granules.

They are the actual precursors of the hormone named *epinephrine*.

These granules are browned by contact with a bichromate solution.

This results from the oxidation of the hormonal substance by the bichromate.

Such an effect is known as the *chromaffin reaction*.

Yet, in fact, any appropriate oxidizing agent will produce similar results.

Cells are oriented with one end abutting on a capillary, the other end on a venule.

Secretion granules collect at the venous pole and discharge into the venule.

A few autonomic ganglion cells also occur in the medulla.

4. Vessels and Nerves.

The *vascular supply* is perhaps the richest of any organ in the body.

The cortex receives blood from multiple arterioles in the capsule.

On entering, these become sinusoids which pass medullaward between cell columns.

The sinusoids are lined with fixed macrophages.

The medulla receives its blood from two different sources.

The major source is venous blood from the cortical sinusoids, just mentioned.

On reaching the medulla, these connect with collecting venules.

A lesser supply is from arterioles that pass directly from capsule to medulla.

In the medulla they open into an ordinary capillary plexus there.

This meshwork is in intimate relation with the medullary parenchyma.

Hence the cortex is favored, over the medulla, with arterial blood.

All the blood of the medulla drains into small collecting veins.

These open into a main, central vein that leaves at the hilus.

The larger veins are atypical, having much longitudinal muscle in the adventitia.

Lymphatics occur in the capsule and in association with medullary veins.

Unmyelinated *nerves*, from the solar plexus, enter the capsule in small bundles.

Following trabeculae, some end in the cortex; most end about medullary cells.

The latter are like preganglionic fibers, the medullary cells taking the place of autonomic ganglia in the ordinary autonomic-system arrangement.

Stimulation of the splanchnic nerves produces a heavy discharge of epinephrine.

POSTNATAL INVOLUTION:

Within two weeks after birth the suprarenal glands lose one-third of their weight.

This is due to the degeneration of the bulky *fetal cortex*, next to the medulla.

Outside the fetal cortex, at birth, is the thin representative of the *permanent cortex*.

This consists of the z. glomerulosa and part of the z. fasciculata.

All layers of the final cortex are represented before the first year has elapsed.

The significance of the fetal cortex, and its loss, are poorly understood.

Enticing is a possible endocrine function dependent, in turn, on placental hormones.

REGENERATIVE ABILITY:

Cells of the z. glomerulosa and of the outermost, transitional region of the z. fasciculata are commonly held to proliferate steadily.

Daughter cells would then be progressively pushed downward toward the medulla.

In the z. reticularis they decline and die; they are removed mainly by macrophages.

There are also local mitoses in the cortex at all levels.

Cortical cells are easily injured by infections, toxins, narcosis, etc.

Repair follows unless the damage leads to scar-formation or eventual death.

In experiments a cortical mass will regenerate from traces of the z. glomerulosa.

Medullary cells show little sign of either degeneration or regeneration.

E. DIAGNOSTIC FEATURES:

It is a parenchymatous organ, without ducts, having an obvious cortex and medulla.
  The medulla is largely missing in the compressed 'wings' of the gland.
The *cortex* is arranged in a palisade of radial, epithelial cords.
  Three concentric zones, with different cell arrangements, are fairly well shown.
  Sometimes sections contain seeming islands of cortex within the medulla.
      These are junctional portions of the cortex that bulged into the plane of section.
The *medulla* consists of cell groups arranged irregularly as masses and cords.
  Such cell groups are highly vascularized, the larger vessels being conspicuous.
  In some regions, veins are about the only medullary component seen.

F. FUNCTIONAL CORRELATIONS:

The cortex and medulla are functionally distinct, like separate organs.
  This is consonant with different developmental origins and cytological structure.
The *cortex* is essential to life, although nine-tenths can be removed safely.
  Cortical destruction by tuberculosis (Addison's disease) has a fatal expectancy.
      Death can be averted by the administration of the cortical extract.
The cortex is necessary in order to maintain a variety of vital functions.
  It maintains the electrolyte and water balance in the body.
      Otherwise there is a concentration of the plasma, a shift of water from tissu
          spaces into cells, and deranged kidney function.
  It maintains the proper carbohydrate balance in the body.
      With derangement of this control, the glycogen stores are depleted.
          Protein fails to convert into carbohydrate.
  It maintains resistance to stress (temperature extremes; fatigue; trauma).
  It maintains properly the intercellular substances of the body.
Forty steroid compounds have been isolated from the cortex.
  Seven have marked cortex-like activity; others have sex-hormone activity.
  But no single one has all the properties of a crude, cortical extract.
There is evidence pointing to a functional specialization of the zones.
  The zona glomerulosa seems to be concerned with the salt-regulating activity.
  The fasciculate and reticular zones appear to be concerned with the regulation (
      carbohydrate metabolism.
  Some claims associate the reticular zone with sex-hormone production.
Overfunctioning manifests itself when cortical (adrenogenital) tumors develop.
  In women there is a masculinizing effect (appearance of beard, etc.).
      Or a premature appearance of male secondary sexual characters in childre
  Tumors that feminize males have also been reported.
The *medulla* is not essential to life, and not surely important to normal functioning.
  It produces the hormones (*epinephrine; norepinephrine*) located in the granules.
  The number of chromaffin granules in a cell is an index of its secretory state.
  Similar granules appear in the suprarenal vein after stimulating the splanchnic nerv
      This is perhaps the only hormone identifiable in its cells of origin, and traceab
          and exactly measurable during discharge.
The medulla is said to be an emergency organ, normally storing most of its product.
  Ordinarily it discharges so little secretion that its effect is unimportant.
  Under emotion it discharges more, and then augments the action of sympathe
      nerve endings, producing effects on smooth and cardiac muscle and
      glands.
Cells recover rapidly after stimulation, and refill with secretory granules.

V. THE PARAGANGLIA

These bodies consist of small masses of *chromaffin cells* (pheochrome cells).
    They lie retroperitoneally, mostly along the course of the sympathetic trunks.
    Minor groups occur in relation to the gonads, liver and heart.
At birth there are some 40 masses, ranging from microscopic clusters to pea size.
    They reach the height of their development in infancy and then regress.
    The largest are the paired or joined *para-aortic bodies* (of Zuckerkandl).
    These lie behind the peritoneum, ventral to the dorsal aorta.
    Each is about 1 cm. long, but by puberty they are no longer macroscopic.
A *paraganglion* may be free or closely associated with sympathetic nerves or ganglia.
    It consists of cell strands, commonly penetrated by rich capillaries.
    The cells resemble those of the suprarenal medulla and have a similar origin.
        Nevertheless, the secretion of epinephrine has never been satisfactorily established.
    There is a rich supply of autonomic nerve fibers.
    The whole mass tends to be encapsulated.

VI. THE EPIPHYSIS

is also called, from its shape, the *pineal body* or *conarium*.
    Epiphysis means 'a sprout upon' (the brain).

. STRUCTURAL PLAN:
    The *epiphysis* is a stalked outgrowth from the roof of the diencephalon.
    It is an encapsulated, lobulated organ about 7 mm. long.
        Internally it is densely packed with cells, and may contain calcareous concretions.

. DETAILED STRUCTURE:
1. Framework.
        A thin *capsule*, supplied by the pia mater, sends *septa* and vessels inward.
        The septa are mostly composed of reticular fibers.
            They enclose incompletely masses of cells that constitute *lobules*.
        Neuroglia (astrocytes) provide a delicate support for the specific *pineal cells*.

2. Parenchyma.
        The organ consists of *epithelioid cells* and *neuroglia cells*, arranged in cords.
            Neither type shows to advantage without special silver techniques.
        The epithelioid cells have long, branched processes with bulbous endings.
            They are specific *pineal cells*, characteristic of the organ.
            Several types have been described, based on cytoplasmic content.
            These include homogeneous, granular and lipoidal cells.
                The granular cells are acidophilic, basophilic or pigmented.
        The neuroglial elements are *astrocytes* and *microglia*.

3. Vessels and Nerves.
        Blood vessels are confined almost exclusively to the capsule and septa.
        Lymphatics have not been demonstrated.
        Many *nerve fibers* enter and supply both vessels and parenchyma.
            Some (unmyelinated) are autonomic; others (myelinated) are from the brain.

C. INVOLUTION:

The epiphysis reaches its fullest development (but not size) in middle childhood.
Later there are regressive changes, but the time of onset is variable.
These changes involve the fibrous stroma rather than the parenchymal cells.
Connective tissue increases and the lobules are more plainly delimited.
The tissue ultimately undergoes hyaline degeneration.
The sharp demarcation between fibrous tissue and parenchyma is lost.
Concretions become more frequent; glial fibers thicken.
Acervuli are concretions ('brain sand'), located mostly in the septa and capsule.
They increase in number with age, and may become 1 mm. or more in diameter.
They are lamellated and are externally pimply or knobbed.
They consist of carbonates and phosphates of calcium and magnesium.

D. DIAGNOSTIC FEATURES:

Cellular masses are separated into imperfect lobules by septa.
The general appearance resembles somewhat a lymphoid organ.
In ordinary sections, the cells appear crowded and without clear boundaries.
The relatively large nuclei are lightly stippled; the cytoplasm is scanty and pale.
Between the cells there is a fine fibrillar mesh.
Darkly basophilic, lamellated 'brain sand' is a characteristic feature.
But even in adults these concretions are absent in one-fourth of all specimens.

E. FUNCTIONAL CORRELATIONS:

Functional relations are obscure, contradictory and unreliable.
There is no histological evidence of secretion or of secretory nerve fibers.
There is no satisfactory experimental or clinical proof of endocrine functions.
This organ is, perhaps, a rudimentary expression of the pineal eye of lower vertebrates.

VII. THE PLACENTA

Among its other functions, the placenta synthesizes hormones important in pregnancy.
These products continue or supplement activities of the hypophysis and ovaries.
The tissue responsible for hormone production is developed by the fetal chorion (p. 296).
It consists of a double layer of *trophoblast*, clothing the chorionic villi.
The inner layer is *cellular trophoblast*, a simple sheet of cuboidal cells.
It elaborates a gonadotrope, much like LTH, that preserves the corpus luteum.
As this layer is used up (see below), the hormone production declines.
The outer layer is *syncytial trophoblast*, derived from cellular trophoblast.
The latter cells divide, and daughter cells merge into a common mass.
By the end of the third month of pregnancy, little cellular trophoblast remains.
This syncytial layer progressively replaces the ovary in hormone production.
Both estrogen and progesterone are secreted by it in large amounts.

Chapter XVII. THE INTEGUMENTARY SYSTEM

The integument comprises the skin and certain specialized derivatives of it.
  The latter are the nails, hair and several kinds of glands.

I. THE SKIN

The *skin* is an organ that provides an external covering to the body.
  It weighs 9 pounds, is 0.5 to 5.0 mm. thick, and has an area of some 18 sq. ft.
At the free surface there is a specialized epithelium known as the *epidermis*.
The *dermis* (officially the corium) is the subjacent dense bed of vascular connective tissue.
  This layer corresponds to the lamina propria of a mucous membrane.
  When tanned, it becomes 'leather.'
The *subcutaneous layer* is a still deeper, looser, fibrous bed beneath the skin.
  It is the 'superficial fascia' of gross anatomy.
  This layer corresponds to the submucosa beneath a mucous membrane.
The boundary between epidermis and corium is usually uneven, but abrupt.
  There is an even, smooth junction on the forehead, ear and scrotum.
  Elsewhere there are net-like systems of ridges and finger-like papillae.
The free surface of the skin is furrowed by criss-crossing systems of delicate creases.
  These form small rhomboidal or rectangular areas.
  The palmar and plantar surfaces bear parallel ridges (*cristae*) and furrows (*sulci*).
    These are structural adaptations to meet heavy mechanical demands.
    The patterns are individually specific in the details of their loops and whorls.

A. EPIDERMIS:
  The *epidermis* is a stratified squamous epithelium, usually about 0.1 mm. thick.
    On the palm and sole it may become 0.8 and 1.4 mm. thick, respectively.
      Moreover, pressure or friction tends to increase the thickness still further.
      Yet there is an hereditary factor, since it is already thick in the fetus.
  This epithelium is characterized by having its superficial layers cornified.
    Hence the entire body is encased within a dead husk.
    The thickness of this husk is related to the mechanical contact encountered.
      It also thickens markedly as an accompaniment of sun-tanning.
  The epidermis is a nonvascular layer, but it is in close relation with the dermis.
    Nutrition is achieved by fluids transuding from out the dermis.
  The epidermis is most highly differentiated on the palmar and plantar surfaces.
    The maximum layering and cellular differentiation occur there.
    The layers are: (1) *germinative;* (2) *granular;* (3) *lucid;* and (4) *horny.*
  As in all stratified epithelia, there is a continuous loss and replacement of cells.
    Cells proliferate at low levels; daughter cells are pushed up by still younger ones.

185

1. Stratum Germinativum.

This so-called *Malpighian layer* is irregularly ridged on its lower surface.

Regions over dermal papillae are much thinner than between papillae.

The basal cells are columnar elements, comprising the *stratum basale*.

They constitute a single layer of deeply basophilic cells.

Tooth-like processes are anchored in the basement membrane beneath.

Next higher are the *prickle cells* of the stratified *stratum spinosum*.

These cells are polyhedrons, somewhat flattened at higher levels in the layer.

They are slightly separated from each other; *intercellular bridges* pass across.

Each 'bridge' represents cytoplasmic extensions meeting at a *desmosome* (p. 33).

Hence the cells, although beset with prickles, are independent entities.

Bundles of *tonofibrils* pass into the bridges and insert on the desmosome.

They are believed to give strength and elasticity to the cell.

Electron micrographs imply that they are the precursors of keratin.

The cytoplasm is decreasingly basophilic (*i.e.*, less RNA) at higher levels.

Mitoses occur in the basal and prickle cells, and mostly at night.

Daughter cells take several weeks to pass through the epidermis.

2. Stratum Granulosum.

The component cells are somewhat flattened elements.

In the thick epidermis of the palm or sole they are 3 to 5 cells deep.

Elsewhere this layer is thinner or lacking.

In vertical section the cells are diamond-shaped, with a thin cell membrane.

The nucleus is pale and indistinct; it shows degenerative changes.

The cytoplasm of some mammals contains irregular-shaped granules of *keratohyalin*.

These refractile granules stain with some acid dyes and certain basic dyes.

In man 'granules' occur as locally-stained regions of tonofibrils.

Intercellular bridges and tonofibrils are recognized with difficulty.

3. Stratum Lucidum.

This is a clear, translucent layer, 3 to 5 cells deep.

It is a constituent only of especially thick epidermis (palm; sole).

The flattened, dying cells are compacted into a homogeneous, glassy plate.

Nevertheless, the individual cells can still be isolated by chemicals.

In vertical sections the lucid layer is a wavy stripe.

It is highly refractile and stains feebly with most dyes.

The nuclei are indistinct or invisible; the cells are dying or dead.

The cytoplasm contains a semifluid substance, named *eleidin*.

Electron micrographs show bundles of tonofibrils merging.

4. Stratum Corneum.

This is a layer of cornified cells, progressively flattened and fused.

On the palm and sole the layer becomes extremely thick.

The component cells are closely packed; yet each retains its cell membrane.

The cell surface is somewhat spiny, but intercellular bridges are lost.

Cytoplasm has been replaced with a homogeneous substance containing filaments.

This material is dry, shiny and highly refractile.

Chemically it is *keratin*, which is consistent with tonofibrils as precursors.

It is a soft type of keratin, low in sulphur; cells are not fused as in nails.

The details of the process of keratization are not sufficiently understood.
At the surface the dried, caked cells are sloughed off as compound scales.

5. Regional Differences.

The thick epidermis of the palm and sole have all the layers just described.
These are the most highly differentiated regions of the total epidermal surface.
The epidermis of the general body surface is both thinner and simpler.
Only the germinative layer and a thin, horny layer are constantly present.
The granular layer is at best two cells thick, and is often lacking.
This is because keratization is less marked and is intermittent.
A lucid layer cannot be demonstrated.
Toward the surface the cells become thin *keratin plates*, firmly joined.
The horny cells are not retained long, and hence the layer remains thin.
At the margin of the lip, nostril, anus and vulva there is a junctional region.
Here the epidermis is transitional into a mucous membrane.
The epithelium is thick and is moistened by mucus.
A thin stratum corneum permits the red blood color to show through plainly.

6. Pigmentation.

The color of skin itself is yellow; this is due to the presence of *carotene*.
Blood, showing through, gives the reddish tints.
Fine granules of *melanin pigment* are responsible for brown colors.
This substance is especially present in the basal cells.
By the time a cell reaches the stratum corneum, at least, it disappears.
Some claim that it then becomes a diffuse coloring matter.
Pigment is said to be elaborated through the interaction of an oxidase (*tyrosinase*) with
a chromogen precursor-substance (*tyrosine*).
Both the formation and fate of melanin need further investigation.
'Tanning' is a secondary pigmentation after exposure to ultraviolet light.
There is an increase in blood inflow, followed by prolonged venous stagnation.
Melanin shows an increase in a few days and soon reaches a maximum.
It then degenerates, producing *melanoid*, which gradually disappears.
Pigment is practically absent from the palm and sole of all races.
In white folk, pigment granules are almost always confined to the basal cells.
Certain regions (areola; circumanal area; etc.) are more richly pigmented.
Local spots with deep pigmentation are known as *pigmented moles*.
In the colored races, pigment may extend even into the stratum granulosum.
Epidermal pigment is elaborated in special cells derived from the neural crest.
These highly branched *melanoblasts* migrate into the basal layer.
Here they elaborate pigment and turn it over to germinative cells.
Melanoblasts appear as 'clear cells' in ordinary stained sections.
They blacken specifically with a special reagent called *dopa*.
This reaction indicates the presence of a precursor substance of melanin.

3. DERMIS:

The *dermis* (or derma, or corium) begins with a thin *basement membrane*.
Its presence, however, is not manifest in ordinary preparations.
The thickness of the closely interwoven dermis varies between 0.3 and 4 mm.
A thin epidermis may have a thin dermis (eyelid)or a thick dermis (back).
The dermis can be subdivided for convenience into two strata, *papillary* and *reticular*.

1. Papillary Layer.

This stratum includes ridges and papillae protruding into the epidermis.

There are as many as 65,000 of these papillae to the square inch.

In the palm and sole the papillae are numerous and tall (50 to 200 μ).

They tend to occur in a double row and are often branched.

They are also tall in the lips, penis and nipple.

Such interlocking with the epidermis is mechanically advantageous.

Where mechanical demands are slight, they are few, low and irregularly arranged.

Example: face; trunk.

Some papillae contain tactile sensory corpuscles; they are *tactile papillae*.

Other papillae contain only blood vessels; they are *vascular papillae*.

The fundamental tissue of the papillary layer is a closely interwoven mesh.

It is composed of thin collagenous and elastic fibers.

2. Reticular Layer.

This stratum comprises the main fibrous bed of the dermis.

It consists of coarse, rather densely interlacing fibers.

Their preponderant direction is parallel to the surface.

Elastic networks intermingle with collagenous fiber-bundles.

Cells are relatively few, but are those typical for connective tissue.

Pigmented, branched connective-tissue cells (*chromatophores*) may occur.

They usually have a superficial location.

They are numerous only in areas where the epidermis is heavily pigmented.

Example: areola; circumanal region.

They are also more abundant in individuals with darker skins.

Such cells do not elaborate their pigment, but merely ingest and store it.

True dermal *melanoblasts* (dopa positive) are known also to occur locally.

They are responsible for the *Mongolian spot* of the sacral region and for certain tumors (*blue naevi*).

Hairs, sweat glands, sebaceous glands and lamellar corpuscles are represented.

The perineum, scrotum, penis and nipple have smooth muscle fibers in the dermis.

This muscle content is responsible for the dartos reflex of the scrotum and for the erection of the nipple.

Small bundles constitute the erector muscles of hair follicles.

In the face and neck, skeletal fibers terminate in the dermis.

They provide the basis for skin movements, better developed in lower mammals.

C. SUBCUTANEOUS LAYER:

This layer constitutes the so-called *superficial fascia*.

It is not a part of the skin, yet blends (unsharply) into the dermis.

It is a looser network of connective-tissue bands and septa.

The density and arrangement of the subcutaneous layer determine the mobility of the skin.

Much of the skin can be displaced considerably, except on the palm and sole.

Here mobility is greatly reduced and the fibers are thick and numerous.

With aging, elasticity declines; the skin wrinkles and loses tone.

The spaces of the subcutaneous mesh are occupied by lobules of fat.

When these are abundant, the subcutaneous layer is called a *panniculus adiposus*.

On the abdomen the panniculus may reach a thickness of 1 in., or more.

Yet there are regions (eyelids; scrotum; penis) where fat never occurs.

. VESSELS AND NERVES:

Arteries form networks beneath the reticular and papillary layers.

They also send extensions into the papillae and form capillary loops there.

The epidermis is nourished by tissue fluid that passes into the intercellular spaces.

The *veins* form a superficial plexus beneath the papillae, and two deeper ones.

There is also a plexus in the subcutaneous tissue.

Lymphatics begin as blind vessels or networks in the papillae and beneath them.

These drain into a plexus at the junction of the dermis and subcutaneous layer.

Efferent nerves supply the smooth muscle of blood vessels, erector muscles of hairs, and the myoid elements and gland cells of sweat glands.

Afferent nerves connect with lamellar corpuscles, tactile corpuscles and hair follicles.

They also form free nerve endings in the dermis and epidermis.

. REGENERATIVE ABILITY:

The capacity for regeneration and the repair of gross losses is highly developed.

Epidermal cells glide across small gaps in mass movement.

Restoration of thickness is achieved secondarily by mitoses.

Larger gaps are bridged by combined movement and proliferation.

The underlying connective tissue produces fibroblasts and a provisional mucous tissue.

The latter is converted into fibrous tissue, but elastic fibers are slow to reform.

. DIAGNOSTIC FEATURES:

The *epidermis* is a stratified squamous epithelium; cornification produces matted scales.

In ordinary skin the cornified layers are few, but begin abruptly.

In the palm and sole the cornified layers make a very thick stratum.

Distinctive granular and lucid layers are plainly seen also.

The epidermis usually is cut to show the scalloped, superficial ridging.

The *dermis* is composed of relatively dense connective tissue.

Sweat glands, sebaceous glands and hairs are usually, but not always, encountered.

On the palm and sole, hairs and sebaceous glands are lacking.

The *subcutaneous layer* is a looser connective tissue.

It contains lobules of fat and the roots of hairs.

. FUNCTIONAL CORRELATIONS:

The external layer of the skin is a practically impermeable coat of dead cells.

It is primarily protective against trauma, bacteria, drying, water absorption, noxious gases and fluids, ultraviolet light, etc.

Cornification (*i.e.*, keratization) is kept in control by vitamin A.

The skin excretes water, fat and various catabolic wastes.

It is important in the regulation of body temperature (by insulation and sweating).

It is the most extensive receptor of tactile, thermal and painful impressions.

The skin is a storehouse for glycogen, cholesterol and water.

In it ergosterol is activated by ultraviolet light to form vitamin D.

Subcutaneous tissue serves to bind the skin to the deep fascia or periosteum.

It also affords mobility to the skin in accordance with local requirements.

Bursae occur between the skin and deeper prominences, such as the elbow and kneecap.

Like bursae elsewhere, they are closed fibrous sacs containing a viscid fluid.

They facilitate the play of skin over bony prominences and also provide cushioning.

II. THE NAILS

Nails are features present only in man and other primates.

A. STRUCTURAL PLAN:

A *nail* is a convex, rectangular specialization of the skin.

It consists of a horny *nail plate*, lying upon a less modified *nail bed*.

The plate is contained within a U-shaped *nail groove*, formed by the skin.

The nail plate has a *free edge*, a *body* (exposed, but attached beneath), and a *root* (covered and attached beneath).

At the junction of body and root is a crescentic whitish zone, the *lunule*.

The lunule often is concealed by the skin fold, except on the thumb.

The *nail groove* is flanked by a similarly coursing skin fold, the *nail wall*.

The nail wall overlaps the nail plate where it lies in the groove.

Laterally the nail groove is shallow; proximally it is a deep pocket.

The *nail bed*, underlying the nail plate, consists of the germinative layer of the epidermis, and the dermis beneath it.

B. DETAILED STRUCTURE:

1. Nail Groove.

This curved furrow is lined with somewhat modified skin.

Approaching the depth of the nail groove, the dermal papillae become lower, and all but the germinative layer of the epidermis give out.

Cells of the horny layer extend from the nail wall onto the free nail plate.

This constitutes the *eponychium*, commonly called cuticle.

2. Nail Bed.

The *nail bed* underlies both the exposed and concealed portions of the nail plate.

It consists of modified epidermis and of dense dermis.

The epidermis of the finger tip extends under the free edge of the nail plate.

Its specialized layers attach to the plate and extend slightly beneath the body.

This horny, cellular tissue is called the *hyponychium*.

The epidermis beneath the exposed nail plate is reduced to the germinative layer.

Irregular projections from the nail substance pass between the germinative cells.

This arrangement serves to attach the nail plate in this region.

The germinative layer under the nail root is thicker proximally than elsewhere.

This region, where nail growth chiefly occurs, is named the *matrix*.

It extends slightly farther back than does the actual nail substance.

The matrix represents a specialized germinative layer.

The cells of this layer contain peculiar *onychogenic fibrils*.

This fibrillar structure is lost, and the cells become homogeneous as they cornify and join the nail plate.

A keratohyalin stage, with granules as in skin, cannot be recognized.

Beneath the exposed nail plate the dermis is longitudinally ridged.

Glands do not occur in the dense connective tissue of the nail bed.

The deepest part of the bed is fused to the periosteum of the terminal phalanx.

3. Nail Plate.

The nail plate consists of intimately fused, horny, epidermal scales.

The cornified cells appear to fuse into homogeneous nail substance.

However, alkalies can make the component cells swell and separate.
This treatment also discloses a shrunken nucleus.
The nail contains 'hard keratin,' like hair (p. 192); its cells do not desquamate.
The component scaly cells of the nail plate are arranged in layers.
This gives a striated appearance when cut in vertical section.
In the root the layers are unequal in length, and so overlap.
The superficial layer extends farthest back into the nail groove.
Deeper layers extend progressively shorter distances.
The deepest layer of all ends at the lunule.
Air spaces between cells cause the well-known white spots.
The plate is thin proximally in the root but quickly reaches its maximum thickness where the root passes into the exposed nail body.
In the finger this thickness is 0.5 mm.; in the toe, it is considerably thicker.
The body of the plate is translucent and transmits the pink color of the bed.
Here the plate tends to be longitudinally ridged.
The root is more opaque than the body; cornification and drying are incomplete.
Its exposed, distal margin shows as the crescentic, whitish *lunule*.

4. Vessels and Nerves.

The vascular and nerve supply of a nail are like that in the skin (p. 189).
Arterio-venous anastomoses occur in the nail bed (and on the finger tips).

C. GROWTH AND REGENERATIVE ABILITY:

New nail substance is added from the matrix (under the root of the nail plate).
The most proximal cells of the matrix form the surface layer.
The most distal cells of the matrix (lunule margin) form the deepest layer.
Beyond the lunule the nail bed does not participate in growth appreciably.
The nail plate merely glides over it, according to most authorities.
A finger nail grows nearly 1 mm. each week, and is renewed in about 6 months.
Unlike hair, nails grow continuously throughout life.
Formation of a new nail will follow the forcible removal of an old one.
Only if the matrix is destroyed will this regeneration fail.

D. DIAGNOSTIC FEATURES:

Sections of the nail, *in situ*, show characteristic surroundings.
These are: nail groove and wall; free edge; epo- and hyponychium; terminal phalanx.
The *nail plate* lies on a typical germinative layer; specialized layers are absent.
The transition in structure between plate and bed is exceedingly abrupt.
The plate is striated, but gives little indication of its cellular origin.
The *nail bed* lacks sweat glands or hair follicles.
There is no subcutaneous tissue, since dermis and periosteum fuse.

E. FUNCTIONAL CORRELATIONS:

Nails, claws and hoofs are homologous epidermal products.
Nails are not only protective, but they also have utility as tools.
Small objects can be picked up and various manipulations performed by them.

III. THE HAIR

Hairs are elastic, tapering, horny threads; they are characteristic of mammals alone.

Their length varies from 1 mm., or less, to an extreme of 5 ft.

Their thickness ranges from 0.005 mm. (lanugo) to 0.2 mm. (beard).

The distribution in men covers the entire skin, except for a few regions.

    Example: palm; sole; neighborhood of anal and urogenital apertures.

Their frequency varies regionally; example: vertex, 1300 per sq. in.; chin, 140 per sq. in.

A. STRUCTURAL PLAN:

    There is a free *shaft*, and a *root* embedded in the skin.

        The hairs are not set perpendicularly, but slope at an angle.

    A tubular *hair follicle*, part epidermal and part fibrous (dermal), encloses the root.

        Toward its deep end, the follicle swells and there is named the *hair bulb*.

        Indenting the basal end of the bulb is a connective-tissue *papilla*.

    Associated with the follicle are a *sebaceous gland* and *erector muscle*.

    Curly hairs and their follicles are flatter than are straight ones.

B. STRUCTURE OF SHAFT AND ROOT:

    A hair consists of epidermal cells arranged in three concentric, cylindrical layers.

1. Medulla.

    The *medullary core* is a looser central axis, two or three cells thick.

        It rarely extends the total length of any hair.

    Hairs of the axilla, beard and eyebrows contain a medulla.

        Hairs of the head may or may not possess this core.

        A medulla is absent in the fine, short hairs of the downy type.

    The cells of the medulla are shrunken, cornified cuboidal cells.

        These are partly separated by air spaces.

        The cells contain refractile droplets and, often, pigment.

        A prominent medulla, combined with pigment loss, makes hair 'silvery.'

    The keratin of medullary cells is of the 'soft' type, as in epidermis (p. 186).

2. Cortex.

    The main bulk of a hair, the *cortex*, appears compact and longitudinally striate.

        It consists of long, flattened, spindle-shaped, cornified, acidophilic cells.

        Maceration can isolate them, and demonstrate nuclei and horny fibrils in them.

    Pigment, in solution and as granules, occurs in and between cells.

        Black hair has much pigment that represents well-oxidized tyrosin.

        Red hair contains pigment that is the product of limited oxidation.

        Air vacuoles, located between cells, probably can modify the hair color.

3. Cuticle.

    Superficially there is a very thin, single layer of cells, known as the *cuticle*.

        These are cornified scales that have lost their nuclei.

    The scales overlap, like shingles, with their free edges directed upward.

        An interlock with cells lining the follicle aids in resisting detachment.

    In surface view the scales are arranged in a wavy, mosaic pattern.

    The keratin of the cortex and cuticle is of the 'hard' type, as in nails and feathers.

        It does not pass through a keratohyalin stage; its compacted cells do not desquamate

        It is an albuminoid (with a large content of sulphur) that resists chemical change.

    Keratin molecules are long polypeptide chains, parallel and connected by side chains.

These threads follow zig-zag courses, but when wet they stretch and bend easily.
Such properties are the basis on which wet hair can be 'set' temporarily in curls.
Permanent waving utilizes heat or chemicals to establish more lasting effects.
Old linkages, in and between molecules, are replaced by new alignments.

C. STRUCTURE OF FOLLICLE:

A hair follicle consists of a compound sheath.
Externally there is a *dermal root sheath;* internally, an *epidermal root sheath.*
Toward its deep end the follicle is expanded into a *hair bulb.*
Here the hair root and its sheaths blend in a mass of primitive cells, the *matrix.*
The base of the bulb is indented by a prominent, connective-tissue *papilla.*
Around the lower half of the papilla is where the hair root and its sheaths merge.
All layers of the follicle are not present at all levels.
They are represented best at some distance above the bulb.

1. Dermal Root Sheath.

This fibrous *sheath* exists only around the lower two-thirds of the follicle.
It is represented best in coarse hairs such as those of the scalp.
There are three layers, corresponding to similar strata of the corium.

A. OUTER LAYER.
This is a poorly defined layer of longitudinally directed fibers.
It corresponds to the deep (reticular) layer of the dermis.

B. MIDDLE LAYER.
This is a thicker, more cellular and denser layer of circular, fine fibers.
It corresponds to the papillary layer of the dermis.
The *hair papilla* is like an ordinary dermal papilla, but far larger.
It contains capillaries, nerve fibers and, sometimes, pigment cells.
Its shape is like an egg, supported by a stalk-like neck.

C. INNER LAYER.
Most internally, next to the follicle, there is a homogeneous *glassy membrane.*
It corresponds to the basement membrane beneath the epidermis.
Similarly it consists of reticular fibers and amorphous ground substance.

2. Epidermal Root Sheath.

There are an outer and an inner *epidermal sheath,* each with subordinate strata.
The outer sheath corresponds to the less modified, deep epidermal layers.
The inner sheath corresponds to the more specialized, superficial layers.

A. OUTER ROOT SHEATH.
Above the outlet of the sebaceous gland, ordinary epidermis lines the follicle.
Below this level the germinative layer alone continues as the outer sheath.
It thins as it approaches the bulb, but can be traced even to its base.
This sheath has its two subordinate layers arranged as in the epidermis.
1. COLUMNAR LAYER. A single layer of taller cells, next to the glassy membrane.
2. PRICKLE-CELL LAYER. Several layers of cells, with intercellular bridges.
This layer is the more internal of the two in position.

B. INNER ROOT SHEATH.
This constitutes a keratinized, cellular sheath enveloping the growing root.
Like the hair, it is pushed up by additions from the bulb.
Unlike the hair, it gives out before reaching the sebaceous-gland level.
It elaborates 'soft keratin,' with a keratohyalin stage, like epidermis.
Nuclei and discernible cells occur only at the deeper levels of the sheath.

There are three layers which may be likened to the specialized epidermal strata.
The corresponding strata of the epidermis are granular, lucid and cornified.
1. HENLE'S LAYER.
   This is an outer, single layer of elongate, low cells.
   The clear cells contain hyaline fibrils at the deeper follicular levels.
2. HUXLEY'S LAYER.
   This consists of several layers of transparent, precornified cells.
   They contain acidophilic *trichohyalin granules*, much like epidermal eleidin.
3. CUTICLE.
   This is a single layer of thin, transparent, horny scales.
   The cells overlap like shingles, with their free edges directed downward.
   Interlocking with similar cells of the hair cuticle explains why the inner root
   sheath is also removed when a hair is extracted.

D. ASSOCIATED MUSCLE AND GLANDS:

1. Arrector Pili Muscle.

The *erector muscle* of a hair is a characteristic accessory.
   It is a band of smooth muscle, 0.05 to 0.2 mm. wide.
   Large hairs have thick bands, but there are exceptions (axilla; beard).
   Some hairs lack an erector muscle (eyelashes; nasal hairs).
A muscle arises high in the dermis and, for a distance, is a single bundle.
   It then subdivides, each division passing to a hair of a hair group.
   Such a terminal bundle usually joins the follicle below the sebaceous gland.
      However, the muscle may be perforated by a large, branched gland.
The muscle inserts on the dermal root sheath, slightly above its mid-level.
   This is on the side that makes an obtuse angle with the epidermis.
Contraction, as by cold or fright, contracts the muscle, erects and lifts the hair, and
      depresses the adjacent skin; this is 'goose flesh.'
   At the same time, sebum is expressed from the squeezed sebaceous gland.

2. Sebaceous Glands.

One to several *sebaceous glands* always connect with a hair.
There is, however, no direct correlation between the sizes of the two.
   On the contrary, some of the smallest hairs have the largest glands.
A gland usually is located in the angle between the follicle and its muscle.
Its short duct empties into the follicle at a level three-fourths of the way up.
(For the structure of sebaceous glands, see p. 197.)

E. GROWTH:

The hair root and its sheaths end in a bulbous enlargement which surrounds the papilla.
   This mass of syncytial-appearing cells is not organized into layers.
   Its nuclei are often seen in mitosis, and it is a proliferating matrix-tissue.
Cells about the apex and sides of the papilla move upward and transform into hair cells.
   Cells at the apex form the medulla (when it is to be represented).
   Cells on the upper slope form the cortex; prior to keratization they are basophilic.
   Cells on the sides form the cuticle.
Pigment is acquired in the same way as that of the epidermis (p. 187).
Cornification is gradual, as the hair cells are moved toward the surface.
   When about half the distance is gained, cornification is complete.
   The hair cells are dead; they have become acidophilic and doubly refractive.

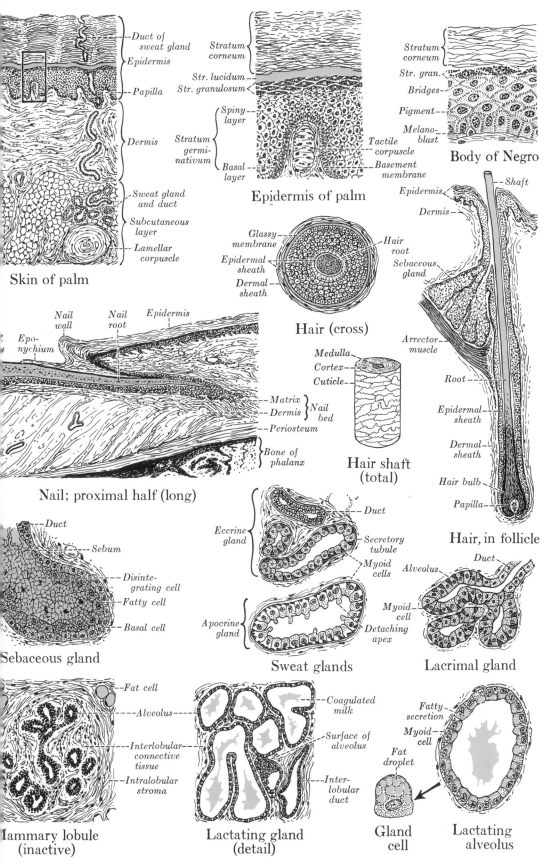

Skin of palm

Duct of sweat gland
Epidermis
Papilla
Dermis — Stratum germinativum
Sweat gland and duct
Subcutaneous layer
Lamellar corpuscle

Epidermis of palm

Stratum corneum
Str. lucidum
Str. granulosum
Spiny layer
Basal layer
Tactile corpuscle
Basement membrane

Body of Negro

Stratum corneum
Str. gran.
Bridges
Pigment
Melanoblast

Hair (cross)

Glassy membrane
Epidermal sheath
Dermal sheath
Hair root

Hair, in follicle

Shaft
Epidermis
Dermis
Sebaceous gland
Arrector muscle
Root
Epidermal sheath
Dermal sheath
Hair bulb
Papilla

Nail; proximal half (long)

Nail wall
Nail root
Epidermis
Eponychium
Matrix
Dermis — Nail bed
Periosteum
Bone of phalanx

Hair shaft (total)

Medulla
Cortex
Cuticle

Sebaceous gland

Duct
Sebum
Disintegrating cell
Fatty cell
Basal cell

Sweat glands

Eccrine gland
Duct
Secretory tubule
Myoid cells
Apocrine gland
Detaching apex

Lacrimal gland

Alveolus
Duct
Myoid cell

Mammary lobule (inactive)

Fat cell
Alveolus
Interlobular connective tissue
Intralobular stroma

Lactating gland (detail)

Coagulated milk
Surface of alveolus
Interlobular duct

Gland cell

Lactating alveolus

Fatty secretion
Myoid cell
Fat droplet

THE INTEGUMENTARY ORGANS

Cells next to the lower papilla-third transform into the inner root sheath.
  Like the hair root this sheath grows upward, but it disintegrates before reaching the level of the sebaceous-gland duct.
Cells at the bottom of the follicle continue into the outer root sheath.
  It is possible that this sheath is pushed up from below, as is the inner sheath.
    Yet most authorities think that it grows from mitoses in its outermost layers.
Weekly growth ranges from 1.5 mm. (leg) to 2.7 mm. (scalp).
  Cutting has no effect on the rate of growth of hair or on its coarseness.

F. SHEDDING AND REPLACEMENT:

Hair has a definite period of growth, after which it ceases growing, is retained for a time in its follicle, and then is lost and replaced.
  At any given time, half of the hair follicles are active and half are inactive.
    Growing and resting periods are about equal, except on the head and face.
  The life-span of an eyelash is 3 to 4 months; of a scalp hair, about 4 years.
  In some mammals there is periodic shedding (winter and summer coats).
  In other mammals, including man, hair loss is irregular and continuous.
    Each follicle has an independent and characteristic rhythmic cycle.

1. Shedding.

When the growth period nears its end, proliferation slows and ceases.
The bulb then changes into a solid, keratinized, club-shaped mass.
This mass, including the cornified inner root sheath which fuses with it, detaches from the papilla but remains bound to the hair-root proper.
Such a *club hair* is forced up to the level of the sebaceous duct.
  This results from the proliferation of indifferent matrix cells.
  (Here it remains until it is pulled out or is pushed out by a new hair.)
The papilla then atrophies and, seemingly, may even disappear completely.
The outer root sheath collapses and becomes an epithelial cord.
  It extends from the atrophic papilla to the lower end of the elevated club hair.
  It shortens and draws the papilla-remnant upward.

2. Replacement.

After a rest period, the epithelial cord at the follicular base (outer epithelial sheath) regains its former length and thickness.
Simultaneously, the papilla-remnant enlarges (or perhaps forms anew).
  It indents the mass of the epithelial sheath, and a new bulb is formed.
From the new cell matrix about the papilla an inner sheath and hair differentiate.
  They grow progressively upward, through the follicle, toward the surface.
For a time the old hair may lie above, or at one side, of the new, upgrowing one.

3. Regeneration after Injury.

Forcible extraction of a growing hair results in only a temporary loss.
  The outer sheath, and probably some matrix, remain; restoration soon follows.
Superficial injuries to skin are followed by a regeneration of follicles and hairs.
  Healing of wounds by scar tissue chokes and destroys any remnants of follicles.

G. AGE CHANGES:

Baldness is more frequent (6:1) in males than in females.
  It is an hereditary and sex-controlled trait.

The genetic factors are effective only when male hormone is present in the body.
Follicles first show declining vigor by forming short hairs of the downy type.
Then they atrophy and disappear totally.
Whitening of the hair is due to the failure of pigment formation at replacement.
Sudden blanching through fear is not proved; it is an irrational folk belief.
Truly gray hair is rare; mingled white and dark hairs give the common gray effect.

H. VESSELS AND NERVES:

Blood vessels of the dermis supply a rich capillary plexus to the papilla.
Other vessels vascularize the fibrous root sheath.
Lymphatic connections have not been demonstrated.
Nerve fibers encircle the follicle in a plexus and make sensory endings within it.
Vasomotor fibers enter the papilla; pilomotor nerves innervate the erector muscle.

I. DIAGNOSTIC FEATURES:

Hair follicles are to be expected in most sections containing skin.
Chief exceptions are the palmar and plantar surfaces.
The cylindrical follicle, with its bulb and papilla, is a unique structure.
In longitudinal section it is wholly distinctive.
The associated sebaceous gland and erector muscle are also unique features.
Transverse sections show a variety of concentric layers at different levels.
All layers are seen best at a level about two-thirds of the way down the follicle.
(Empty follicles, with the hair dropped out, are sometimes encountered.)

J. FUNCTIONAL CORRELATIONS:

Hair is primarily for protection, warmth and tactile reception.
The coarser hairs, appearing after childhood, are controlled by the sex hormones.
Some hairs (axillary; pubic) are common to both sexes.
Other hairs of the male (beard; chest) are a secondary sexual characteristic.
They also appear after puberty, but only when the male sex hormone is adequate.
Subsequently they are maintained by the hormone, supplied in proper amounts.
Hair follicles provide foci of epidermal regeneration after superficial loss of skin.

IV. THE CUTANEOUS GLANDS

Several kinds of glands differentiate from the epidermis; and some are highly specialized.
There are: *sebaceous glands; lacrimal glands; sweat glands; mammary glands.*

A. SEBACEOUS GLANDS:

These are holocrine glands in which secretory cells are lost along with the secretion.
In most instances they occur in company with a hair (p. 194).
Usually several glands drain into a hair follicle; hence the total number is large.
Glands independent of hairs occur in a few locations.
The duct then opens onto the free surface of the skin.
Example: margin of lips; glans penis; inner surface of prepuce; labia minora;
nipple; tarsal (Meibomian) glands of eyelids.
These glands are entirely lacking from the palm and sole.

1. Structural Plan.

Sebaceous glands are located in the dermis of the skin.

The duct opens typically into the neck of a hair follicle.

Each gland is encapsulated by a thin layer of connective tissue.

The diameter of groups of glands ranges from 0.2 to 2.0 mm.

There is somewhat of an inverse relation between gland size and hair size.

The largest, as on the nose, are associated with a delicate hair.

Sebaceous glands belong to the saccular group of glands.

Some small glands consist of but one saccule.

Most glands have several saccules opening into a short, relatively wide duct.

The largest are compound glands, with a branching duct.

The saccules are pear-shaped and ordinarily appear filled with puffy cells.

2. Detailed Structure.

A. SECRETORY PORTION.

The *saccule* consists of a stratified epithelium, supported by a delicate basement membrane and a thin layer of connective tissue.

The epithelium tends to fill the saccule completely.

The basal glandular cells are small, low, cuboidal elements.

They are continuous with the basal cells of the epidermis.

Toward the center of the sac the cells become progressively larger.

They are also more globular and have a greater fat content.

A fatty metamorphosis of cytoplasm occurs, leaving only cytoplasmic strands.

These thin, basophilic strands separate the fat droplets.

The nuclei shrink, condense and disintegrate.

Finally, the whole cell breaks down into a fatty mass and cellular debris.

The lost cells are replaced by proliferation from the basal cells.

The neck region is no longer viewed as the source of replacements.

Glands are subject to change; new buds grow out from ducts or saccules.

B. EXCRETORY DUCT.

The short, wide *duct* of a gland is lined with stratified epithelium.

This lining is continuous with the epithelial sheath of the hair.

(Or with the germinative layer of the epidermis if the gland opens on skin.)

Toward the saccule the layering decreases progressively.

Finally it merges with the low basal cells of the saccule.

The mouth of a large, exposed duct is visible; it often shows as a 'blackhead.'

A retention cyst in the scalp is a 'wen.'

C. SEBUM AND ITS DISCHARGE.

The secretion, formed by fatty metamorphosis and cell-disintegration, is *sebum*.

It is an oily product, containing also cellular remnants.

It fluoresces in ultraviolet light; sebum in undischarged glands glows also.

Discharge is aided by contraction of the erector muscle and by general pressure.

D. VASCULAR SUPPLY.

Capillary basketworks closely invest the saccules.

3. Specialized Sebaceous Glands.

The *tarsal glands* (of Meibom) of the eyelids have an unusual arrangement.

There is one long, axial duct into which saccules open from all sides.

Tyson's glands are twisted tubes of undetermined status.

They occur inconstantly on the glans penis and inner surface of the prepuce.

Sebaceous cells have been described in them.

4. Diagnostic Features.
Saccules, simple or branched, lie in the dermis.
Except for some special locations, they are always associated with hair follicles.
The peripheral cells are cuboidal.
The more central cells are large, puffy and pale.
The largest often show signs of disintegration.
The cytoplasm appears frothy because of vacuoles left by dissolved fat droplets.
The short duct usually opens into a hair follicle, not far below the epidermis.

5. Functional Correlations.
Sebum is a grease that oils hair, lubricates the epidermis and keeps it supple.
It is mildly bactericidal and helps protect epidermis against water penetration.

B. LACRIMAL GLAND:
This derivative of the conjunctival, modified skin is a *tear gland;* see p. 313.

C. SWEAT GLANDS:
The ordinary *sudoriparous glands* are unbranched, coiled tubular glands.
They are more highly developed in man than in other mammals.
They occur throughout the skin, except upon the nail bed, eardrum, glans penis, inner su
face of the prepuce and margin of the lip.
The frequency of ordinary merocrine sweat glands (*eccrine glands*) varies regionally.
In general, they are more abundant than sebaceous glands or hairs.
On the palm and sole there are about 3000 per sq. in.; on the back, about 500.

1. Structural Plan.
The *secretory tubule* lies deep in the dermis or even in the subcutaneous tissue.
This portion is coiled into a mass 0.3 to 0.4 mm. in diameter.
The tubule is about 3.0 mm. long and 0.06 mm. wide in ordinary sweat glands.
(Certain larger, specialized glands will be described separately on p. 199.)
The *duct* is a narrower, inactive continuation of the secretory tubule.
It rises to the epidermis by a slightly tortuous course.
The duct joins the epidermis, and spirals through it to the free surface.
Its opening, the *sweat pore*, is a minute pit.
These pores are best seen on the ridges of the palmar and plantar surfaces.
Here they are easily visible under a magnifying lens.

2. Detailed Structure.
A. Secretory Tubule.
This tubule consists of a simple epithelium, bordered by peculiar 'myoid cells.'
A basement membrane supports it, and connective tissue embeds it.
1. gland cells.
There is a single layer of faintly basophilic, cuboidal to columnar cells.
Their height varies with the functional state of the gland.
Hence the size of the lumen is also a variable feature.
Cell boundaries are commonly not plain.
The prominent, round nucleus is located about midway of the cell.
The cytoplasm contains vacuoles filled with watery secretion.
It also contains fat droplets and, occasionally, pigment granules.
The exact appearance depends upon the secretory stage of these cells.

Typical *secretory capillaries* occur between the gland cells and in them.

The glandular epithelium rests upon an acidophilic *basement membrane*.

2. MYO-EPITHELIAL CELLS.

At the periphery of the tubule there are peculiar spindle-shaped cells.

They lie mostly wedged between the bases of gland cells.

They wind in longitudinal spirals about the tubules.

These *myo-epithelial cells* are slender, flattened cells, 30 to 90 μ long.

The nucleus is elongate; the cytoplasm is fibrillar and acidophilic.

They are usually considered to be specialized, smooth-muscle fibers.

Their contractions are supposed to help empty the gland.

The origin (ectodermal) is unlike that of ordinary smooth muscle.

The largest and most numerous myoid cells occur in the largest glands.

These are the specialized sweat glands, to be described presently.

B. EXCRETORY DUCT.

The secretory tubule suddenly narrows into a slenderer *excretory duct*.

This tube consists of two layers of dark-staining, cuboidal cells.

The layer next the lumen bears a specialized cuticular border.

Myo-epithelial cells are not represented.

The duct joins the germinative layer at a thicker region, where it dips between connective-tissue papillae.

A spiral duct then continues through the epidermis to the free surface.

This part of the duct is merely a cleft-like tunnel.

It is bordered by concentrically arranged epithelial cells.

C. VESSELS AND NERVES.

Blood vessels and capillaries fashion plexuses about the gland tubules.

Nerve fibers form periglandular networks, from which fibers enter the tubules.

These end on the myo-epithelial cells and between the gland cells.

3. Specialized Sweat Glands.

Certain large, branched sweat glands have a distinctive method of secretion.

The apices of the gland cells, with contained secretory products, break off.

In this way the secretion is liberated.

Such glands are known as *apocrine glands*.

This group is less coiled than are ordinary sweat glands.

The lumen of the secretory tubule is conspicuously wider.

Also the myo-epithelial cells are larger and more numerous.

The secretion is thicker, more pigmented and contains larger fat droplets.

A. CERUMINOUS GLANDS.

These glands occur in the external auditory canal (p. 315).

The secretion (*cerumen*) is a yellow, pigmented, fatty fluid.

B. CILIARY GLANDS (OF MOLL).

These glands of the eyelids are twisted, spiraling tubes.

They sometimes branch.

C. RUDIMENTARY MAMMARY GLANDS.

This group occurs along the course of the mammary ridge of the embryo.

Representatives are found in the axilla, mammary areola, mons pubis, labia majora, scrotum and circumanal region.

The coiled tube may reach a length of 30 mm. and make a mass 5 mm. in diameter.

Its duct opens into a hair follicle, as do sweat glands of lower mammals.

Some ducts, however, become separate secondarily and open independently.

The *axillary glands*, for example, acquire their large size at puberty.
At this time they begin to secrete, apocrine style, an odoriferous fluid.
Its characteristic odor results secondarily from bacterial action.
Periodic changes, paralleling the menstrual cycle, remain unsubstantiated.

4. Regenerative Ability.
Sweat glands can regenerate if their deeper ends escape destruction.

5. Diagnostic Features.
Sweat glands can be expected in almost every section of the skin.
The coiled, secretory portion lies at about the dermal-subcutaneous junction.
Its coils, sectioned in various planes, make a characteristic group.
The secretory cells are low columnar; peripherally there are myoid cells.
The duct passes vertically to the epidermis and channels through it in a spiral.
It is relatively long; its double layering in the free portion is distinctive.

6. Functional Correlations.
The sweat glands, in excreting sweat, act as accessory excretory organs.
The secretion contains many of the ingredients of urine.
It is an oily fluid that becomes watery on nervous stimulation of the gland.
These glands are also important in the regulation of body temperature.
Evaporation of sweat from the skin surface has a cooling effect.
The nature and significance of the axillary type of gland is poorly understood.

D. MAMMARY GLAND:
The *mammary gland* is a specialized, cutaneous gland located in the subcutaneous tissue.
It resembles the modified sweat glands of the apocrine type.
Development and structural conditions in lower mammals support this conclusion.
Glands are represented in both sexes, and they progress slightly during childhood.
At puberty they advance rapidly in the female, but very slowly in the male.
At 20 years the male glands stabilize in a feebly developed state.
They then correspond to the female glands in early puberty.
Moreover, the female glands remain imperfectly developed until pregnancy occurs.
Full differentiation and function are attained only after childbirth.

1. Structural Plan.
The mammary tissue comprises the *corpus mammae*, covered by skin.
The skin-cover is capped by a circular, pigmented area, the *areola*.
At the center of the wrinkled, pebbly areola lies the elevated *nipple*.
The glandular substance comprises 15 to 20 *lobes*.
Actually each is an independent gland with its own duct system.
A lobe is surrounded by interlobar connective tissue and much fat.
The fatty and fibrous tissue also subdivides a lobe into many lobules.
The epithelial parenchyma is embedded in loose, delicate connective tissue.
The *intralobular ducts* drain into *interlobular ducts*, and these into a main duct.
This single excretory duct from each lobe is a *lactiferous duct*.
It dilates, near its end, into a *lactiferous sinus*.
The duct then narrows again and opens at the summit of the nipple.
The functioning mammary gland is typical of the compound saccular type of gland.
It then differs greatly from its relatively undeveloped, inactive state.

2. Detailed Structure.

A. AREOLA AND NIPPLE.

The columnar *nipple* is traversed by *lactiferous ducts,* 2 mm. in diameter.

At the base of the nipple, each main duct bears a local dilatation.

This spindle-shaped *lactiferous sinus* attains a maximal diameter of 5 to 8 mm.

During lactation it is supposed to serve as a little reservoir for milk.

A duct opens by a *pore,* about 0.5 mm. in diameter, at the top of the nipple.

There are fewer pores (8 to 15) than main ducts, owing to terminal fusions.

Ducts have a one- to two-layered columnar epithelium until near the outlet.

The *areolar region,* including the nipple, has a thin, pigmented epidermis.

Pigmentation is deeper in brunettes and during pregnancy.

The dermis contains tall papillae and smooth-muscle fibers.

The muscle is arranged both circularly and radially.

In the nipple it is mostly circular, but some fibers follow the ducts.

Contraction of the muscle elevates and hardens the nipple.

The *areola* contains special *areolar glands* which open on surface elevations.

These glands (of Montgomery) are large, branched glands of the apocrine type.

They are regarded as transitions between sweat glands and mammary glands.

The areola also contains ordinary sweat glands and large sebaceous glands.

B. INACTIVE GLAND.

The *ducts* are the chief epithelial tissue seen, both inside and outside lobules.

The lining changes from a simple cuboidal to a two-layered epithelium.

Peripheral to the lactiferous sinus, the epithelium stratifies progressively.

At the pore, it becomes continuous with the epidermis.

Between the epithelium and basement membrane are stellate *myo-epithelial cells.*

The glandular *lobules* are small and have a rudimentary appearance.

The *intralobular ducts* appear narrow or collapsed.

Alveoli at best are mere buds, as in a sprouting embryonic gland.

Many believe that actual alveoli are entirely lacking prior to pregnancy.

Intralobular connective tissue is loose and fine in texture.

It is cellular and vascular, but contains no fat.

It furnishes a nutritive and expansible bed for future, functional alveoli.

This field of the potentially active lobule is plainly recognizable.

Interlobular connective tissue is relatively abundant, dense and coarse.

Cells are few, but fat is present and sometimes plentiful.

Here also course the *interlobular ducts.*

Some periodic swelling of the breasts accompanies the menstrual cycle.

This is perhaps due largely to vascular engorgement and fluid infiltration of the interstitial connective tissue.

Some epithelial increase, nevertheless, occurs cyclically in the monkey.

Similar evidence from precisely-timed, human biopsies is lacking.

C. ACTIVE GLAND.

The gland arouses during pregnancy and becomes functional after childbirth.

The cessation of nursing is followed by marked retrogression.

1. DURING PREGNANCY.

In the first half of pregnancy, *secretory ducts* extend and *alveoli* appear.

These result from rapid proliferation at the ends of existing ducts.

Their lumina hollow out by the middle of pregnancy.

Interlobular fat disappears to make room for lobular expansion.

The 15 to 20 lobes become plainly recognizable entities.

At the same time lymphocytes infiltrate the stroma within lobules.

In the second half of pregnancy the proliferation declines.

The alveoli, however, enlarge and elaborate secretion-precursors.

Some fluid (*colostrum*, p. 203) is secreted and the alveoli dilate.

Lobules fill out internally, expand grossly and become well demarcated

This is partly at the expense of the abundant intralobular stroma.

Yet even at the end of pregnancy some lobules are still laggard.

2. DURING LACTATION.

The prominent *alveoli* are closely packed within well demarcated *lobules*.

They become saccules and comprise most of the tissue of the breast.

Conversely, the interlobular stroma is reduced to thin septa.

The alveoli show regional differences in appearance.

That is, not all parts of the gland, or even of the same lobule, are in t

same functional state at the same time.

Many alveoli are dilated by milk and have a thin epithelial wall.

Others are resting; they have a relatively thick wall and small lumen.

The basophilic *gland cells* have indistinct cell boundaries.

Between them and a delicate basement membrane are stellate *basket cel*

These are *myo-epithelial cells*, presumably contractile.

Gland-cell shapes range from low cuboidal to columnar in active alveo

The taller cells often have rounded tops.

The nucleus is rounded to oval, and centrally situated.

Small fat droplets appear locally, apparently by active synthesis.

One or more large fat globules collect at the free, bulging end.

Also albuminous granules and vacuoles occur there.

Secretion is, at least in part, of the apocrine type.

The swollen tops of the cells detach with their contained secretion.

These losses leave low, frayed cells which regenerate their cytoplasm.

The secretory cycle is then repeated.

Intralobular ducts are much like alveoli in structure and function.

Hence they are a true *secretory duct*.

They contain cuboidal cells and elongate myo-epithelial elements.

The latter are supposed to express milk from the ducts.

Excretory ducts (both small and large) change but little.

3. AFTER LACTATION.

Secretion ceases and milk in the lumina of alveoli is absorbed.

Regressive changes return the gland to the resting state.

The alveoli dwindle, lose their lumina, and some cells degenerate.

However, the gland usually does not return to the nulliparous state.

After the first pregnancy, many alveoli remain recognizable as such.

Secretory residues may be retained in the ducts for a long time.

Connective tissue apparently increases, and again infiltrates with fat.

D. VESSELS AND NERVES.

The *vascular supply* becomes much richer in the active gland.

Blood vessels ramify in the stroma and terminate in capillary plexuses abc

alveoli and intralobular ducts.

Lymphatic networks surround the secretory portions of the gland.
> They drain chiefly to the axillary lymph nodes.

Efferent nerves supply the smooth muscle of vessels and of the areolar region.
> Secretory fibers also innervate the glandular epithelium.

Afferent nerve fibers supply numerous sensory endings in the nipple.
> Some of these endings resemble those on the genitalia.

3. Involution.

After the menopause the mammary gland undergoes regressive development.
The secretory epithelium atrophies, as do the excretory ducts to a less degree.
> Only a few scattered remnants (mostly of the duct system) persist.

The stroma becomes less cellular and the collagenous fibers decrease in number.
> The fibers appear as if 'melted down' into a more homogeneous mass.
> Elastic fibers increase in amount.

4. Diagnostic Features.

Intralobular ducts are poorly distinguished from alveoli, or not at all.
> Interlobular ducts lie in the coarse fibrous stroma.
>> In the active gland they occur in the compressed septa between lobules.

The *inactive gland* consists of scattered groups of epithelial cords or tubules.
> These appear like a sprouting, fetal stage of a gland.
> Such groups of rudiments occur within a cellular, connective-tissue bed.
> These unit areas (lobules) are embedded in a coarse, fibrous and fatty stroma.

The *lactating gland* shows sharply demarcated, crowded lobules.
> The interlobular connective tissue is compressed into thin septa.
> Secretory alveoli often differ in appearance regionally.
>> The larger ones are very closely packed saccules with wide lumina.
>> The cell tops tend to bulge and appear vacuolate (or ragged, if discharged).
>> Milk in the lumen appears as a granular mass.
> (There is a superficial resemblance to the lung, thyroid and prostate.)

During pregnancy, conditions are intermediate between inactivity and lactation.
After the menopause, conditions are simpler than before the first pregnancy.
> The appearance is one of wasting; epithelial strands and ducts persist variably.

5. Functional Correlations.

The mammary gland is controlled by hormones.
> The growth of the duct system, at puberty, is induced by *estrogen*.
> The completion of growth in pregnancy is a further action of estrogen.
>> *Progesterone* apparently aids, but its exact role is disputed.
> The initiation of secretion is induced by the lactogenic hormone, *prolactin*.
>> This hypophyseal hormone is identical with the luteotrophic hormone.

The secretion during the first few days after delivery is known as *colostrum*.
> It also follows the termination of lactation.
> Similar to it is the *witch milk* of the newborn of both sexes.
> Colostrum is a watery milk, containing protein but little fat.

Colostrum contains a characteristic component known as the *colostrum corpuscle*.
> These are large, globular cells that contain numerous fat droplets.
> Such corpuscles have often been interpreted as detached gland cells.
> Actually, they seem to be outwandered lymphoid cells, capable of amebism.
>> They acquire fat globules from the lumen by phagocytosis.

Within a few days after childbirth, the colostrum is replaced by *milk*.

Milk is a complex solution and emulsion.

It contains casein, lactose and inorganic salts in solution.

It also contains fat globules (mostly 2 to 5 μ) in suspension.

Each droplet is enclosed in an albuminous envelope.

This prevents ready coalescence of the droplets.

Free nuclei and some cellular fragments can be found in milk.

Chapter XVIII. THE MOUTH AND PHARYNX

The *digestive system* comprises the mouth, pharynx and digestive tube.
    In addition, it includes the salivary glands, pancreas and liver which open into these parts.
The hollow passage, from mouth to anus, is called the *digestive tract*.
    It exhibits regional specializations at various levels along its course.
    These modifications are correlated with the successive functions performed locally.
        The primary functional component in each instance is the lining of the hollow canal.
        This lining is a *mucous membrane*, adapted at each level to its specific purpose.

I. STRUCTURAL PLAN OF THE MOUTH AND PHARYNX

The lining is a mucous membrane connected to firmer supporting structures.
    Teeth project through the epithelium, and glands open onto it.

1. Mucosa.
    The *epithelium* is mostly of the stratified squamous type.
        It is not as highly flattened as epidermis, and it is not truly cornified in man.
        Its superficial cells desquamate into the saliva.
    A *basement membrane* serves for the basal attachment of the epithelium.
    The *lamina propria* bears vascular papillae that indent the epithelium.
        In the pharynx, lymphocytic infiltration occurs into the layer.
    A *lamina muscularis mucosae* is lacking throughout the mouth and pharynx.
        In the pharynx an elastic network occupies its position.

2. Submucosa.
    This stratum is present in certain regions as a lax layer, but is not delimited sharply.
        Where existent as an entity, it permits the mucosa to be lifted as a fold.
        It serves to attach the mucosa to the underlying muscles or bone.
    A submucosa is absent in the hard palate (in part), gums and dorsum of the tongue.

3. Glands.
    These are compound, tubulo-alveolar elements, not present in all regions.
        They may be serous, mucous or mixed sero-mucous.
    They lie in the submucosa, wherever this stratum is recognizable, or even deeper.

4. Supporting Wall.
    In all regions the superficial tissues attach to deep-lying skeletal muscle or bone.

5. Vessels and Nerves.
    Blood vessels, lymphatics and nerves form coarse plexuses in the submucosa.
        Finer subdivisions pass into the mucosa and extend into the papillae.
        The mucosa is a well vascularized, highly sensitive membrane.

II. THE VESTIBULE

This is a sort of anteroom to the oral cavity proper.

Superficially it is bounded by fleshy folds that constitute the lips and cheeks.

Internally it is separated from the mouth by the gums, alveolar bone and teeth.

The parotid glands open into the vestibule; they are described with similar glands (p. 233).

1. Lip.

On the outer side is typical *skin*, with a thin cornified epidermis.

Hair follicles, sebaceous glands and sweat glands are conspicuous features.

Centrally within the lip is a plate of skeletal muscle (mostly the *orbicularis oris*).

Slips of muscle insert among the fibers of the dermis, so that the skin is mobile.

These constitute the *mimetic muscles* (*i.e.*, of expression) of this region.

On the inner side is a typical *mucous membrane* and a less definite *submucosa*.

The stratified (but uncornified) epithelium is markedly thicker than the epidermis.

The lamina propria indents the epithelium with moderately prominent papillae.

Rounded groups of *labial glands* lie deep in what can be termed a *submucosa*.

They are mixed sero-mucous, and are preponderantly mucous.

Their ducts open onto the surface epithelium of the vestibule.

At the free margin of the lip is a *transitional zone*.

Here the thick epithelium contains much translucent eleidin.

Tall vascular papillae indent the epithelium far toward the surface.

Blood in the capillaries shows through, and the lip appears red.

The virtual absence of glands in this region favors drying.

Hence the lips have to be moistened by wiping with the tongue.

The lips, like the cheeks, are regions that enjoy marked mobility.

They aid in eating, drinking, phonation and facial expression.

They restrict the opening of the mouth to a convenient size.

2. Cheek.

These parts continue laterally the general plan and composition of the lips.

Even the transitional zone of the lips extends outward from the angles of the lips.

In this middle strip of mucosa the papillae are very tall; glands lack completely.

In general the *mucosa* has short papillae; elastic fibers are abundant (unlike the lips).

The rather compact lamina propria is bound down at intervals to the muscle layer.

This prevents large folds and lessens the opportunity of injury when biting.

The *submucosa* is definitely a looser, fat-containing layer.

Mixed glands (mostly mucous) even invade the stratum of muscle (the buccinator).

3. Gum.

It comprises that part of the oral mucosa which attaches to the alveolar bone.

At the gum margins, the surface epithelium turns inward for a distance of about 2 mm.

It is separated from the surface of the tooth by a groove (*gingival sulcus*).

At the bottom of the groove there is an *epithelial attachment* to the teeth.

As the gum recedes in later years, this zone of attachment undergoes a shifting.

The shift is from the enamel to the enamel and cementum, and finally to cementum.

The *epithelium* resembles that of the labial mucosa.

The *lamina propria* is dense, fibrous tissue.

It binds the gum to the cementum and to the alveolar bone.

Near the gum line, or free margin, the papillae are very tall and vascular.

The vicinity of the epithelial attachment is devoid of papillae.

There is reason to suspect that the lamina may be unusually active metabolically.

It contains large numbers of mast cells.

4. Teeth.

Teeth, gums and alveolar bone provide a wall between the vestibule and mouth proper.

Since the teeth are complicated structurally, they will be treated as a separate topic.

III. THE TEETH

The *teeth* are modified, soft papillae, covered by peculiar, hard substances.

The exposed part of the hard coating develops from an ectodermal epithelium.

All concealed portions of a tooth, in its natural position, are mesenchymal in origin.

Teeth are unique among organs by having the childhood set replaced by a permanent set.

A. STRUCTURAL PLAN:

A *tooth* consists of a free *crown* and one to three concealed *roots*.

Crown and root meet at the *neck*, which is surrounded by the *gum margin*.

The root of a tooth occupies an *alveolus*, or socket, in the bone of the jaw.

A *periodontal membrane* attaches the root of the tooth to the alveolar wall.

The hollow *pulp chamber* of the crown extends into *root canals*.

At the tip of each root, the canal opens by an *apical foramen*.

The entire cavity is occupied by a soft core of *dental pulp*.

The hard wall of the tooth consists of three different kinds of specialized substance.

Dentine borders the pulp and furnishes the body of the entire tooth.

It is interrupted only at the apical foramen.

Enamel covers the crown, becoming thinner at the neck.

Cementum encrusts the root; it is thinner at the neck.

B. DETAILED STRUCTURE:

1. Dentine.

Like bone, it consists of a collagenous mesh and calcified ground substance.

Unlike bone, it contains neither vessels nor total cells.

Dentine is harder than ordinary bone; it is 72 per cent inorganic.

In the crown, uncalcified areas produce the so-called *interglobular spaces*.

Next to the cementum, similar spaces constitute the *granular layer* (of Tomes).

Dentine appears radially striate because of countless *dentinal canaliculi*.

These tubules pursue S-shaped courses with many minor spiralings.

A canaliculus is a tiny tubule, 1 to 3 μ in diameter and up to 4 mm. long.

It branches, tapers peripherally and may end in anastomosing loops.

Each canal is lined with a dark-staining, uncalcified *dentinal sheath* (of Neumann).

The sheath is dense, refractile and resistant to chemicals.

The lumen of the canaliculus is occupied by a *dentinal fiber* (of Tomes).

It belongs to a specialized osteoblast (*i.e.*, odontoblast) in the pulp cavity.

Hence this canal is a type of bone-canaliculus, with its peculiar capsule.

In old age the dentinal tubules are often obliterated by calcification.

Incremental lines (of Owen and of Ebner) represent layered deposits of dentine.

In transverse sections they resemble the growth rings of a tree.

Abrasion or irritation can stimulate the deposit of *secondary dentine*.
This irregularly arranged dentine may even obliterate the pulp cavity.

2. Enamel.

This highly specialized epithelial product is the hardest tissue of the body.
It is composed almost totally (97 per cent) of inorganic salts.
The chief component (90 per cent) is calcium phosphate.
The structural unit is a rod-like *enamel prism*, radially arranged.
Each is surrounded by a thin *prism sheath*, richer in organic matter.
Union is by a scanty, cementing *interprismatic substance* that also calcifies.
Each prism was formed by a separate cell; it extends from dentine to surface.
The diameter varies from 3 to 6 μ; it thickens progressively toward the surface
As many as 12 million prisms occur in a molar tooth.
In surface view a prism is evenly cross-banded and often slightly beaded.
The banding presumably reflects daily rhythms in lengthwise growth.
In transverse section a prism is basically hexagonal.
In man most of them appear semicircular, but with indented bases.
The arrangement resembles the pattern made by the scales in fish skin.
The prisms are grouped in bundles that may cross at acute angles.
The enamel as a whole is arranged in series of arching, superposed layers.
These layers represent periods of rhythmic growth.
Successive layers are demarcated by the *incremental lines* (of Retzius).

3. Cementum.

A thin layer of bone invests the dentine of the root.
It contains some bone cells occupying lacunae within a typical matrix.
There is irregular and inconstant lamellation, but vessels are usually lacking.
In old age, Haversian systems may appear, as the cementum continues to thicken

4. Dental Pulp.

The main *pulp chamber* and *root canals* together comprise the *pulp cavity*.
This cavity is filled with a soft, gelatinous core which is the *pulp*.
The pulp is popularly called the 'nerve' of the tooth.
Its cells are fusiform and stellate; most of them are much like mesenchyme.
Reticular fibers are interspersed in a viscid ground substance.
At the periphery occurs an epithelioid layer of columnar cells, the *odontoblasts*.
These are peculiar, specialized osteoblasts, of mesenchymal origin.
Each cell sends a long process into an adjacent dentinal canaliculus.
These slender, branching processes are the *dentinal fibers* (of Tomes).
Vessels and nerves are described below, under a separate heading.

5. Periodontal Membrane.

This is a kind of periosteum that lies between the alveolus and the root.
It also supports the gum, with which it merges in the region of the neck.
At this level it helps form the so-called *circular dental ligament*.
The membrane consists of densely arranged, coarse collagenous fibers.
It contains fibroblasts and osteoblasts; elastic fibers are lacking.
Sharpey's fibers extend away from both surfaces and bind the membrane to th
alveolar wall in one direction, and to the cementum in the other direction
The membrane also serves as a suspensory ligament for the teeth.

6. Vessels and Nerves.

Usually a single *arteriole* enters each root-tip and ascends into the pulp chamber.

Capillary loops supply the odontoblasts and then open into thin-walled venules.

These more centrally located *venules* retrace the course of entering arterioles.

The presence of *lymphatics* within the pulp is still a subject of dispute.

Myelinated nerves accompany the arterioles and branch with them.

Nearing the periphery of the pulp, the fibers lose their sheaths.

Naked twigs pass between odontoblasts, but do not enter dentinal tubules.

The dentinal fibers apparently serve as pain receptors.

These intermediaries transmit sensory stimulations to the free nerve endings.

Unmyelinated nerve fibers also enter the pulp; they are vasomotor in function.

C. DIAGNOSTIC FEATURES:

Enamel and dentine are histological tissues that specifically characterize teeth.

The spatial relations of enamel, cementum, dentine and pulp are diagnostic.

The relation of the tooth to its alveolus is also unique.

D. FUNCTIONAL CORRELATIONS:

The teeth serve to bite and grind food to proper size.

They are of considerable use in speech.

Experiments with radioactive tracers show mineral turnovers in both dentine and enamel.

Active interchanges of calcium and phosphorus occur between teeth and the blood.

IV. THE TONGUE

The *tongue* is an organ that belongs partly to the mouth and partly to the pharynx.

It rises above the floor of these regions as a mobile organ.

A. STRUCTURAL PLAN:

A mass of *skeletal muscle* is largely contained within a covering of *mucous membrane*.

The under-surface of the tongue is smooth, and in places there is a *submucosa*.

The top-surface is uneven, with a tightly adherent *mucosa* (but no submucosa).

A longitudinal, *median sulcus* overlies a deeper *lingual septum*.

The anterior two-thirds and posterior one-third are separated by a V-shaped boundary.

The angle opens forward and has the *foramen caecum* at its apex.

The larger oral portion is the *body;* the smaller pharyngeal portion is the *root*.

The dorsum of the tip and body of the tongue bears numerous *lingual papillae*.

This area includes two-thirds of the entire top surface.

The dorsum of the root presents irregular bulgings, containing the *lingual tonsils*.

The floor of the mouth has a loose *submucosa;* it contains fat and the *sublingual glands*.

B. DETAILED STRUCTURE:

1. Mucosa.

The fairly thick *epithelium* is of the stratified squamous type.

The epithelium is tightly bound down (except under the tongue).

The *lamina propria* is compact and intimately united to muscle bundles.

The superficial portion, throughout the dorsum, bears vertical projections.

Overdraped with epithelium, they constitute the *lingual papillae*.

These gross elevations are quite different from the ordinary connective-tissue papillae, also present, which merely indent the epithelium.

Lingual papillae are of four types: *filiform; fungiform; vallate;* and *foliate.*

A. FILIFORM PAPILLAE.

These are so numerous as to constitute the 'plush' of the tongue.

They are arranged in parallel rows, diverging from the median sulcus.

A typical papilla begins as a primary columnar elevation of the lamina propria.

This bears 5 to 30 tall, secondary, connective-tissue *papillae.*

Epithelium clothes these papillary tufts and ends in tapered points.

The whole papilla resembles a 'cat of nine tails,' about 2 to 3 mm. long.

The surface of the epithelium is hard and scaly, but not truly cornified in man.

B. FUNGIFORM PAPILLAE.

These are knob-like projections, scattered singly among filiform papillae.

Many vessels and a thin, translucent epithelium give them a red color.

They are larger than the filiform papillae, but much less numerous.

They have a narrow stalk and a broader, rounded top.

The shape resembles a button-mushroom (whence their name, 'fungiform').

The largest papillae are as much as 1.8 mm. high and 1 mm. wide.

The primary connective-tissue core bears many secondary papillae.

They merely indent the epithelium, however; the free surface is smooth.

Some fungiform papillae bear one to several *taste buds.*

Large, *conical papillae,* up to 3 mm. long, occur sparingly.

They are considered to be a modified, fungiform type.

C. VALLATE PAPILLAE.

This type makes a V-shaped row that demarcates the body and root of the tongue

The total number is usually 7 to 11.

It is much larger than any other type; (height, 0.5 to 1.5 mm.; width, 1 to 3 mm.).

This papilla does not extend much above the lingual surface.

On the other hand, it sinks well beneath the surface level.

Each papilla is encircled by a deep *trench;* beyond this is a facing *wall.*

A papilla has the shape of an inverted, truncated cone with a nearly flat top.

It resembles the fungiform type in shape, but it is larger and counter-sunk.

The connective-tissue core forms secondary papillae on its top surface alone.

The covering epithelium is indented by them, yet has a smooth free-surface.

The lateral surface of a vallate papilla contains many *taste buds* (about 200).

The opposite wall, across the trench, has fewer buds (about 50).

These totals are highly variable; the numbers decrease greatly in old age.

Von Ebner's glands, purely serous, are associated with each papilla.

They intermingle with the muscle, and some 30 ducts empty into the trench

D. FOLIATE PAPILLAE.

These are parallel mucosal folds on the lateral margins of the tongue.

They are located at the junction of its body and root.

In adult man, foliate papillae are regressive or rudimentary.

Infants may have 4 to 8 well-developed, vertical folds on each side of the tongue.

These bear *taste buds* along the middle region of their vertical surfaces.

Von Ebner's glands, purely serous, open into the bottom of the trenches.

In some mammals (*e.g.,* rabbit), foliate papillae are highly developed.

E. TASTE BUDS.

These prominent, ovoid bodies embed in the epithelium of some lingual papillae.

As the receptor organs of taste, they are described on p. 305.

2. Lingual Tonsil.

Its multiple, lymphoid units in the root of the tongue cause surface bulgings.

These tonsillar structures are described on p. 142.

3. Glands.

The *lingual glands* lie deep in the lamina propria and extend into the muscle.

A. ANTERIOR LINGUAL GLANDS.

These are located under the apex of the tongue, at each side of the median line.

They are mixed sero-mucous glands, with several ducts.

B. GLANDS OF VON EBNER.

This group is limited to the region of the vallate and foliate papillae.

All of the alveoli are purely serous.

Numerous ducts (4 to 38) can be traced to the trench of each vallate papilla.

C. MUCOUS GLANDS OF THE ROOT.

These occur in the lymphoid area, but encroach slightly onto the body.

They are pure mucous glands, whose ducts open onto the dorsum of the tongue.

Some of the ducts empty into the pits of the lingual tonsils.

None, however, open into the trenches of the vallate papillae.

The submaxillary and sublingual glands open alongside the tongue.

Both types will be described with similar major glands (p. 234).

4. Muscle.

The muscle mass is halved incompletely by the median, fibrous *lingual septum*.

The skeletal muscle fibers belong to two general groups.

Intrinsic fibers of the m. lingualis lie wholly within the tongue limits.

Extrinsic fibers enter from without and serve also to anchor the tongue.

These include the hyo-, genio-, stylo-, palato- and chondroglossus muscles.

The muscle fibers are arranged in definite bundles, interlacing at right angles.

Different bundles are longitudinal, vertical and transverse in direction.

The muscle fibers are embedded in loose, fatty areolar tissue (endomysium).

The fibers insert into the perimysial connective tissue which surrounds bundles.

Some of the fibers branch near their insertions.

5. Vessels and Nerves.

Blood vessels supply the lingual muscles and form a plexus in the lamina propria.

From the latter, capillaries extend to the papillae.

Lymphatics drain the papillae and produce plexuses in the lamina propria.

Efferent nerve fibers distribute to the muscle, glands and blood vessels.

Some *sensory nerve fibers* end freely; these mediate general sensibility.

Others terminate within taste buds and are gustatory in function.

DIAGNOSTIC FEATURES:

Bundles of skeletal muscle interlace in three planes; this is a unique feature.

They are divided incompletely by a fibrous median septum.

Stratified squamous epithelium provides an external covering.

Lingual papillae project from the mucosa of the dorsal surface of the body.

Tonsillar pits characterize the mucosa of the dorsal surface of the root.

Small glands occur constantly in sections through the root.

They may be present or absent in sections through the body.

Taste buds occur dependably only about the trench of each vallate papilla.

They are ovoid bodies, prominent and pale staining, set in the epithelium.
The component cells are elongate, and most of them extend the length of a bud.

D. FUNCTIONAL CORRELATIONS:

The tongue is of use in selecting food, and in directing it to the teeth and pharynx.
Chewing and swallowing are thus furthered; the tongue also aids in speech.
The sense of taste resides in taste buds whose cells respond to substances in solution.
Distinctive taste-bud types have not been correlated with taste discrimination.
General chemical sensibility exists where taste buds do not occur.

V. THE PALATE

The *palate* furnishes a roof, separating the mouth from the nasal passages and nasopharynx.
The oral side bears the oral type of mucosa.
The nasal side bears the respiratory type of mucosa.
Between the two mucosae is a middle lamina of bone (in front) or of muscle (in rear).

1. Hard Palate.

The *oral side* bears a mucosa, covered with a stratified squamous epithelium.
It is indented with tall papillae extending from a densely fibrous lamina propria.
A submucosa exists except in a midline seam (the *raphe*) and near the gum.
The anterior one-third contains fat.
The posterior two-thirds contains pure *mucous glands*.
The *middle layer* is supplied by horizontal parts of the maxillary and palate bones.
The *nasal side* bears a mucosa with a pseudostratified, ciliated epithelium.
There are mixed *sero-mucous glands* and a deep layer of elastic fibers.

2. Soft Palate.

This is a backward continuation of the palate, ending in a conical, free *uvula*.
The *oral side* continues its covering of stratified squamous epithelium.
The lamina propria bears tall papillae and is infiltrated with lymphocytes.
Mucosa and submucosa are separated by a dense network of elastic fibers.
The loose submucosa contains pure *mucous glands*.
The *middle layer* is a sheet of skeletal muscle.
The *nasal side* continues the structures from the hard palate, as already described.
Near the free posterior margin, however, there is stratified epithelium.
(This is reflected for a distance from the oral surface onto the nasal surface.)

3. Diagnostic Features.

The palate is a plate bearing two mucous membranes, back to back.
On the oral side the mucosa has stratified squamous epithelium.
The submucosa contains mucous glands.
On the nasal side the mucosa has a pseudostratified, ciliated epithelium.
The mucosa has sero-mucous glands; there is no submucosa.
The middle support is either bone (hard palate) or skeletal muscle (soft palate).

4. Functional Correlations.

The palate, in general, was developed to separate nasal passages from mouth.
The *hard palate* is firm, as an adaptation to the action of the tongue.

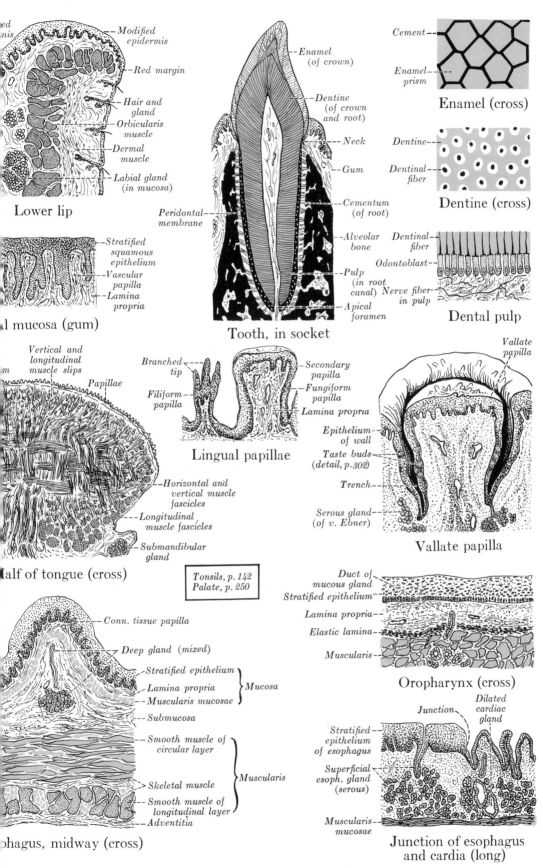

Modified epidermis

Red margin

Hair and gland

Orbicularis muscle

Dermal muscle

Labial gland (in mucosa)

Lower lip

Enamel (of crown)

Dentine (of crown and root)

Neck

Gum

Cementum (of root)

Peridontal membrane

Alveolar bone

Pulp (in root canal)

Apical foramen

Tooth, in socket

Cement

Enamel prism

Enamel (cross)

Dentine

Dentinal fiber

Dentine (cross)

Dentinal fiber

Odontoblast

Nerve fiber in pulp

Dental pulp

Stratified squamous epithelium

Vascular papilla

Lamina propria

al mucosa (gum)

Vertical and longitudinal muscle slips

Papillae

Branched tip

Filiform papilla

Secondary papilla

Fungiform papilla

Lamina propria

Lingual papillae

Vallate papilla

Epithelium of wall

Taste buds (detail, p.302)

Trench

Serous gland (of v. Ebner)

Vallate papilla

Horizontal and vertical muscle fascicles

Longitudinal muscle fascicles

Submandibular gland

alf of tongue (cross)

Tonsils, p. 142
Palate, p. 250

Conn. tissue papilla

Deep gland (mixed)

Stratified epithelium

Lamina propria

Muscularis mucosae

Mucosa

Submucosa

Smooth muscle of circular layer

Skeletal muscle

Muscularis

Smooth muscle of longitudinal layer

Adventitia

phagus, midway (cross)

Duct of mucous gland

Stratified epithelium

Lamina propria

Elastic lamina

Muscularis

Oropharynx (cross)

Junction

Dilated cardiac gland

Stratified epithelium of esophagus

Superficial esoph. gland (serous)

Muscularis mucosae

Junction of esophagus and cardia (long)

THE UPPER ALIMENTARY CANAL

It withstands the force applied in crushing, mixing and swallowing food.
The mucosa as a whole is firmly attached to prevent slippage.
The *soft palate* is movable during the act of swallowing.
It is then drawn upward, thereby closing off the naso-pharynx.

VI. THE PHARYNX

he *pharynx* is a somewhat flattened conical chamber, through which air and food pass.
is partly divided at the level of the soft palate into a superior and inferior region.
The superior part, respiratory in function, is called the *naso-pharynx*.
Its mucosa continues the general structure of the nasal passages farther in front.
The inferior part consists of an *oro-pharynx* (behind the palatine arches) and of a *laryngo-pharynx* (behind the larynx).
This region progressively approaches the structural plan of the digestive tube proper.
group of *tonsils* encircles the beginning of the pharynx.

. MUCOSA:
1. Epithelium.
The *naso-pharynx* is lined chiefly by a pseudostratified epithelium.
The columnar cells are ciliated; some are specialized as goblet cells.
Lower levels have first stratified columnar epithelium, then stratified squamous.
This is a result correlated with the circumstance that the soft palate comes frequently in contact with the posterior pharyngeal wall.
The *oro-* and *laryngo-pharynx* are lined with a soft, stratified squamous epithelium.
Here the opposed surfaces come into contact, and are rubbed by passing food.

2. Lamina Propria.
Only the naso-pharynx has a distinct *basement membrane* beneath its epithelium.
The stratified epithelium is indented by small connective-tissue papillae.
The lamina, composed of fibro-elastic tissue, contains *lymphoid infiltrations*.
On the posterior surface of the naso-pharynx is the *pharyngeal tonsil* (p. 143).
Laterally, at the junction of mouth and oro-pharynx, are *palatine tonsils* (p. 141).
Basally, in the root of the tongue, is the *lingual tonsil* (p. 142).
In the oro- and laryngo-pharynx are scattered, solitary lymph nodules.
Regions associated with pseudostratified epithelium have small *sero-mucous glands*.
Regions associated with stratified epithelium have small *mucous glands*.
The deepest stratum of the lamina is occupied by fibers of a thick *elastic layer*.
This takes the place of the muscularis mucosae of the digestive tube proper.

. ACCESSORY COATS:
1. Submucosa.
This tunic is well developed in two localities only.
These are laterally in the naso-pharynx and in the approach to the esophagus.
Elsewhere the elastic stratum of the lamina propria abuts against the muscle.
Regions of the pharynx having stratified epithelium have small *mucous glands*.
These may even extend deep into the muscular layer.

2. Muscularis.
The muscular tunic consists of two layers of *skeletal muscle*.
The inner layer is longitudinal; the outer layer is oblique or circular.

3. Adventitia.

A thin, fibrous sheath occurs in most regions.
In other regions the muscles attach directly to the skull.

C. DIAGNOSTIC FEATURES:

The general *naso-pharynx* resembles the respiratory nasal cavities in structure.
The absence of a venous plexus and the presence of a muscular coat are differences.
The *oro-* and *laryngo-pharynx* increasingly resemble the esophagus as they near it.
The presence of an elastic layer (instead of a muscularis mucosae) is distinctive.
The submucous glands are purely mucous, not mixed.
The muscle layers are reversed from the order in the digestive tube.
The several types of tonsils are distinctive features of their regions (pp. 141–143).

D. FUNCTIONAL CORRELATIONS:

The pharynx is a common passageway for air and food; their pathways cross.
Air, reaching it, has been warmed and filtered; food has been prepared for digestion.
The phase of swallowing performed by the pharynx is a complicated, involuntary act.

Chapter XIX. THE DIGESTIVE TUBE

The *digestive tube* is a canal that begins with the esophagus and ends with the anus.
It is a typical example of the hollow organs of the body.

I. THE STRUCTURAL PLAN OF HOLLOW ORGANS

Most tubular and saccular organs are constructed according to a common plan.
Typically there are four concentric coats, named *tunics*.

    In certain organs there is a reduction within a coat or even the elimination of a coat.
    There are also minor structural variations to meet local requirements.
The tunic commonly called a *mucous membrane* has four component layers.

Tunica Mucosa.
    A. EPITHELIUM.
        This may be of any type, correlated with the function performed.
        The *epithelium* borders on the cavity of a hollow organ, which is called the *lumen*.
        In the relaxed condition an actual cavity does not exist to any degree.
            The folded epithelial surfaces are then in contact; the lumen is potential only.
        A lumen exists wherever fluid or solid material is passing, or is retained.
            In special situations the lumen is kept open by a reinforced outer wall.
                Example: trachea; auditory tube.
    B. MEMBRANA PROPRIA.
        The epithelium usually attaches to a sheet-like support of firm consistency.
            This is the membrana propria, or *basement membrane* as ordinarily named.
        It consists of reticular fibers and a structureless ground substance.
            If thin, its presence may be unnoticed in sections stained in a routine manner.
            The thickness is not always correlated with the amount of stress encountered.
    C. LAMINA PROPRIA MUCOSAE.
        Areolar tissue, reticular tissue, or both, form the basis of the *lamina propria*.
        There may be a *lymphoid infiltration*, and even *lymph nodules*.
        The superficial portion may be elevated into papillae, villi or folds.
        Smaller vessels and nerves invade the lamina propria throughout.
        Simple or compound *glands* are abundant in some organs.
    D. LAMINA MUSCULARIS MUCOSAE.
        When present, this layer consists of smooth muscle; usually there are two layers.
            An inner layer is circular; the outer is longitudinal.
        Its presence establishes the exact boundary between the mucous membrane and
            submucosa.

Tunica (or Tela) Submucosa.
    Coarse areolar tissue comprises this web-like membrane, usually called the *submucosa*.
        Its considerable laxity and elasticity provides mobility to the mucosa.

The submucosa also supports the larger blood vessels, lymphatics and nerves.
It contains a vascular plexus, nerve plexus and, commonly, small autonomic ganglia.
In a few organs there are compound *glands* in the submucosa.

3. Tunica Muscularis.

The *muscular tunic* is often relatively thick; in a few locations it is omitted.
Almost without exception, it is composed of smooth muscle.
The commonest arrangement is two concentric tubes (rarely three or one).
The inner layer is usually circular in arrangement; the outer, longitudinal.
Knowing the arrangement of these layers in a given organ, the plane of a section taken from that organ can be determined.
A vascular plexus, nerve plexus and small ganglia commonly lie between the two layers.
The muscularis maintains tonus in a tube and also propels its contents onward.

4. Tunica Adventitia or Serosa.

The outermost coat is primarily fibrous—an *adventitia*, or fibrosa.
In a few organs the adventitia becomes strengthened with cartilage.
Hollow organs lying in the peritoneal cavity, or projecting into it, are surfaced with a reflection of the peritoneum.
The entire outer tunic is then known as a *serosa*.
Through the adventitia or serosa, vessels and nerves pass to deeper levels of the wall.

II. THE ESOPHAGUS

This simple tube, the *esophagus* or gullet, is 10 in. long; it connects pharynx with stomach.
There is a fairly gradual transition from the structure of the pharynx into the esophagus.
In effecting this, a muscularis mucosae replaces the elastic layer of the pharynx.
Also the tunica muscularis becomes more regularly arranged.

A. MUCOSA:

1. Surface Epithelium.

The stratified squamous epithelium is continued from the pharynx unchanged.
There is, however, an abrupt transition into the simple epithelium of the stomach.
The line of junction of the two epithelial sheets follows a jagged course.
The *epithelium* is highly stratified (about 25 cell-layers).
It is indented by tall connective-tissue papillae of the lamina propria.
In man the epithelium is not cornified or highly flattened, as in some mammals.

2. Lamina Propria.

This layer consists of areolar tissue, poor in elasticity, and not highly cellular.
Tall *papillae* indent the epithelium (even for two-thirds of its thickness).
A few solitary *lymph nodules* occur in relation to the ducts of mucous glands.
Superficial glands occur at the extreme upper and lower ends of the esophagus.
They are variable in number and sometimes fail (especially the upper set).
These are compound tubular glands that sometimes take a weak mucin stain.
Each duct opens at the summit of a connective-tissue papilla.
They resemble the cardiac glands of the stomach, and the lower set joins them.
For this reason, they are sometimes called 'cardiac glands.'

3. Muscularis Mucosae.

This layer of smooth muscle is thicker than anywhere else in the body.

At the upper end it occurs as bundles that do not make a complete layer.

Toward the stomach it is complete and increasingly robust (0.2 to 0.4 mm. thick).

Its muscle fibers are arranged longitudinally; a circular layer is lacking.

ACCESSORY COATS:

1. Submucosa.

The submucous layer is lax and elastic, to allow dilatation when food is swallowed.

When the esophagus is empty, 7 to 10 prominent longitudinal folds are formed.

These involve both the mucosa and submucosa and give the lumen a star-shape.

Deep glands, which are the *esophageal glands* proper, lie within the submucosa.

Their number is variable (60 to 740), and their distribution irregular.

Each is a small, compound tubulo-alveolar gland; it produces typical mucus.

The chief duct of each gland, in passage, pierces the muscularis mucosae.

A duct enters the epithelium where the latter dips downward between papillae.

2. Muscularis.

Two thick layers of muscle are conspicuous features.

The inner layer is circular; the outer layer is longitudinal.

The composition of the muscle coat varies at different levels.

The upper quarter consists of skeletal muscle, not arranged very regularly.

A middle segment contains a mixture of skeletal and smooth muscle.

The lower third consists of smooth muscle, regularly arranged.

(The smooth- and skeletal-muscle extents are subject to individual variation.)

3. Adventitia.

The most external tunic is a typical, loose, fibrous investment.

It connects with surrounding structures and conducts many vessels and nerves.

. VESSELS AND NERVES:

The distribution of blood vessels, lymphatics and nerves within the entire digestive tube follows a similar, fundamental pattern.

These features will be summarized at the end of this chapter (p. 232).

. DIAGNOSTIC FEATURES:

The esophagus is characterized by its stratified squamous epithelium, robust muscularis mucosae and strong, regularly arranged muscular coat.

The mucosa and submucosa tend to be thrown into alternate major and minor folds.

In transverse section they produce a characteristically branched, stellate lumen.

That is, the main arms of the star subdivide peripherally into Y-shaped endings.

The muscularis mucosae is by far the thickest present in any organ.

Mucosal glands are too local in extent to be dependable as a general diagnostic aid.

When present they indicate an extreme upper or lower level of section.

(Whether upper or lower, can be told by the composition of the muscularis.)

Submucosal glands are commonly encountered in sections, but may be lacking.

The composition of the muscularis establishes the general level of the section.

If skeletal muscle only is present, the upper quarter of the tube can be assumed.

No other organ contains skeletal muscle and a muscularis mucosae.

If mixed skeletal and smooth muscle are present, the middle third can be assumed.
No other organ has a muscularis of this sort.
If smooth muscle only is present, the lower third can be assumed.

E. FUNCTIONAL CORRELATIONS:

The esophagus is a conducting tube that completes the warming or cooling of food to a appropriate temperature for reception into the stomach.
Food and drink are carried downward rapidly by muscular contractions and gravity.
Glandular secretions are mucoid and solely for lubricative purposes.

III. THE STOMACH

The *stomach* is a tube that has become dilated and distorted into a capacious sac.
To aid description, the stomach is divided into cardia, fundus, corpus and a pyloric region.
Fundus and corpus are similar structurally; hence the histological regions are but three.

A. MUCOSA:

The thickness varies from about 0.3 mm. at the cardia, to 1.5 mm. at the pylorus.
The mucous membrane (and submucosa) are thrown into longitudinal folds, or *rugae*.
The height and number of these depend on the degree of gastric distention.
Also there is a finer system of furrows, marking off *gastric areas* (1 to 5 mm. across).
On these bulging mounds open the gastric pits, or *foveolae*.
The foveolae range from 17 (in fundus) to 9 (in pylorus) per sq. mm.
In all, there are some 3,400,000 foveolae; they serve as ducts to the gastric glands.
Several gastric glands empty into the bottom of each foveola.

1. Surface Epithelium.

Tall columnar cells are regularly arranged in a simple *epithelium*.
At the cardia they continue into the basal layer of the esophageal epithelium.
The transition from stratified to simple epithelium is abruptly precipitous.
All of the component cells are mucus-secreting, so none has a goblet shape.
The mucus, however, is peculair since not all 'specific' mucous stains color it.
In life, mucigen fills the cytoplasm above the level of the depressed nucleus.
These globules are preserved with great difficulty.
As a result, routinely stained sections show clear, pale cells.
Terminal bars encircle the cell tops; electron micrographs demonstrate microvill
The surface cell-type continues into the foveolae; here they produce less mucige

2. Glands.

The *gastric glands* are of the simple, branched tubular type.
They extend more or less vertically through the full thickness of the mucosa.
Each foveola serves as a short duct to several glands.
The total number of glands is estimated at 15,000,000.
Most of these differentiate after birth; one-half, after 10 years.
The total secreting area of the glands is large (30 sq. ft.).
There are three regional types of gland in the stomach: *cardiac; fundic; pyloric*.
A. CARDIAC GLANDS.
This type occupies a narrow band next to the cardio-esophageal junction.
The zone varies in width between 5 mm. and 40 mm.

They are essentially like the superficial glands of the lower esophagus.

Both make a continuous series of small, sometimes compound, tubular glands.
The foveola (about one-half the total length) receives several glands.
The secreting portions are tortuous; their component cells are mucous elements.

These cells are much like the mucous cells of fundic and pyloric glands.
The gland-lumen is of fair diameter; ducts sometimes dilate prominently.
At lower levels within the zone transitions into the fundic type occur.
The significance of cardiac glands is obscure.

B. FUNDIC GLANDS.

This type is poorly named, since it occurs in both the fundus and corpus.

The term *gastric gland* is also used to designate this particular type.

It is obviously an inappropriate name for glands of a limited region.
Each is a fairly straight, tubular gland that branches somewhat.

Branching occurs from the sides, and especially at the ends.
Several regional segments are recognized in a total gland.

There are: a short duct (the *foveola*); a short, constricted *neck;* a long *body;*
a slightly dilated and bent blind end, or *fundus.*
From three to seven glands open into each foveola.
The largest glands attain a length of about 1.5 mm.

The ratio of duct length to the gland proper is about 1:4.
The lumen of the secretory portion is narrow and often scarcely noticeable.
The component cells of the secretory portion show four cytological types.

Cell-types 1 to 3, below, bear microvilli on their free surface.

1. MUCOUS NECK-CELLS.

This type is characteristic of the neck region of fundic glands.

They become progressively abundant in glands nearer the pyloric region.
In routine preparations they stain palely and resemble chief cells.

But they differ in having basally located nuclei, usually flattened.
Specific mucus-stains differentiate mucigen in them.

Nevertheless, the mucus is watery and of a special nature.

2. CHIEF CELLS.

This type is progressively abundant in glands nearer the cardiac region.

They constitute most of the tubule below the level of the gland neck.
Such cells are pyramidal, granular elements, with basophilic cytoplasm.

Basally in the cell there is striate, *chromidial substance* (p. 13).
The spherical nucleus is located not far below the center of the cell.
After a period of rest, a cell contains coarse *presecretion granules.*

After activity, the cells are smaller and the granules fewer.
Preservation is difficult, and postmortem disintegration is prompt.

In ordinary preparations much of the cytoplasm is clear and vacuolate.

With proper fixation and staining, the *zymogen granules* corresponding to
these spaces can be demonstrated.

They consist of *pepsinogen,* the precursor of pepsin.

3. PARIETAL CELLS.

This cell type is progressively abundant in glands nearer the pyloric region.
Parietal cells are wedged in singly between the mucous neck-cells, where they
are most common, and between the chief cells.

For this reason, they tend to occupy a peripheral position in the tubule.

Especially is this true toward the base of the gland.

Here they may even bulge prominently (when chief cells are depleted).
The cell shape is wedge-like to spheroidal.

The nucleus (sometimes two or more) is spherical and centrally located.
The finely granular cytoplasm stains strongly with acid aniline dyes.
There are, however, no distinctive secretory granules.
No cytological changes during functional activity are demonstrable.
Intracellular secretory channels form coarse spaces within the cytoplasm.
The main canaliculus is a tubular groove between neighboring chief cells.
This *secretory capillary* opens into the lumen of the gland proper.
Only special impregnation methods demonstrate well such capillaries.
The function of parietal cells is to 'secrete' hydrochloric acid.
Free acid occurs in secretory capillaries, but not in the cytoplasm.
The actual mode of acid formation is not surely established.
This is the only cell in the human body known to produce acid.

4. ARGENTAFFIN CELLS.

These *enterochromaffin elements* occur occasionally in fundic glands.
They lie between the basement membrane and the chief cells.
A slender extension often reaches the gland lumen.
Granules in the broad cell-base stain with chrome salts or silver.
They are precursors of *serotonin*, a potent vasoconstrictive hormone.

C. PYLORIC GLANDS.

This type occupies one-seventh, or more, of the gastric area.
An *intermediate zone*, between fundic and pyloric areas can be recognized.
Here the glands combine certain features of both types.
The *pyloric glands* are simple, branched, convoluted-tubular glands.
They are more branched than the fundic type, and their foveolae are deeper.
Their foveolae are at least as long as the secretory tubules.
Several glands open into each foveola.
The body of the gland is short, tortuous and contains a prominent lumen.
Only one cell type is found in the body (except for a few argentaffin cells).
This cell may be identical with the mucous neck-cell of fundic glands and the
secretory cell of the cardiac glands.
It stains palely in routine preparations, but colors with mucigen stains.
The secretion-antecedent is definitely mucoid in nature.
The nucleus is often flattened against the cell base.
Pyloric glands are intermediate in sequence and composition between the fundic
type and the duodenal glands (of Brunner).
They are usually said to function solely as slime-producing glands.
Yet pyloric (and cardiac) glands contain dipeptidase enzymes.

3. Lamina Propria.

The surface and glandular epithelium rest upon a *basement membrane*.
The connective tissue of the *lamina* is scanty because the glands are so numerous.
Especially is this true of the region supplied with crowded fundic glands.
The most abundant tissue is located high in the lamina, between foveolae.
It merely fills-in the narrow spaces between the glands proper.
The basic tissue is a delicate network of collagenous and reticular fibers.
There is a diffuse infiltration of lymphocytes and some other cells.
Solitary lymph nodules occasionally are seen.
They are more abundant in the cardiac and pyloric regions.
The *muscularis mucosae* is mostly thin, yet it is arranged in layers.
The inner layer consists of circular fibers.
Delicate strands of muscle pass from this sheet upward between the glands.

The outer layer consists of longitudinal fibers.
In some regions there is still another layer; this outermost one is circular.

ACCESSORY COATS:

1. Submucosa.

This coat is a loose, fibrous and vascular layer, with considerable elasticity.
It participates in producing the folds that comprise the *rugae*.
These folds are effaced as the stomach distends with food.

2. Muscularis.

There are three thick layers of smooth muscle, arranged somewhat irregularly.
The *inner layer* consists of oblique fibers.
It occurs on the front and back surfaces in the fundus-corpus region.
The *middle layer* consists of circular fibers.
It is the best developed and most regular of the three.
At the pyloric orifice it forms the thick *pyloric sphincter*.
The *outer layer* consists of longitudinal fibers.
It is best represented along the inner and outer curvatures.

3. Serosa.

There is the usual connective-tissue layer, surfaced with mesothelium.
This investment is continuous with the gastric mesenteries (here called *omenta*).

REGENERATIVE ABILITY:

Surface replacements come from the deeper parts of foveolae where mitoses are frequent.
Cells are pushed up to replace those lost in cardiac, fundic and pyloric regions.
In the secretory tubule of the fundic type of gland, replacements occur also.
New mucous neck-cells probably are recruited downward from foveolae.
Undifferentiated cells deep in the foveolae gradually transform into neck-cells.
Chief cells, in turn, seem to be recruited from neck-cells.
These transformed mucous neck-cells presumably move downward to deeper levels.
Neck-cells and parietal cells exhibit mitoses; chief cells are not known to divide.
In the glands of the cardia and pylorus, mitoses occur at the deeper levels.
These are among the mucous cells of the gland-tubules proper.
Regeneration of the mucosa, even to restore total losses, is also successful.
Cells resembling foveolar cells migrate from the wound margin.
Moving in a centripetal direction, they cover the denuded area.
Presently new foveolae appear and glands bud from them.
In the fundus and corpus, glands soon consist entirely of mucous neck-cells.
Mucous neck-cells then differentiate into both chief and parietal cells.

DIAGNOSTIC FEATURES:

The stomach is thick-walled and heavily musculatured.
The plane of section is often hard to determine from sections.
This is partly because of the skewed muscle arrangement.
Also, sections are often cut at random from unoriented blocks of tissue.
The lining epithelium is subject to prompt autolysis after death.
This results in poor preservation, or even surface erosion in many instances.
The free surface is covered (and foveolae are lined) with pale, columnar cells.
The mucosa between foveolae, when cut vertically, resembles intestinal villi somewhat.

The epithelium, however, lacks the obvious striate border that characterizes villi.
It also lacks goblet cells, scattered among ordinary columnar cells.
Fundic glands are nearly straight and are several times longer than their foveolae.
The gland lumen is unusually inconspicuous.
Most of the gland cells (chief cells) are pale in routinely stained specimens.
In addition there are parietal cells (usually wedged in) farther from the lumen.
These stain brightly with acid dyes and are most numerous near the gland neck.
Pyloric glands are somewhat shorter than their very long, prominent foveolae.
The glands are tortuous and are never cut to include their full length.
Instead, short segments are seen; many are cut transversely or slantingly.
All the cells are clear and pale-staining; the lumen is conspicuous.
Cardiac glands are mucoid, the gland cells resembling somewhat the pyloric type.
The foveolae are much shorter than those of pyloric glands.
Since the gland is compound, the tubules show a disorderly arrangement.
Dilated tubules, resembling cysts, are common.

E. FUNCTIONAL CORRELATIONS:

1. Mechanical.

The muscular coat serves to churn the food and progressively empty the stomach.
The pyloric sphincter controls the intermittent escape of food into the duodenum.
The muscularis mucosae produces independent mucosal movements.
It is able to orient objects that have been swallowed (fish bones; pins; etc.).
Contraction of the muscular strands lying between glands compresses the mucosa.
This presumably helps to empty the glands of their secretion.
The lax submucosa allows the mucosa to shift position independently of the muscularis.
It also accommodates marked changes in the volume of stomach contents.
The mucus lubricates, moistens and, perhaps, protects against autodigestion.
The living mucosa, however, may protect itself by producing an antienzyme.

2. Chemical.

The 1.0 to 1.5 liters of gastric juice, secreted daily, contain various products.
Hydrochloric acid is supplied by the parietal cells of the fundus and corpus.
The amount of acid present regionally varies with the abundance of these cells.
Consequently, the pyloric region, which lacks such cells, is alkaline.
Pepsin is elaborated by the chief cells, as various facts attest.
The content of pepsinogen in the gastric mucosa varies regionally.
The local amount is proportional to the abundance and fullness of chief cells.
It splits proteins, in an acid medium, into proteoses and peptones.
Why the surface epithelium is not digested in life is not well explained.
Neck-cell *mucus* contains a substance necessary to erythrocyte production.
Rennin is an enzyme that curdles milk; it is apparently a product of chief cells.
Unlike the peptic glands, the pyloric glands secrete continuously.
Enzymic secretion, in significant amounts, does not occur.
Some absorption takes place in the stomach, but it is relatively slight.
Substances absorbed include water, salts, sugar, alcohol (and some other drugs).

IV. THE INTESTINE (GENERAL FEATURES)

The *intestine* is a tube, much longer than the cavity that contains it.
Hence it follows a coiled and irregular course between the pylorus and anus.

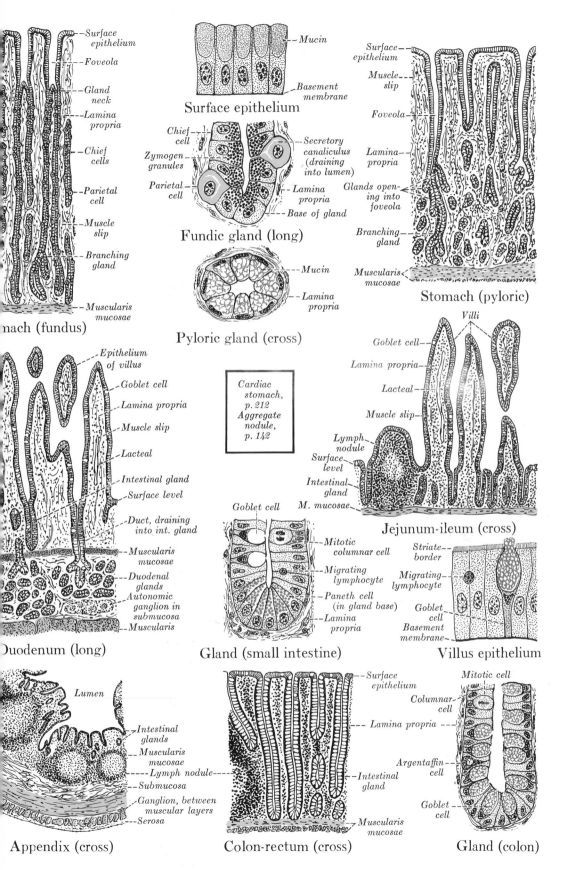

Surface epithelium
- Surface epithelium
- Foveola
- Gland neck
- Lamina propria
- Chief cells
- Parietal cell
- Muscle slip
- Branching gland
- Muscularis mucosae

...mach (fundus)

Surface epithelium
- Mucin
- Basement membrane

Fundic gland (long)
- Chief cell
- Zymogen granules
- Parietal cell
- Secretory canaliculus (draining into lumen)
- Lamina propria
- Base of gland

Pyloric gland (cross)
- Mucin
- Lamina propria

Stomach (pyloric)
- Surface epithelium
- Muscle slip
- Foveola
- Lamina propria
- Glands opening into foveola
- Branching gland
- Muscularis mucosae

Cardiac stomach, p. 212
Aggregate nodule, p. 142

Duodenum (long)
- Epithelium of villus
- Goblet cell
- Lamina propria
- Muscle slip
- Lacteal
- Intestinal gland
- Surface level
- Duct, draining into int. gland
- Muscularis mucosae
- Duodenal glands
- Autonomic ganglion in submucosa
- Muscularis

Gland (small intestine)
- Goblet cell
- Mitotic columnar cell
- Migrating lymphocyte
- Paneth cell (in gland base)
- Lamina propria

Jejunum-ileum (cross)
- Villi
- Goblet cell
- Lamina propria
- Lacteal
- Muscle slip
- Lymph nodule
- Surface level
- Intestinal gland
- M. mucosae

Villus epithelium
- Striate border
- Migrating lymphocyte
- Goblet cell
- Basement membrane

Appendix (cross)
- Lumen
- Intestinal glands
- Muscularis mucosae
- Lymph nodule
- Submucosa
- Ganglion, between muscular layers
- Serosa

Colon-rectum (cross)
- Surface epithelium
- Lamina propria
- Intestinal gland
- Muscularis mucosae

Gland (colon)
- Mitotic cell
- Columnar cell
- Argentaffin cell
- Goblet cell

THE LOWER ALIMENTARY CANAL

t is composed of a long, slender portion and a shorter, but thicker, portion.

These divisions are named the *small intestine* and *large intestine*, respectively.

Both segments are typical, tubular organs that have many features in common.

Yet both the small and large intestine possess important, distinctive characteristics.

t will be simplest to discuss first those features shared by the entire intestine.

Subsequently the individual peculiarities of the subdivisions can be made clear.

A. MUCOSA:

1. Epithelium.

A layer of simple epithelium constitutes the actual intestinal lining.

It also drapes over the finger-like villi, and dips into the glands.

Its component cell-types are the same throughout the entire intestine.

(An exception is the local epithelium comprising the special duodenal glands.)

Four types of epithelial cells can be recognized at all levels of the tube.

Their frequencies, however, are not uniform at the various levels.

A. SIMPLE COLUMNAR CELLS.

There are some five trillions of these cells in the small intestine alone.

Each is a tall cell, plastic and quite elastic.

The cytoplasm is finely granular; the ovoid nucleus is somewhat basal.

At the free surface it elaborates a prominent, vertically *striate border*.

The striation is produced by closely packed, cytoplasmic rodlets.

This appearance is revealed clearly by the electron microscope alone.

The border is best developed on epithelium that is exposed to the main lumen.

It thins on cells extending into glands and finally fails entirely.

Just beneath the border there is a felt-like ectoplasm, the *terminal web*.

The columnar cells of the free mucosal surfaces are primarily absorptive.

There is no evidence of secretion into the lumen, but it possibly occurs.

B. GOBLET CELLS.

These cells are typical unicellular mucous glands.

All stages of the secretory cycle (filling; discharge; recovery) are seen.

They lack a striate border; mucus is extruded from the thin cell-top.

The number of goblet cells increases progressively from duodenum to rectum.

This increase is accompanied by a compensatory decrease in columnar cells.

Since mitoses almost never occur, these cells are not self-perpetuating.

Replacement is believed to be through the transformation of columnar cells.

C. PANETH CELLS.

These rather large cells occur at the bottom of the simple intestinal glands.

They are most numerous in the small intestine and appendix.

They are serous, zymogenic cells—labile and often not well preserved.

The base of the cell is dark-staining and striated.

It consists of basophilic, iron-containing *chromophil substance*.

Above the nucleus are large, round, refractile, *acidophilic granules*.

These accumulate during fasting and disappear during digestion.

Although it is a special secretory cell, its function is in doubt.

D. ARGENTAFFIN CELLS.

These cells are also known as *enterochromaffin cells*.

They occur chiefly in the intestinal glands; rarely, on villi.

Present in moderate numbers, they are scattered throughout a gland.

They are most numerous in the duodenum and appendix.

The flask-shaped cell has small granules beneath its nucleus.

These granules are yellow when fresh; they are acidophilic.
They brown with chromates and blacken with silver.
The function of these cells has been a long-standing mystery.
Now their granules are identified with *serotonin* production.
This hormone is an effective vasoconstrictor.

2. Surface Covering.

The epithelium covering the general surface of the mucosa is limited in area.
It occupies the intervals between the myriads of glands and villi.
Its components are the columnar cells and goblet cells.

3. Intestinal Glands.

Another name for this pit-like gland is the *intestinal crypt* (of Lieberkühn).
There are about 180,000,000 glands in all; each resembles a miniature well.
A gland is a simple epithelial tube that dips below the general surface.
It extends vertically through the lamina propria to a distance of 0.1 to 0.7 mm.
The base of a gland almost reaches the muscularis mucosae.
The epithelium contains columnar, goblet, Paneth and argentaffin cells.
There is a thin striate border in cells that occupy the upper half of the gland.
Goblet cells are more numerous in the upper half of a gland.
Paneth and argentaffin cells occur, the former at the base of the gland.

4. Lamina Propria.

Its substance fills-in between the glands and forms cores to the villi.
It is mostly a reticular-tissue framework, infiltrated with free cells.
In addition, there are delicate collagenous white fibrils and many elastic ones.
The composition is somewhat different from ordinary lymphoid tissue.
Besides lymphocytes, there are many other kinds of cells.
These include plasma cells, eosinophils and mast cells.
Many lymphocytes pass between the epithelial cells; their fate is unknown.
Reticular networks condense into a delicate *basement membrane* under the epithelium.
Solitary lymph nodules occur frequently (some 30,000 in all).
They are conspicuous features that push aside the neighboring glands.
They often encroach on the submucosa, and become large and pear-shaped.
Aggregate nodules, or Peyer's patches, are commonest in the ileum.
(Their structure has already been described, p. 140.)
The *muscularis mucosae* is thin, yet contains two layers of smooth muscle.
The inner layer is circular; the outer layer, longitudinal.
Fibers, derived from the inner layer, extend into the villi.
These layers are often broken by large, solitary nodules and by Peyer's patches.

B. ACCESSORY COATS:

1. Submucosa.

This layer is composed of loose areolar tissue, which contains some fat cells.
It bears the customary plexuses of vessels and nerves.
In the small intestine it is elevated into ring-like folds, the *plicae circulares.*
The submucosa of the duodenum harbors the specific *duodenal glands.*

2. Muscularis.

The inner coat of smooth muscle is arranged circularly.

The outer coat of smooth muscle is arranged longitudinally.
>   In most of the large intestine it thickens into three equally-spaced bands.

3. Serosa.
>   The typical serosa is continuous with the mesentery of the free intestine.
>   Some regions of both the small and large intestines have an incomplete serous coat.
>>   That is, these 'bare' portions are pressed against the body walls.

V. THE SMALL INTESTINE

This division of the intestine is about 23 feet long, and hence is thrown into coils.
>   Such ample length provides a large internal expanse for absorptive purposes.

The small intestine is divided, without sharp limits, into three portions.
>   The *duodenum* is short, the *jejunum* much longer, and the *ileum* still longer.
>   The jejunum and ileum have no important structural differences.

Both the small and large intestine are characterized by simple *intestinal glands*.
>   These dip into the lamina propria like so many tubular pits.

The entire small intestine is distinctive because it alone possesses *villi*.
>   These elevations give a velvety appearance to the mucosal lining.
>   The duodenum is further distinguished by special *duodenal glands* in its submucosa.

A. MUCOSA:
1. Surface Epithelium.
>   The epithelium of the general surface is limited in extent.
>>   This is because the villi and glands are closely crowded.
>   The general surface is seen best in the ileum, and especially toward its end.
>>   Here the glands and villi are spaced farther apart.

2. Intestinal Glands.
>   These secretory glands, or *crypts*, are only of moderate length (0.1 to 0.3 mm.).
>   Due to crowding, glands often look in sections like mere intervals between villi.
>>   Actually, villi are elevations of the mucosa, while glands are wholly separate, tubular invaginations into its substance.
>   Paneth and argentaffin cells are relatively abundant.

3. Villi.
>   These structures are local elevations of the mucosa, 0.3 to 1.0 mm. tall.
>>   Each is a projection above the level of the general surface.
>   Their abundance varies with the absorptive activity of a region.
>>   (Duodenum, up to 40 per sq. mm.; ileum, as few as 18 per sq. mm.)
>>   The total for the small intestine is about 4,000,000.
>   The main purpose of villi is to enhance the absorptive area of the epithelium.
>>   They increase this area at least five times in man.
>>   In the small intestine the total surface expanse thereby becomes 60 sq. ft.
>   The shape of the villi varies in different mammals, and also at different levels.
>>   In the human duodenum they are leaf-shaped plates, and shortest.
>>   In the human jejunum they are still compressed and have clubbed ends.
>>   In the human ileum they are finger-shaped and tallest.
>   Structurally, a villus is projecting lamina propria, covered with epithelium.
>>   The relation of these is somewhat like a finger enclosed within a glove-sheath.

The axis of a villus is a blind lacteal, set in a core of lamina-propria tissue.
An arteriole and venule course nearby and supply a capillary net.
The stroma contains groups of smooth muscle fibers, longitudinally oriented.
The epithelium is composed mostly of the ordinary columnar-type cells.
There are some goblet cells and, rarely, argentaffin cells.
Goblet cells become progressively more numerous at lower levels of the tub
Epithelial cells of the villi are shed rather abundantly.
With mucus, they constitute the feces of starving individuals.
In preserved specimens, especially at the tip of villi, the epithelium tends to separa
from the basement membrane and lamina propria.
This is an artefact produced by the agonal contraction of local muscle fibers.

B. ACCESSORY COATS:

1. Submucosa.

The only special features of the submucosa are the *plicae* and *duodenal glands*.

A. PLICAE CIRCULARES.

Elevations of the submucosa produce about 800 incomplete ring-like ridges.
These permanent laminae, the *plicae circulares*, are covered with mucosal folds.
Plicae appear near the pylorus and are tallest (8 mm.) in the jejunum.
They become less abundant in the ileum, and largely disappear at its middl
Plicae are not effaced by distention or stretching of the bowel.
In this they differ from the impermanent rugae of the stomach.

B. DUODENAL GLANDS.

These mucous glands (of Brunner) are continuous with the pyloric glands.
Once in the duodenum, however, they promptly descend into the submucos
Here they become distinctive glands of this region.
The *duodenal glands* occur in lobules and tend to occupy the cores of plicae.
In the upper duodenum they are abundant and crowded.
In the lower two-thirds of the duodenum they decrease in size and frequenc
They disappear entirely before the duodenum comes to an end.
The glands are compound tubular in type; the tubules have a prominent lumen
The *secretory cells* are low, columnar elements that secrete mucin.
Yet they stain weakly with some specific dyes for mucin.
They resemble the mucous neck-cells of gastric glands.
The *ducts* are mucoid in nature, much like the long secretory tubules.
They pass through the muscularis mucosae and open into intestinal glands.
Rarely they terminate on the surface, between glands and villi.

2. Muscularis and Serosa.

There are no unusual features in these tunics.
Wherever the intestine is free, its serosa continues into a suspending mesentery.

C. MESENTERIES:

A *mesentery* arises when the serosa leaves the abdominal wall to reflect around the gut.
The parietal peritoneum, from each side, unites into a double sheet.
This mesentery (visceral peritoneum) contains an internal sheet of connective-tissue.
On each exposed, flat surface is a layer of mesothelium.
The connective-tissue carries blood vessels, lymphatics and nerves to the intestine.
It also contains lymph nodes and, usually, considerable fat.
Where the mesentery meets the intestine it splits into its component halves.
These continue as the *serosal coat* which envelops the digestive tube.

The dorsal and ventral mesentery of the stomach are called by a special name, *omenta*.
The omenta, and associated 'ligaments,' are similar to the intestinal mesentery.
Yet they are perforated in places by many holes, and here are net-like.

. REGENERATIVE ABILITY:
Mitoses occur abundantly in intestinal glands, and occasionally in duodenal glands.
These proliferative cells lie somewhat above the bottom of the intestinal gland.
They are somewhat shorter than the columnar cells of the surface and villi.
They also lack the striate border of those cells.
Many become columnar and goblet cells, as transitional stages prove.
They pass upward in the gland and onto the surface and villi.
Also this migration has been traced by tagging nuclei with radioactive phosphorus.
All superficial cells are said to be replaced in less than two-day intervals.
Other cells presumably move downward and replace the Paneth and argentaffin cells.
Removal of an area of duodenal mucosa and submucosa imitates local destruction by ulcer.
Cell migration and mitosis take place from duodenal glands at the wound margin.
After resurfacing is accomplished, villi and duodenal-type glands differentiate.
The glands occupy the position of intestinal glands; the latter do not regenerate.

. DIAGNOSTIC FEATURES:
Columnar cells of the general surface and villi possess a well-developed striate border.
This feature and goblet cells distinguish intestinal mucosa from stomach.
Otherwise pyloric mucosa is sometimes confused with that of the small intestine.
This is because the interspaces between pyloric foveolae are mistaken for villi.
Simple tubular glands in the mucosa identify the intestine throughout its length.
Villi are specific features that are diagnostic of the small intestine alone.
Submucosal plicae are characteristic of the small intestine alone.
Nevertheless, plicae are lacking near the pylorus and in the lower ileum.
Also, they are seen to advantage only in longitudinal sections.
Longitudinal sections through villi and glands are readily distinguished from each other.
Their position in the intestinal lumen or lamina propria, respectively, suffices.
Transverse sections through villi and glands can also be distinguished easily.
Both show bands of epithelium facing on a free space.
The glands are smaller, are almost perfectly circular and surround a small lumen.
Villi are much larger, are mostly elliptical and are surrounded by free space.
In villi, the epithelial bands border on a voluminous space (intestinal lumen).
(This space, however, may contain mucus or food debris.)
A prominent striate border caps the free ends of the component, columnar cells.
The sizable interior of the villus is filled with lymphoid tissue and vessels.
Nuclei of the epithelial cells lie nearer this central core.
In glands, the epithelial circular bands lie in a bed of solid lymphoid tissue.
A striate border is either lacking or thin, depending on the level of section.
The interior is a small open space (the lumen), often containing mucus.
Epithelial nuclei lie nearer the periphery of the circular band.
The *duodenum* is recognized by the compound mucous glands in its submucosa.
Only the esophagus, among tubular organs, also possesses submucosal glands.
But its stratified squamous epithelium is an obvious differential feature.
The *jejunum* and *ileum* are structurally similar and are mostly indistinguishable.
The lower ileum has its villi spaced slightly farther apart.
Plicae are absent (determinable only in longitudinal sections).

Aggregate follicles are highly characteristic of the ileum, but not exclusively so. However, their presence in sections cannot be depended upon.

F. FUNCTIONAL CORRELATIONS:

The activities of the entire intestine are treated as a unit on p. 230.

VI. THE LARGE INTESTINE

This tube is about 5 ft. long, and about double the width of the small intestine.
It includes the *caecum, appendix, colon* and *rectum*.
The lining lacks the transverse plicae and villi that characterize the small intestine.
Consequently, the epithelium that covers the general surface is plainly seen.
Intestinal glands are longer and lie closer together than do those of the small intestine.
Although more conspicuous than the latter, their only differences are quantitative.
Epithelial cell-types are identical with those in the small intestine.

A. ILEO-CAECAL VALVE AND CAECUM:

The *ileo-caecal valve* is formed by apposed folds of the mucosa and submucosa.
Each fold is supported by a central plate of smooth muscle.
This is supplied by the circular muscle layer.
The parallel free-edges of the two folds guard a slit-like orifice into the caecum.
The blind sac known as the *caecum* is like the rest of the colon in structure.
At its junction with the ileum there is an abrupt change in structural character.

B. VERMIFORM APPENDIX:

This is a blind, finger-like process of the caecum, also called the *vermiform process*.
Its wall is relatively very thick, and its lumen proportionately small.
Deep pockets between mucosal folds give the lumen an irregular, often angular, form
In adults the lumen tends to become more rounded.
The lumen frequently contains detritus; sometimes it is even obliterated.

1. Mucosa.

The *glands* decrease in number and length in middle age and later.
They contain many goblet cells and occasional Paneth cells.
Argentaffin cells are perhaps more numerous than elsewhere in the intestine.
Lymphoid tissue in the lamina propria constitutes a conspicuous layer.
It is responsible for the relatively great thickness of the total wall.
It contains closely spaced, solitary *lymph nodules* (except in old age).
These often show in sections as a fairly complete, confluent lymphoid ring.
Germinal centers tend to be very large, like those of the tonsil.
The *muscularis mucosae* is poorly represented.
It is often interrupted and broken by the large lymph nodules.
These nodules, pushing far into the submucosa, make the boundary between m
cosa and submucosa indefinite and hard to follow.

2. Accessory Coats.

A. SUBMUCOSA.
This layer is of the ordinary type and quite thick.
It usually contains fat cells and is encroached on by the lymphoid tissue.
After middle age the mucosa, and the submucosa (in part), may fibrose.

B. MUSCULARIS.

The muscular coat is somewhat thin, but contains the two typical layers.

Taeniae, such as characterize the caecum and colon, are lacking.

C. SEROSA.

The serous coat is like that of the intestine in general.

A rudimentary mesentery is continuous with it.

On the other hand, the appendix may lie wholly or partly behind the peritoneum.

C. COLON:

1. Mucosa.

The mucous membrane, by itself, does not form folds, plicae or villi.

The *surface epithelium* consists chiefly of simple columnar cells.

Each has a thin, striate border.

There are scattering goblet cells, as well.

The *glands* are longer (0.4 to 0.6 mm.) than in the small intestine.

Hence the mucous membrane, as a whole, is thicker.

The glands are arranged in regular vertical rows, set close together.

They are characterized by an abundance of goblet cells.

Often the glands appear as if almost composed of these cells alone.

Argentaffin cells occur occasionally, but Paneth cells are rare.

The *lamina propria* is organized as in the small intestine.

Eosinophils are numerous among the other cell types.

Solitary *lymph nodules* are larger and more numerous than in the small intestine.

As many as 21,000 nodules have been estimated as a total number.

They commonly intrude well into the submucosa.

The *muscularis mucosae* has the two typical layers of smooth muscle.

2. Accessory Coats.

A. SUBMUCOSA.

There are no peculiarities in this tunic.

B. MUSCULARIS.

The internal, circular coat of smooth muscle is typical.

The external, longitudinal coat is peculiar and unique.

It contains three longitudinal, ribbon-like thickenings, named *taeniae*.

These narrow bands are spaced equally from each other.

Between the bands the longitudinal coat is thin, yet usually complete.

Since taeniae are shorter than the rest of the wall, sacculations are produced.

These *haustra* disappear when the taeniae are cut or stripped off.

Between sacculations the wall is thrown into crescentic *plicae semilunares*.

These crescentic folds involve the entire wall and project into the lumen.

C. SEROSA.

The peritoneal reflection does not surround most of the colon completely.

This is because the colon tends to be pressed against the body wall.

Attached scatteringly to the colonic serosa are small sacs or fringes.

These structures, usually containing fat, are named *appendices epiploicae*.

They represent a redundant serosa that balloons away from the wall proper.

D. RECTUM:

For the most part the *rectum* differs from the colon only quantitatively.

This is true of all but its lowest region, which is the *anal canal*.

The *intestinal glands* are the longest (up to 0.7 mm.) of the entire intestine.
They become small, sparse and then cease at the beginning of the anal canal.
Lymphoid tissue is less abundant than in the upper colon.
The *muscularis* has the typical two layers, which are thick; it lacks taeniae.
A *serosa* is replaced, at progressively lower levels, by an *adventitia*.

E. ANAL CANAL:

This short tube is, in a sense, a lower portion of the rectum (*pars analis recti*).
The mucosa is folded into about eight longitudinal *anal columns*.
The ends of these folds, bordering the anal orifice, join one another.
Thus pocket-like *anal valves* are created, whose cavities are *anal sinuses*.
Above the valves the epithelium has changed into a stratified cuboidal type.
At the level of the valves the epithelium becomes stratified squamous.
Also, the muscularis mucosae, which has suffered fragmentation, disappears.
The uncornified epithelium of the canal changes into *epidermis* at the anal orifice.
Here hairs and cutaneous glands make their appearance.
Some of the sweat glands resemble the specialized sweat glands of the axilla.
These apocrine glands are named *circumanal glands* (*cf.* p. 199).
The submucosa is notable for its rich plexus of hemorrhoidal vessels.
The circular layer of smooth muscle thickens terminally as the *internal anal sphincter*.
More superficially the nearby skeletal muscle forms the *external anal sphincter*.

F. DIAGNOSTIC FEATURES:

The *large intestine* is diagnosed by its prominent intestinal glands, associated with a smooth
internal surface (that is, negatively by the absence of villi).
Goblet cells are extremely plentiful in the glands.
A taenia, if included in a section, is a specific characteristic feature.
The *appendix* is a 'miniature colon,' but with certain identifying features.
The wall is very thick in comparison to the size of the lumen.
The lumen is often angular in shape, and may contain compacted material.
Intestinal glands are less numerous and often show an altered condition.
There is an abundance of lymph nodules, usually forming a lymphoid ring.
The germinal centers tend to be very large.
The muscular coat lacks the taenial thickenings that occur in the colon.
The *colon* and *rectum* are, for the most part, only quantitatively different.
On the whole, the rectal glands are somewhat longer than in the colon.
Yet the increase to this maximal length is gradual in the lower colon.
The colon has taeniae, whereas the rectum lacks them.
The inclusion of a taenia in a section, however, cannot be relied on.
The longitudinal muscle coat of the rectum is thick.
In the colon, except for taeniae, it is thin.
(Yet a longitudinal section along a taenia would show a thick outer layer.)

VII. FUNCTIONS OF THE INTESTINE

1. Motility.

The muscular coat causes local segmental movements and propulsive peristalsis.
Peristaltic movements are the only ones that occur in the large intestine.
The muscularis mucosae produces ridging, grooving and pitting of the mucosa.
Displaced fibers in the villi are responsible for shortening and waving movements.

Secretion.

Goblet cells, throughout the intestine, produce lubricative mucus for the lining.

In the large intestine, the abundant mucus also binds the contents into a semifluid, progressively dehydrating, fecal mass.

The duodenal glands secrete a mucous, alkaline fluid continuously.

The secretion contains *dipeptidase*, a proteolytic enzyme.

It is similar to the enzyme produced by the cardiac and pyloric glands.

It is supposed to digest the collagen of adipose tissue.

This would make fat more accessible to the action of the lipases.

The intestinal glands secrete the yellowish, alkaline *intestinal juice*.

Those of the small intestine presumably produce the various enzymes.

It is not known which cells elaborate the different constituents.

Glands of the large intestine secrete much mucus, and little else.

There are several enzymes in the intestinal juice.

Erepsin reduces partly digested proteins to amino acids.

Several enzymes (*maltase; lactase; invertase*) split carbohydrates into simple sugars.

Lipase splits fats into glycerol and fatty acids.

Nuclease breaks down nucleic acid.

Enterokinase activates trypsinogen into trypsin.

Certain hormones are passed into the blood from the duodenum.

The exact cellular source of these secretions is unknown.

Secretin activates the pancreas; *cholecystokinin*, the gall bladder; *serotonin*, blood vessels.

Excretion.

Water and lipids (including cholesterol) are excreted into the lumen.

Absorption.

This is a vital phenomenon performed by the columnar epithelium.

Both the length of the intestine and its internal folds expedite absorption.

But it is the villi that are especially concerned in these absorptive activities.

Large quantities of *water* are taken up, especially in the large intestine.

Inorganic salts in solution are absorbed readily by the epithelial cells.

Iron, fed as compounds, can be followed through the striate border.

Proteins are broken down into amino acids and absorbed as such.

Their course through the epithelium and into the portal vein cannot be traced.

Carbohydrates are admitted as glucose and other simple sugars.

They cannot be followed through the epithelium.

Yet they enter the capillaries and leave the intestine by the portal vein.

Digested fat, as fatty acids and glycerol, gains ready entrance into the epithelial cells.

In the cytoplasm they are resynthesized into droplets of neutral fat.

Some *neutral fat*, in emulsified droplets, may also enter, passing between microvilli.

The course of fat droplets, stained with osmic acid, can be followed easily.

Course: distal cytoplasm → intercellular space → basement membrane → lamina propria.

Lacteals of villi absorb fat droplets; they eventually reach the blood stream.

Bile salts and excreted lipids are largely recaptured and re-utilized.

Bacterial Action.

Bacteria are abundant in the large intestine.

They constitute at least one-tenth of the dry weight of the feces.

Some of them digest cellulose, on which digestive juices have no effect.

VIII. VESSELS AND NERVES OF THE DIGESTIVE TUBE

Blood vessels, lymphatics and nerves enter the tube by way of its mesentery, when present.

1. Blood Vessels.

Arteries and veins form a prominent plexus in the submucosa.

Branches from this plexus extend into both the mucosa and the muscularis.

Capillary networks supply the coats of the gut-wall, and their special contents.

In the small intestine, additional branches supply the villi.

One (or more) arterioles pass up the villus, breaking down into a capillary plexus.

This superficial network is drained by one (or two) venules.

The venule usually takes a position opposite to the arteriole.

2. Lymphatics.

The mucosa has lymphatic loops or blindly ending vessels.

Each villus has a blind, axial *lacteal*, which collects fatty lymph (*chyle*).

Their total absorptive surface equals 34 sq. ft.

The submucosa and muscularis have typical plexuses.

The free lymphatic vessels, leaving the wall, drain into lymph nodes.

3. Nerves.

The innervating fibers come from the vagus nerves and from autonomic ganglia.

There is a *myenteric plexus* (of Auerbach) and a *submucous plexus* (of Meissner).

Included in these intramural plexuses are small autonomic ganglia.

In the myenteric plexus some neurons are interconnecting, or associative, units.

Terminal nerve fibers end in muscles and vessels; these are motor in function.

Sensory endings in the epithelium have also been claimed, but are usually denied.

Parasympathetic fibers are those from the vagi, and also from the sacral outflow.

They terminate on cells of the intrinsic ganglia of the gut wall.

Axons from such ganglion cells pass to the muscle cells of the wall and its vessels.

They excite muscular activity, vascularity and secretion.

Sympathetic fibers arise in the ganglia of autonomic plexuses external to the gut wall.

They pass directly to their endings upon muscle of the wall and of vessels.

Their action is inhibitory, and hence antagonistic to the parasympathetics.

Chapter XX. THE MAJOR GLANDS OF DIGESTION

The small glands, located in the wall of the alimentary canal, have already been described.

These include the intrinsic glands of the mouth, pharynx and digestive tube.

In addition, there are extrinsic glands: the larger *salivary glands*, *pancreas* and *liver*.

These constitute the major gland-masses related to digestion.

I. THE MAJOR SALIVARY GLANDS

The extrinsic *salivary glands* occur in three paired sets.

Each is a merocrine gland of the branching, tubulo-alveolar type.

Each compound, lobulated gland opens into the oral cavity by an excretory duct.

Saliva is a viscid fluid containing a mixture of all the oral secretions.

The daily amount for man is about 1.5 quarts; for the cow, 65 quarts.

Saliva contains mucus, proteins, salts, and enzymes (*ptyalin* and *maltase*).

Desquamated epithelial cells, and lymphocytes are characteristic constituents also.

These components were long ago named *salivary corpuscles*.

The details of merocrine-gland structure are described on pp. 164–167.

Here will be presented only the distinctive features of the large salivary glands.

A. PAROTID GLAND:

Each gland is situated below and somewhat in front of the closely associated ear.

Its main *excretory duct* (of Stenson) opens into the vestibule of the mouth.

The parotid is *purely serous* in man, but this is not true of all mammals.

Also in human infants there are some cells that respond to stains for mucus.

The glandular mass is enclosed within a fibrous sheath, or *capsule*.

Septa pass inward to divide the organ into *lobes* and *lobules*.

This tissue often contains many fat cells.

A fine connective-tissue *stroma* embeds the alveoli and ducts.

The *alveoli* are somewhat elongate and often exhibit branching.

Their cuboidal cells are typical serous elements with granular cytoplasm.

Secretory capillaries extend from the inconspicuous lumen between alveolar cells.

Clasping *basket cells* are well developed and numerous.

Intercalated ducts are slender and relatively long tubules, attached to the alveoli.

Their component cells are flat and elongate.

Secretory ducts, intermediate in position, likewise are relatively long.

They are a type of duct, peculiar to the salivary glands.

Their columnar cells, bright staining and basal striations make them conspicuous.

Excretory ducts begin as a simple columnar epithelium, and then become pseudostratified.

They finally gain true stratification near the main outlet.

A similar epithelial gradation is found also in the other large salivary glands.

B. SUBMAXILLARY GLAND:

Each gland is situated in the floor of the mouth, under shelter of the mandible.

Hence it is also called the *submandibular gland*.

The submaxillary is a *mixed gland* in man and most other mammals.

In man purely serous alveoli outnumber the remaining (mixed) alveoli about 5:1.

A typical connective-tissue *capsule*, *septa* and *stroma* are present.

The *parenchyma* is divided by septa into *lobules*.

Most of the secretory end pieces are *serous alveoli*, rounded to somewhat elongate.

All other end pieces are *mixed tubules* of sero-mucous composition.

Slanting sections may appear to show them as purely mucous tubules.

Actually, all such tubules have clusters of serous cells at their blind ends.

In general, these serous terminations do not overlap as typical demilunes.

Sections often show caps of serous cells overlying mucous cells.

Such sections do not pass through the long axis of the tubule.

Secretory capillaries occur between the serous components of the gland.

Stellate *basket cells* occur between gland cells and the basement membrane.

The *duct system* includes representatives of all three subtypes.

Most of the *intercalated ducts* are short, but some equal those of the parotid gland.

On the other hand, the *secretory ducts* tend to be longer than those of the parotid.

Hence these ducts are conspicuous features within the lobules.

The main *excretory duct* (of Wharton) opens at the frenulum of the tongue.

C. SUBLINGUAL GLAND:

This is a composite organ, situated in the floor of the mouth, near the midplane.

There are one *major gland* and several *minor glands* on each side of the tongue.

Each glandular mass has its individual excretory duct opening on a separate papilla.

The *major duct* of the major gland opens near the frenulum of the tongue.

The sublingual gland is a *mixed gland* in man and various other mammals.

It is more variable in composition than the other salivary glands.

The several gland-masses are not identical in composition.

Neither is any one mass uniform among different individuals.

Yet the minor glands are always highly mucous.

The secretory *end pieces* are tortuous, branching tubules.

In man their mucous cells are much more numerous than serous cells.

Secretory tubules are either *purely mucous* or *mixed* (with demilunes).

The existence of purely serous alveoli is an exceptional local phenomenon.

It is noteworthy that even the serous cells have semimucoid characteristics.

Basket cells are present, as in other salivary glands.

There is no definite, common capsule, but *septa* and *lobules* are prominent.

The duct system is distinctive in a negative way.

Intercalated ducts, of the ordinary sort, are mostly lacking.

They are largely replaced by *mucous tubules*, continuous with secretory tubules.

In fact, the two are indistinguishable.

Some *secretory ducts* occur, but they are very short segments that escape attention.

They bear only a patch of basally striated cells.

Hence sections show very few obvious ducts within a lobule.

Extralobular ducts are ordinary *excretory ducts*.

D. VESSELS AND NERVES:

See the general account on p. 167.

. REGENERATIVE ABILITY:

Removal of large portions of glands can be followed by successful regeneration.

In experiments even a five-sixths loss is tolerated.

But the replacement of lost tissue is never complete.

Restoration is accomplished by proliferation from ducts and secretory cells.

. DIAGNOSTIC FEATURES:

The distinguishing characteristics of serous and mucous cells are summarized on p. 164.

The *parotid gland* has serous alveoli only.

Both the submaxillary and sublingual glands are mixed (serous and mucous) glands.

The *submaxillary* is preponderantly serous.

The *sublingual* is preponderantly mucous.

The parotid and submaxillary glands have numerous secretory ducts within each lobule.

These stain brightly acidophilic, and hence are conspicuous.

The parotid and submaxillary glands also have numerous slender, intercalated ducts.

These, however, are not conspicuous features.

The sublingual gland has but few obvious ducts of any kind within its lobules.

The sublingual gland is the only one to lack a distinct external sheath or capsule.

Yet all of these glands are divided by connective tissue into prominent lobules.

. FUNCTIONAL CORRELATIONS:

Saliva moistens and lubricates food, thus preparing it for stimulating the taste buds, for salivary digestion, and for being swallowed.

It is also chemically active, making salivary digestion possible.

This is because enzymes are produced by the serous cells.

Hence it is the parotid gland that is especially concerned with enzyme elaboration.

Ptyalin converts starch into maltose.

Maltase converts maltose into the simple sugar, glucose.

The *small oral glands* probably serve mostly to moisten and lubricate the mucosa.

In doing this they seemingly secrete continuously.

The *major salivary glands* secrete, following reflex stimulation of the secretory nerves.

Such stimulation is brought about by the presence of food in the mouth.

II. THE PANCREAS

The *pancreas* is a large digestive gland (9 inches long), connected to the duodenum.

It is really a double gland, whose two components are separate in some fishes.

The *exocrine part* is a typical serous gland that elaborates a digestive juice.

The *endocrine part* is a diffusely scattered assemblage of epithelial islands.

. STRUCTURAL PLAN:

The connective-tissue *framework* is like that of the salivary glands.

A sheath of areolar tissue, which is not a typical *capsule*, invests the organ.

Thin, fibrous *septa* continue into the pancreas and subdivide it.

In this way many distinct *lobules* and less complete *sublobules* are formed.

These lobules are loosely connected, but their interiors are quite compact.

Delicate fibrous tissue (*reticular tissue*) embeds the individual alveoli.

The *parenchyma* is glandular epithelium of two quite different sorts.

The *exocrine part* is organized as a compound, tubulo-alveolar gland.

It has purely *serous alveoli*, resembling the parotid gland.

This tissue makes up the greatest bulk of the organ, by far.

Its *duct system* drains into the duodenum by a main excretory duct.

The *endocrine part* consists of many, scattered, epithelial masses (*pancreatic islands*).

These islands elaborate a hormone that regulates carbohydrate metabolism.

This secretion is carried away by intimate capillary channels.

B. EXOCRINE PANCREAS:

1. Alveoli.

The secretory end-pieces, or *alveoli*, vary between a pear shape and short tubules.

Each is surrounded by a *basement membrane* of reticular fibers.

Basket cells, such as clasp the alveoli of salivary glands, apparently lack.

The component *gland cells* are pyramidal in shape and serous in quality.

A rounded, unflattened, chromatic nucleus lies toward the cell base.

A distinction between basal and apical halves of the gland cells is plain.

The *basal cell-half* contains very finely granular cytoplasm, often striated.

This is strongly basophilic *chromidial substance*, rich in RNA granules.

It is better developed and darker staining than in salivary glands.

The cell base contains mitochondria which are oriented vertically.

These seem to be responsible for the striated appearance of this region.

The *apical cell-half*, bordering the lumen, contains numerous *zymogen granules*.

When fresh they are highly refractile, semifluid globules.

When preserved and stained, they appear as acidophilic 'granules.'

The breadth of the two zones varies with the functional state.

During rest, the outer zone is thick and the basal zone relatively thin.

After secretory discharge, the outer granular zone is thinner.

The basal zone then becomes thicker by cytoplasmic regeneration.

The *Golgi apparatus* is a prominent feature, located above the nucleus.

It bears a close relation to the developing zymogen granules.

These granules arise initially at the expense of the chromidial cytoplasm.

The basophily of this cytoplasm is due to the presence of ribonucleic acid.

The ribonucleoproteins decrease steadily as the zymogen droplets accumulat

2. Ducts.

A. SECRETORY CAPILLARIES.

Tiny *canaliculi* occur between gland cells, as in other serous glands (p. 164).

Such capillaries drain between centro-alveolar cells into the central lumen.

B. CENTRO-ALVEOLAR CELLS.

These elements do not occur with any frequency except in the pancreas.

The gland cells of a pancreatic alveolus usually do not become directly continuo
with an intercalated duct in the manner typical of exocrine glands.

Instead, they tend to surround the beginning of the duct on all sides.

They may also overlap the duct along one side, or replace the duct-wall alo
one side and overlap it on the other side.

The appearance is as if the customary lumen were clogged with cells.

Hence the name *centro-alveolar* or 'centro-acinar.'

Wherever the gland cells overlap duct cells, secretory capillaries exist.

C. INTERCALATED DUCTS.

These ducts are more extensively developed than in any other digestive gland.

This is because typical secretory ducts are wanting in the pancreas.

Hence the largest intercalated ducts exceed the size limit in salivary glands

The component epithelial cells are somewhat flattened to cuboidal in shape.

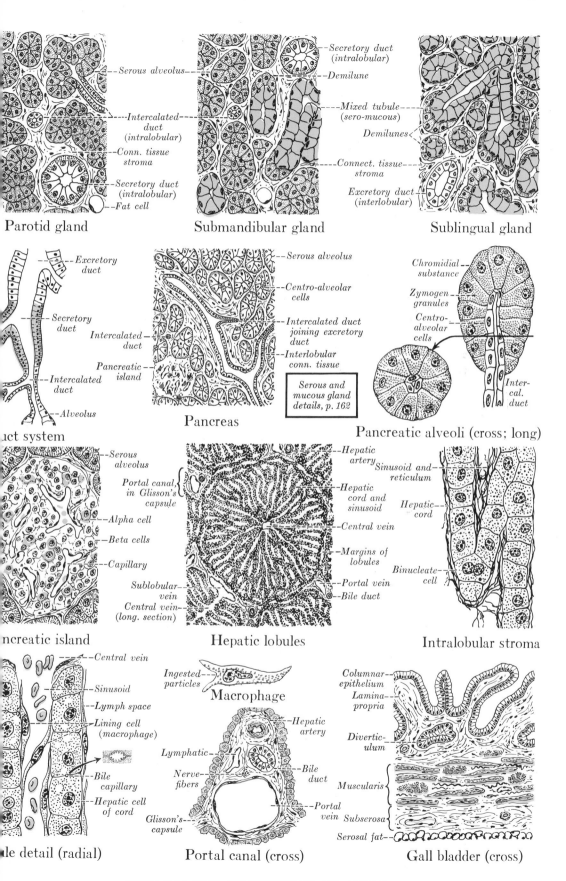

Parotid gland

--Serous alveolus--

--Intercalated duct (intralobular)

--Conn. tissue stroma

--Secretory duct (intralobular)

--Fat cell

Submandibular gland

--Secretory duct (intralobular)

--Demilune

---Mixed tubule (sero-mucous)---

Demilunes

---Connect. tissue stroma

---Excretory duct (interlobular)

Sublingual gland

--Excretory duct

--Secretory duct

Intercalated duct

--Intercalated duct

--Alveolus

uct system

--Serous alveolus

Centro-alveolar cells

Intercalated duct joining excretory duct

Interlobular conn. tissue

Intercalated duct

Pancreatic island

Pancreas

Serous and mucous gland details, p. 162

Chromidial substance

Zymogen granules

Centro-alveolar cells

Inter-cal. duct

Pancreatic alveoli (cross; long)

--Serous alveolus

Portal canal, in Glisson's capsule

--Alpha cell

--Beta cells

--Capillary

Sublobular vein

Central vein (long. section)

ncreatic island

Hepatic artery

Hepatic cord and sinusoid

--Central vein

--Margins of lobules

--Portal vein

--Bile duct

Hepatic lobules

Sinusoid and reticulum

Hepatic cord

Binucleate cell

Intralobular stroma

--Central vein

--Sinusoid

--Lymph space

--Lining cell (macrophage)

--Bile capillary

--Hepatic cell of cord

le detail (radial)

Ingested particles

Macrophage

--Hepatic artery

Lymphatic--

Nerve fibers

--Bile duct

--Portal vein

Glisson's capsule

Portal canal (cross)

Columnar epithelium

Lamina propria

Diverticulum

Muscularis

Subserosa

Serosal fat--

Gall bladder (cross)

THE MAJOR DIGESTIVE GLANDS

D. EXCRETORY DUCTS.

These ducts course in the interlobular connective tissue.

The size of a duct is correlated with the amount of tissue served.

Short lateral ducts drain the lobules and open into the axial main duct.

This main excretory tube then discharges into the duodenum.

Such a penniform arrangement of ducts is unique among the digestive glands.

The epithelial lining is composed of columnar cells (and some goblet cells).

C. ENDOCRINE PANCREAS:

This tissue is unevenly scattered as the *pancreatic islands* (of Langerhans).

Each island is an epithelial mass, tunneled by labyrinthine capillaries.

The position of islands is mostly within lobules rather than between them.

The total number for man varies widely, but averages about one million.

The size ranges from a few clustered cells to aggregates 3 mm. in diameter.

About each spheroidal island is a thin, delimiting membrane of reticulum.

Islands are sometimes connected to ducts by slender epithelial tubules or cords.

These strands are remnants, indicative of the manner of island origin.

It is also claimed that they are able to regenerate islands, and perhaps alveoli.

Such connections are rarely seen in routine preparations.

They do not serve as functional ducts.

The island tissue is arranged in irregular, anastomosing cellular *plates*.

These epithelial 'cords' are separated by closely applied, tortuous *blood capillaries*.

Only delicate reticular tissue occurs within the island and about its periphery.

In routine preparations the component, polyhedral cells appear paler than alveoli.

They also look as if they were syncytial, homogeneous and all of one type.

Special techniques demonstrate distinctive cytoplasmic granules.

Several cell types can be distinguished on the basis of staining, solubility, etc.

Alpha cells, or A-cells, are only fairly numerous in most islands.

Their granules are soluble in water but not in alcohol.

Beta cells (B-cells), alcohol soluble, are smaller and usually much more numerous.

Their granules are coarser, but often are more sparsely distributed.

A third element of mammals in general, the *delta cell* (D-cell), is the rarest.

Whether it is a separate cell-type or a developmental stage is unknown.

All three kinds are quite unlike alveolar cells.

Chromophil substance and zymogen granules are lacking.

D. VESSELS AND NERVES:

The arrangements follow the patterns that are typical for exocrine glands (p. 167).

Small *autonomic ganglia* and lamellar corpuscles occur in the interlobular tissue.

E. REGENERATIVE ABILITY:

The pancreas is able to differentiate a few alveoli and even whole islands after injury.

The restoration may follow duct ligation, surgical excision or disease.

This regeneration comes from proliferating duct tissue.

F. DIAGNOSTIC FEATURES:

The pancreas is a *purely serous* gland; it resembles the parotid.

The following features are, however, distinctive of the pancreas:

Scattered *pancreatic islands* occur throughout the exocrine parenchyma.

There are *no conspicuous ducts* within the lobules.

Any alveolar cell, cut through its full length, shows two *distinct zones*.
  With ordinary stains the basal zone is dark; the apical zone, light.
  With special stains for zymogen granules, these appearances may be reversed.
Alveoli cut lengthwise tend toward a short *tubular shape*.
Centro-alveolar cells are seen within alveoli cut along or across their main axes.

G. FUNCTIONAL CORRELATIONS:
1. External Secretion.
About 2 to 3 pints of alkaline pancreatic juice are secreted daily.
Several digestive pro-enzymes are elaborated by the alveoli.
  These give rise to *trypsin, amylase, lipase* and an enzyme like *rennet*.
  Yet all the alveolar cells are apparently cytologically alike.
Secretion is induced by a hormone, *secretin*, elaborated in the duodenal mucosa.
  It also can be stimulated directly through the vagal nerve supply.

2. Internal Secretion.
The intimate, sinusoidal blood supply of the islands and the absence of ducts strongl
    suggest endocrine function.
Various facts connect the islands with a specific endocrine activity.
  Pancreatic extirpation, or impairment of islands alone, leads to *sugar diabetes*.
    Carbohydrates cannot then be utilized and are lost in the urine.
  On the other hand, duct ligation leads to degeneration of the alveoli alone.
    The islands are not affected, and diabetes does not ensue.
  Autopsies on diabetics often show disease-alterations in island tissue.
    Moreover, in experimentally induced diabetes, B-cells are chiefly injured.
  Certain tumors, composed mostly of B-cells, have been accompanied by a decreas
    of sugar in the blood (indicative of oversecretion of insulin).
An alcoholic extract of the islands is *insulin*, obtainable in pure crystalline form.
  The active principle comes from B-cells, whose granules are alcohol soluble.
  Administration of insulin can make carbohydrates oxidizable and muscle-storabl
    for diabetic patients.
It is believed that A-cells secrete a hormone, *glucagon*, that offsets insulin influence.
  This counterbalancing would serve to maintain a better controlled functioning.

III. THE LIVER

The *liver* lies beneath the diaphragm and is attached to it.
  It is the largest gland of the body and weighs about 3.5 lbs.
The liver is a compound tubular *serous gland*, but it is highly modified in mammals.
  The tubules are replaced by *cellular plates* that branch and anastomose.
  In many of the lower vertebrates, on the other hand, there are real glandular tubules.
Internal *lobulation* is realized only in adult birds and mammals.
  A remodeling of the parenchyma into lobular units has paralleled changes that occurre
    simultaneously in the scheme of vascularization.
  That is, an originally exocrine organ has reorganized its structural plan in order to perfe
    activities that are primarily related to the blood stream.

A. STRUCTURAL PLAN:
The liver contains four incompletely separated *lobes*.
  These are surrounded by a thick *capsule*, mostly overlaid with reflected peritoneum.

There is a definite *hilus* where vessels enter and ducts leave.

The *parenchyma*, in the interior, is subdivided into myriads of small *lobules.*

Each lobule is incompletely isolated by connective tissue named *Glisson's capsule.*

The interior of a lobule consists of radially arranged plates of liver cells.

These *hepatic plates* (often called cords) are separated by *hepatic sinusoids.*

The axis of a lobule is the *central vein*, which drains into a *sublobular vein.*

Sublobular veins unite and produce branches of the hepatic veins.

Connective tissue, at the edges of a lobule, constitutes the so-called *portal canals.*

It comprises most of the Glisson's capsule of that local region.

Each canal contains a branch of an *hepatic artery, portal vein* and *bile duct.*

This lobular arrangement is repeated hundreds of thousands of times.

To understand the liver, therefore, one needs to know well only a single lobule.

LOBULATION:

The hepatic parenchyma is subdivided into obvious anatomical units, called *lobules.*

Each is an irregular prism, measuring about 1 x 2 mm.

It is partially bounded and contained within its incomplete *Glisson's capsule.*

The total number of lobules is approximately one million.

The arrangement of lobules, except close to the surface of the liver, is irregular.

Each lobular unit consists of two chief components.

One is a *parenchyma*, composed of closely packed glandular epithelium.

It is arranged in *plates* radiating from an axis, which is the central vein.

The other is a system of *sinusoids* that converge radially into the central vein.

In their radial courses they tunnel the parenchyma into plate-like cords.

Such channels communicate with both the central vein and vessels at the periphery.

The *hepatic lobule*, just described, is quite unlike lobules of ordinary glands.

That is, its central axis is a vein instead of the customary duct.

This sort of lobulation is an adaptation to certain activities (glycogenic, etc.).

Such lobules are organized with respect to the flow and drainage of blood.

In addition, a different kind of lobule can be recognized; this is the *portal lobule.*

It is arranged with reference to exocrine function (bile secretion).

This unit is formed from parts of three hepatic lobules that adjoin a portal canal.

It is the territory drained by an interlobular bile duct in a portal canal.

The functional boundary of such a portal lobule runs from one central vein to another.

Its axis is a bile duct, located in the common portal canal where the edges of three hepatic lobules meet.

In the seal the portal lobule, as a structural unit, is seen at its best.

Human livers show no physical demarcation into such recognizable units.

. DETAILED STRUCTURE:

1. Framework.

The finest division of the supporting tissue is a *reticulum* of delicate fibrils.

This makes a close network between the sinusoids and plates of glandular tissue.

It serves to hold the plates in place and to keep the sinusoids open.

At the periphery of each lobule there is some ordinary, loose *connective tissue.*

Reticulum of the lobule and such ordinary fibrous tissue merge in this region.

A complete encapsulation of the lobule occurs in the hog, camel and polar bear.

A similar connective-tissue sheath is incomplete in man and most other mammals.

It is largely limited to the edges of lobules, where it acts as a bed (the *portal canal*) for the vessels and bile duct serving adjoining lobules.

All of this perilobular tissue in the liver comprises *Glisson's capsule.*
It should be understood that the same tissue-mass of Glisson's capsule
any local region serves two or three contiguous lobules.
The entire liver is encased within a fibro-elastic *hepatic capsule.*
In most regions it is overlaid by a *serosa* that represents reflected peritoneum.
At the hilus this external capsule is continuous with Glisson's capsule internally.

2. Portal Canals.

This term refers to the *portals,* or gateways, through which blood reaches the liver.
The basis of a 'canal' is the fibrous tissue of Glisson's capsule.
It is located mostly along the edges where the sides of adjoining lobules meet.
This connective-tissue bed of a *portal canal* contains several functional components.

A. PORTAL VEIN.
This vessel is the largest component, but it is very thin-walled.
Its venous blood has already passed through capillary beds of splanchnic orga

B. HEPATIC ARTERY.
Although rather thick-walled, it is usually the smallest component.
There is a well-developed muscular coat and a distinct internal elastic membra

C. BILE DUCT.
Its size is commonly intermediate between that of the two blood vessels.
The epithelium is low cuboidal to columnar in shape.
A connective-tissue investment surrounds the epithelium.
Due to branching, more than one duct is often seen in a canal.

D. OTHER COMPONENTS.
Several delicate *lymphatic vessels* can usually be observed.
They are mere endothelial-lined clefts.
Nerves are present, but they are not conspicuous in routine preparations.

3. Parenchyma.

The *hepatic plates* (commonly called hepatic cords) branch and anastomose.
The center of radiation is the axially situated central vein.
From here the plates spread peripherally in a branching, spoke-like manner.
A plate is mostly one cell thick, except at regions of branching or union.
Between the component cells pass microscopic *bile capillaries.*
These drain toward the periphery and thence into a bile duct in a portal can
The plates are interrupted by frequent perforations of considerable size.

A. HEPATIC CELLS.
The component *cells* of the parenchyma are large and polyhedral in shape.
They measure about 22 x 30 μ, but vary with storage- and secretory activity
A layer of ectoplasm bounds the cells and provides a delicate *cell membrane.*
The *nucleus* is rounded and vesicular, with one or more prominent nucleoli.
Certain large cells have a large nucleus, or two or four of ordinary size.
Such cells have multiples of the ordinary diploid number of chromosom
The *cytoplasm* is granular, but its appearance varies with the functional state.
Many of the 'granules' are *glycogen droplets,* specifically stainable.
Also there are *protein granules* and *fat droplets.*
(In ordinary sections the glycogen and fat have usually been dissolved out.
The periphery of a lobule is its most actively functional region.
Here is the first deposit and loss of glycogen and bile precursors.
An intermediate zone, centralward in the lobule, is progressively less active

The central 'zone of repose' is called on only when demands are excessive.

Here fat and pigment may accumulate and become visible.

There is no *basement membrane* on which the cells rest.

However, the parenchyma is supported by a meshwork of reticulum.

Apparently dying cells are common in normal liver, yet mitoses are rare.

Probably increase in cell-size compensates largely for cell losses.

B. BILE CAPILLARIES.

The tubular *lumen* of the liver cord is easily visible in many lower vertebrates.

A lumen is not seen in the ordinary examination of mammalian liver.

Yet it exists, and the electron microscope demonstrates it plainly.

Also silver treatment or certain dyes (excreted with bile) reveal it.

A *bile capillary* is a tubule coursing between the apposed faces of hepatic cells.

It develops as a pair of grooves on facing cell membranes.

These combine and produce a canal with a tiny lumen.

The tubule gives off side-branches, but rarely reaches the cells' surface.

Thus it lies one-half of a cell-breadth from the adjacent sinusoids.

In an hepatic plate the total system looks like chick netting.

A bile capillary is a true secretory canaliculus, as in other serous glands.

Bile, leaving the cells, passes through it toward the periphery of a lobule.

C. INTRAHEPATIC BILE DUCTS.

At the periphery of a lobule the bile capillaries open into *bile ducts*.

These smallest ducts are called the *canals of Hering*.

In this region there is a transition from the epithelium of the liver cord to that of a bile duct, the lumina of the two becoming continuous.

The canals of Hering continue directly into the twigs of interlobular ducts.

An *interlobular bile duct* is a characteristic component of a portal canal.

Its epithelium varies according to the size of the duct.

The range is from low cuboidal to low columnar epithelium.

The component cells are distinct and have a clear cytoplasm.

The duct is surrounded by fibrous tissue; the larger ones become ensheathed.

4. Vessels.

A. HEPATIC SINUSOIDS.

The *sinusoids* are tortuous channels that form a labyrinth of spaces, 9 to 12 μ wide.

They receive blood from vessels at the periphery of the lobule.

They discharge blood into a central vein in the axis of the lobule.

A sinusoid is lined by two kinds of cells, but this lining seemingly has gaps in it.

One is a thin '*endothelial cell*' that hugs the hepatic cords loosely.

It has a dark, flattened nucleus, and its cytoplasm is a thin film.

Cell boundaries are not demonstrable, as in ordinary endothelium.

The other type is a larger cell with a large, oval, vesicular nucleus.

It has an irregular shape and prominent cytoplasmic processes.

These cell processes extend into or across the sinusoidal channel.

For many years it has been called the *stellate cell* of von Kupffer.

It is intensely phagocytic and belongs to that group of fixed macrophages called the macrophage system or reticulo-endothelial system.

It is disputed as to whether the Kupffer cells are an integral part of the sinusoidal 'endothelium,' with which they may be physically continuous.

Some think they are separate entities, resting on the endothelium.

However, transitional forms are seen, and the ordinary 'endothelial' ce
can, on occasion, become phagocytic.
The two are probably variations of the same general cell type.
That is, they are like the primitive reticular cells and fixed macrophag
of reticulo-endothelium elsewhere in the body.

B. BLOOD VESSELS.

The blood-flow through the liver makes it one of the richest vascularized orga
The vessels of the liver are important since their arrangement is intimately relat
to function, both normal and abnormal.
There are two supplies of blood entering the liver; there is but one path out.
The large, entering vessels first follow the connective tissue between lobes.
They are *interlobar blood vessels* (hepatic artery; portal vein).
From them arise dwindling *interlobular branches* which follow portal cana
The liver is drained by *hepatic veins* and their tributaries.

1. PORTAL VEINS.

Their venous blood is the primary supply (75 per cent) of hepatic lobules.
Small interlobular branches pass between the surfaces of lobules and bre
down into precapillaries which connect directly with intralobu
sinusoids.

2. HEPATIC ARTERIES.

These vessels supply, on the average, some 25 per cent of the total blood.
Such blood is distributed primarily to the connective tissue of the liver.
(It also nourishes the extrahepatic bile ducts and gall bladder.)
Some terminal arterial twigs connect directly with the sinusoids of a lobule.
Such local regions of a lobule may receive arterial blood only.
Blood returns from the capillary bed in the tissue of Glisson's capsule.
It feeds into small branches of the portal vein.
In this way it ultimately (and indirectly) reaches the hepatic sinusoids

3. HEPATIC VEINS.

This system begins with a *central vein* that is axial within the lobule.
It drains the converging sinusoids of the lobule.
It is about 45 μ wide, lacks muscle and has but few collagenous fibers.
Each central vein connects at right angles with a *sublobular vein*.
This stouter, collecting vessel courses alone along the base of a lobule
A solitary, isolated position is a specific characteristic of these veins.
Sublobular veins are tributary to branches of the *hepatic veins* proper.
The latter, also solitary, open into the inferior vena cava.

4. INTERMITTENCE OF FLOW.

It is said that three out of four lobules have inactive sinusoids at any time.
Inactive lobules may have their sinusoids packed with blood, or be empty.
Apparently sphincters exist at both the periphery and center of a lobule.

C. LYMPHATIC VESSELS.

The smallest definite lymphatic vessels occur within the portal canals.
These increase in size until main vessels finally emerge at the hilus.
Yet more lymph arises in the liver than in any other organ of the body.
The unsolved problem is its initial site of origin.
Some investigators claim that *lymph spaces* exist within the lobule.
Spaces (of Disse) do occur between the liver plates and sinusoidal lining.
Or, more precisely, between the plates and a membrane made of reti
lum and ground substance.

The direction of lymph drainage would be toward the periphery of a lobule.
Others are skeptical, since injections fail to show connections with lymphatics.

5. Nerves.

The fibers are chiefly unmyelinated, from the autonomic system.
They accompany the blood vessels and bile ducts, and supply them.
Extensions from these plexuses into lobules, often asserted, are subject to doubt.

STRUCTURAL PECULIARITIES:

The liver shows marked divergences from other compound tubular glands.
All hepatic cells are alike, in spite of a wide diversity in functions performed.
The secretory 'end tubule' is replaced by a continuous system of thin, cellular plates.
No lumen (*i.e.*, bile capillary) is in contact with more than two cells.
On the other hand, a single cell abuts against more than one bile capillary.
The structural unit (lobule) is based on a relation to vessels, not ducts.
The interdigitation of hepatic and portal veins governs lobule formation.
The axis of the lobule is a central vein; in an ordinary gland the axis is a duct.
The relation of hepatic cells to sinusoids is unusually extensive and intimate.
Each cell is bathed on two surfaces by blood.
In this regard the liver resembles various endocrine glands.
Hepatic cells release substances both into the duct system and into the blood stream.
The afferent blood supply to the parenchyma is double, but mostly venous.
That is, most of the blood has already passed through capillary plexuses elsewhere.
The course within a lobule is from periphery to center, rather than the reverse.
The efferent veins take courses independent of the afferents, rather than following them.
The ducts are at the periphery of lobules, rather than at the centers.
The path of secretion within a lobule is from center to periphery, not the reverse.
Connective tissue within the lobule is lacking, except for a reticulum.
Interlobular connective tissue is restricted in extent in man and most other mammals.
It does not enclose lobules, but is largely limited to the edges of lobules.
Yet this tissue receives most of the arterial blood delivered to the liver.

. REGENERATIVE ABILITY:

The liver has a marked capacity for repairing even extensive tissue losses.
Such losses from toxic agents or surgery are recouped (as to liver weight) promptly.
New lobules bud out of old ones, hepatic cells enlarging and increasing by mitosis.
Bile ducts also proliferate and probably also form some new hepatic cells.

. DIAGNOSTIC FEATURES:

The *parenchyma* is arranged in polygonal areas; these are *hepatic lobules*.
The axis of a lobule is an endothelium-lined tube (central vein).
Sections cutting across this axis reveal a radiate arrangement.
Slender, branching cell rows alternate with sinusoidal spaces.
No other structures are seen within a lobule in routine examination.
Sections cutting along the axis show a finger-shaped central vein.
Cell rows pass horizontally from each side of this vertical vessel.
Connective tissue separates lobules at their angles, where *portal canals* occur.
Within the canal occur the conspicuous components of the *hepatic triad*.
These are an artery, vein and a bile duct (with pale cuboidal epithelium).
These three associated structures are specifically diagnostic of the liver.

G. FUNCTIONAL CORRELATIONS:

The liver is essential to life; death promptly follows its total removal.

Yet only a fraction of the parenchyma is necessary; 9 per cent is sufficient (dog).

The secretory product of the exocrine gland is *bile*, a complex fluid.

Included are bile acids, bile pigment, cholesterol, lecithin, fats, urea, etc.

Bile is apparently secreted continuously; a pint or more is the daily output.

1. Secretion.

Bile acids are believed to arise as a synthesis by the liver cells.

As salts they aid in the emulsification of fats during intestinal digestion.

The fat is thereby made vulnerable to the action of lipase.

Bile salts are reabsorbed by the intestine and re-utilized.

2. Excretion.

Bile pigment is derived from hemoglobin through the activity of reticulo-endothelium

The macrophages of this system occur in the liver, spleen and lymph nodes.

The pigment is not reabsorbed, but is eliminated in the feces.

Urea is formed, at least mainly, in the liver from the break-down of amino acids.

It is a by-product of protein metabolism.

Cholesterol, lecithin and fats also are eliminated into the bile.

3. Storage.

An intermittent blood flow makes the liver a major storehouse for blood.

The liver cells store *glycogen* and release it to the blood, when needed, as glucose.

This constitutes the so-called endocrine function of the liver.

In this way the blood-sugar level is maintained under diverse dietary condition

Vitamins (particularly A and B) are stored in the liver, as are *enzymes* and *hormones*.

Fat exists in the liver cells, mostly in a masked form.

It can be transformed into carbohydrates.

4. Extractives.

Heparin is an anticoagulant that is stored in the liver, but not exclusively so.

It originates in mast cells which are abundant in the liver, among other sites.

Fibrinogen is formed in the liver and is given off to the passing blood plasma.

It occurs as a dispersed protein that is instrumental in blood clotting.

An *anti-anemic substance* incites the regeneration of red corpuscles.

It is useful in combating pernicious anemia.

5. Phagocytosis.

The Kupffer cells act like the macrophages of reticulo-endothelium in general.

There is both a filtering action and a tendency to build up immunities.

Conditions in the sinusoids are favorable for phagocytosis.

The current is sluggish and the blood pressure is low.

The Kupffer cells remove particulate matter from the blood stream.

Bacteria, worn-out blood elements and foreign particles are phagocytosed.

IV. THE EXTRAHEPATIC PASSAGES

A main-line duct connects the liver with the duodenum.

The upper part is the *hepatic duct;* the lower part, the *common bile duct.*

he *gall bladder* and its *cystic duct* represent an offshoot from the main conduit.
The union of cystic and hepatic ducts produces a common drain, the *common bile duct*.

GALL BLADDER:
This simple organ is a pear-shaped sac, about 4 x 1.5 inches in size.
It consists of a blind *fundus*, a *body* and a *neck*.

1. Mucosa.

The *mucosal lining* is markedly folded, so that the surface appears honeycombed.
This appearance is largely effaced when the gall bladder is distended.
The *epithelium* consists of tall, palely staining cells with ovoid basal nuclei.
They contain some mucigen that responds feebly to the usual specific stains.
A very thin *striate border* can be demonstrated on the exposed surface.
It is usually overlooked, because it is destroyed by routine fixation.
A *basement membrane* cannot be identified.
The epithelium disintegrates rapidly after death, if still bathed in bile.
Glands do not occur, except for a few mucous glands at the neck of the organ.
However, far-outpouching diverticula (*Rokitansky-Aschoff sinuses*) are common.
These are said to result from prolonged distention of a weakened wall.
They may extend through the muscular coat.
The *lamina propria* consists of delicate, richly vascular connective tissue.
Some smooth muscle fibers occur in it, and solitary lymph nodules also.

2. Submucosa.

This layer is not represented in the gall bladder.

3. Muscularis.

Interlacing bundles of smooth muscle form a thin, irregular *muscular coat*.
Most of the fibers are circularly disposed.
Fibro-elastic tissue is interspersed between the flat bundles of muscle.

4. Serosa.

This tunic becomes an adventitia where contact is made with the liver.
It lies on a thick, loose, vascular layer which is a *subserosa* or *perimuscular layer*.
Luschka ducts are peculiar tubular structures sometimes occurring here.
They connect with bile ducts belonging to the liver itself.
They are probably aberrant bile ducts, formed during development.

5. Vessels and Nerves.

Blood vessels form plexuses in the serosa and lamina propria.
Lymphatics are abundant, and are distributed much like the blood vessels.
Nerve fibers come from the vagus and the sympathetic system.
They are distributed to the muscular wall and blood vessels.

6. Diagnostic Features.

The *mucosa* is highly folded in an irregular manner.
The *epithelium* consists of very tall, pale cells, with a weakly specialized border.
Glands are lacking, but epithelial diverticula may extend well into the wall.
The thin *muscularis* consists of bundles, separated by layers of connective tissue.

The outermost layer is either a *serosa* or *adventitia*, depending on the region viewed. Between it and the muscle is a thick, loose, vascular layer.

7. Functional Correlations.

Some mammals normally lack a gall bladder.

Example: rat; horse; certain ruminants; etc.

Removal of the human gall bladder does not cause serious functional disturbance.

There is commonly a compensatory dilatation of the biliary passages.

The gall bladder is a highly distensible reservoir for *bile storage* between meals.

Its capacity ranges from 15 to 90 ml.

It absorbs water, fat and some salts from the bile, and concentrates bile greatly.

Evidence of secretion is small (except mucus from glands at the neck).

The gall bladder empties its contents on the entry of chyme into the duodenum.

This is controlled by a hormone (*cholecystokinin*) produced in the duodenum.

B. EXTRAHEPATIC DUCTS:

There are three large ducts outside the liver.

The *hepatic duct* receives the smaller ducts that converge from within the liver.

The *cystic duct* drains the gall bladder.

The *common bile duct* is the main tube that continues downward to the duodenum.

1. Structure.

The *mucosa* has a tall columnar *epithelium*, resembling that in the gall bladder.

The apices of the cells contain a slight amount of mucigen.

Mucous glands occur in the lamina propria and drain into the duct lumen.

The mucosal lining of the ducts is thrown into many folds.

Near the neck of the gall bladder it makes the *spiral valve* (of Heister).

These folds contain smooth muscle.

A *fibro-muscular coat* constitutes the rest of the wall.

For the most part this sheath is fibro-elastic tissue.

Smooth muscle is present only to a slight degree, mingled with the fibrous sheath.

In the cystic duct it is almost wholly lacking.

The hepatic duct has longitudinal bundles in occasional specimens.

The common bile duct usually contains muscle, especially in its lower portion

These longitudinal bundles, however, do not form a complete sheath.

A *sphincter muscle* (of Oddi) encircles the outlet into the duodenum.

2. Diagnostic Features.

The *bile ducts* are tubes with a highly folded lining.

The *epithelium* is composed of pale, tall columnar cells.

The relatively thick wall is mostly fibro-elastic tissue.

Mucous glands occur in the wall.

Smooth muscle is deficient or lacking.

It occurs dependably only in the lower levels of the common duct.

Even here it does not constitute a complete longitudinal coat.

3. Functional Correlations.

All tubes of the duct system, inside the liver or outside it, transport bile.

In addition, the extrahepatic ducts add mucus to the biliary fluid.

Chapter XXI. THE RESPIRATORY SYSTEM

This apparatus conducts air and provides for gaseous interchanges in the lungs.
It consists of two portions, specialized for different purposes.
> One is a set of *conducting passages*, whose function is piping air to and from the lungs.
> > These are: *nose; naso-pharynx; larynx; trachea; bronchi;* and *bronchioles.*
> The other is the *respiratory seat* where intimate interchanges occur between air and blood.
> > This comprises: *respiratory bronchioles; alveolar ducts; atria;* and *alveolar sacs.*

I. THE NASAL CAVITY

The *nose* is a hollow organ covered with skin, provided with muscles, supported by cartilage and bone, and lined with a mucous membrane.
A *nasal septum* partitions it into two passages.
Each *nasal cavity* consists of a *vestibule*, and of *respiratory* and *olfactory regions.*

1. Vestibule.

> This dilated region is a sort of anteroom, supported by cartilages on its medial side.
> Its lining is continuous with the skin, but changes character as it advances inward.
> > The stratified, squamous *epithelium* loses cornification and layering.
> Coarse *hairs* are numerous near the external orifice.
> *Sebaceous* and *sweat glands* occur also.

2. Respiratory Region.

> This territory includes nearly all of the septum and lateral walls.
> > The surface area of each lateral wall is increased by shelf-like *conchae.*
> > The mucosal lining is also known as the *Schneiderian membrane.*
> The *epithelium* is pseudostratified and ciliated, with numerous *goblet cells.*
> > The exact composition varies in regions sheltered or exposed to passing air.
> > *Cilia* beat backward, in the direction of the pharynx.
> > Goblet cells sometimes concentrate in intra-epithelial, glandular pits.
> > The *basement membrane* varies regionally from thin to very thick.
> The fibrous *lamina propria* becomes infiltrated with lymphocytes.
> > Eosinophils, plasma cells and macrophages may also be represented.
> > There are mixed *sero-mucous glands*, especially in the more exposed regions.
> A type of cavernous *erectile tissue* occurs in the deeper levels of the lamina propria.
> > This is a vascular plexus; it is composed of large, thin-walled, modified veins.
> > The system of vessels ordinarily serves to warm the passing air.
> > In response to irritation they can distend with blood and produce turgidity.
> > > However, they are unlike the erectile tissue of the genitalia in two respects.
> > > > They are supplied by small veins, not by arterioles.
> > > > The muscle is in the walls of vessels, not in septa between cavernous spaces.

247

A definite *submucosa* is lacking, although the deep, cavernous lamina propria is unusual.
The deepest level of the lamina propria fuses with the subjacent periosteum.

3. Olfactory Region.
This specialized portion of the wall occurs on the superior concha and adjacent septum.
The epithelium contains slender cells that continue brainward as *nerve fibers*.
Serous glands occur in the lamina propria.
Further details will be found in the account dealing with sense organs (p. 304).

4. Diagnostic Features.
The *respiratory mucosa* is surfaced with pseudostratified, ciliated epithelium.
Goblet cells are fairly abundant in it.
Mixed, *sero-mucous glands* and prominent, broad *veins* occur in the lamina propria.
The deepest level of the lamina merges with the periosteum of underlying bone.
The *olfactory mucosa* has characteristics summarized on p. 305.

5. Functional Correlations.
The entire tract, from the nostrils into the lungs, is a two-way thoroughfare for air.
These parts also warm, humidify and filter it in transit.
Mucus serves to entrap particulate matter, and cilia to expel it.
The nasal glands alone furnish nearly one quart of fluid daily.
These secretions inactivate bacteria rapidly.

II. THE PARANASAL SINUSES

The *sinuses* are sacculations that extend from the nasal cavities into nearby bones.
They include the *frontal, sphenoidal, maxillary* and *ethmoidal sinuses*.
The *mucosa* resembles that of the respiratory region, but is thin and less specialized.
The *epithelium* is lower and contains fewer goblet cells.
A *basement membrane* is, for the most part, lacking.
Glands are fewer and smaller, and venous *erectile plexuses* do not occur.

III. THE NASO-PHARYNX

The *naso-pharynx* is lined regionally with either pseudostratified or stratified epithelium.
Its structure is described on p. 213.

IV. THE LARYNX

The *larynx* is a short, firm tube that is supported by *cartilages* and *muscles*.
It also contains the *vocal folds*, commonly called *vocal cords*.
The larynx is interposed between the naso-pharynx and trachea.

1. Mucosa.
The lining *epithelium* is not uniform in type throughout.
Surfaces subject to wear and tear are covered with *stratified squamous epithelium*.
These are the vocal folds, ary-epiglottic folds and most of the epiglottis.
A few *taste buds* occur on the epiglottis and nearby surfaces.
Below the level of the vocal folds, the epithelium is *pseudostratified*.
It contains *goblet cells* and bears *cilia*.

The cilia, as in all the respiratory passages, stroke toward the pharynx.

A *basement membrane* is present, but it is thin.

The *lamina propria* is rich in elastic fibers.

It contains small, mixed *sero-mucous glands*, except in the vocal folds.

A diffuse lymphocytic infiltration and a few *solitary nodules* occur.

There is no definite *submucosa*.

Yet the glands and richest elastic tissue occupy a deep, special level.

The *vocal folds* are two apposed folds of the mucous membrane.

Each encloses an elastic band that constitutes a *vocal ligament*.

The exposed surface is covered with stratified squamous epithelium.

Bordering and paralleling each fold laterally is a *vocal muscle*.

2. Cartilaginous Wall.

The supporting wall contains *cartilaginous plates*, united by ligaments.

The cartilages maintain the larynx as a constantly open tube.

The larger plates are composed of *hyaline cartilage*.

Included are the thyroid, cricoid, and arytenoids (in large part).

These begin to calcify early (the thyroid of males, at puberty).

Other (mostly smaller) cartilages are composed of *elastic cartilage*.

Included are the cuneiform, corniculate, arytenoids (tips), and epiglottic.

3. Laryngeal Muscles.

Some neighboring muscles attach to the cartilages; these are *extrinsic muscles*.

Other muscles interconnect the cartilages themselves; these are *intrinsic muscles*.

Important in this group are the muscles controlling the vocal folds.

4. Diagnostic Features.

The larynx is mostly lined with ciliated *pseudostratified epithelium*.

The vocal folds and epiglottis are covered with *stratified squamous epithelium*.

The *lamina propria* contains small, mixed, sero-mucous glands.

Sectioned *cartilages* (mostly hyaline) are encountered in the peripheral wall.

Attached to them are *skeletal muscles*.

The highly elastic *epiglottis* and *vocal folds* are distinctive features.

One or both should be included in a representative section.

5. Functional Correlations.

The *extrinsic muscles* elevate and depress the larynx; they aid in *swallowing*.

The *intrinsic musculature* of the larynx is concerned with changing the *pitch* of sound.

The size of the opening between the vocal folds is varied for the passing air.

The tension on the vocal folds is increased and diminished.

V. THE TRACHEA AND CHIEF BRONCHI

The *trachea* is a relatively thin-walled rigid tube, about 4.5 inches long and 1 inch wide.

Near the lungs it bifurcates into two chief *bronchi*, similar to the trachea in structure.

The mucosa-lined tube is supported and held open by prominent *cartilages*.

1. Mucosa.

The lining *epithelium* is pseudostratified and ciliated.

It contains many goblet cells and rests upon a very thick *basement membrane*.

The *lamina propria* is a relatively thin, fibrous layer.

There is no muscularis mucosae, but a substitute stratum occupies the same level.

Here elastic fibers form a longitudinally directed *elastic layer*.

Accumulations of lymphocytes occur in the *reticular tissue* of the lamina propria.

2. Submucosa.

A deeper, gland-containing stratum can be designated a *submucosa*.

Many small, *sero-mucous glands* characterize this layer.

They are most frequent at the level of the interspaces between successive cartilages.

Fat cells may be represented, as well.

3. Adventitia.

This tunic contains cartilages, interconnected by fibrous membranes.

There are 16 to 20 *tracheal cartilages*, and about half as many in each chief bronchus.

Each is shaped like a C or Y; they nearly encircle the trachea, but open posteriorly.

This open interval, facing the esophagus, is filled-in by two components.

One is a membrane of fibro-elastic tissue.

The other is the *trachealis muscle*, composed of mostly circular smooth-muscle fibers.

Mixed glands often penetrate into the muscle and even extend outside of it.

The oblique direction and irregular shape of some cartilages may give an appearance in sections like separate plates.

Cartilages show degenerative changes in old age, and may partially calcify.

4. Diagnostic Features.

The lining *epithelium* is pseudostratified, bearing cilia and goblet cells.

The *basement membrane* is one of the thickest in the body.

Mixed *sero-mucous glands* occur in the submucosa.

The *adventitia* tends to show a thick, horseshoe-shaped cartilage 'ring.'

Some transverse sections, however, may contain more than one cartilage-unit.

Sections cut between rings usually lack cartilage.

Longitudinal sections display a series of oval, cartilaginous masses.

Muscle is lacking, except some *smooth muscle* between the ends of cartilages.

5. Functional Correlations.

The walls of the air tubes, large and small, are held open mechanically.

This prevents their collapse and makes breathing easier.

In the larynx, trachea and bronchi patency is accomplished by firm cartilages.

In bronchioles and all smaller passages it is accomplished in another manner.

These parts are attached on all sides to the elastic spongework of lung tissue.

Cartilaginous rings provide the trachea and bronchi with flexibility and extensibility.

Membranous regions of the tube, facing the esophagus, yield to its expansions.

This includes the membranes between rings and muscle between cartilage ends.

Certain functions are shared with other portions of the respiratory passages (p. 255).

VI. THE LUNG

The *lungs* occupy paired pleural cavities in the chest that are lined with a serous membrane.

Each lung lies free within its cavity, except for a stalk carrying an air tube and vessels.

These organs develop like a gland, and maintain a similar structural plan.

Their fundamental component is a system of branching *air tubes*, ending in compound *sacs*.

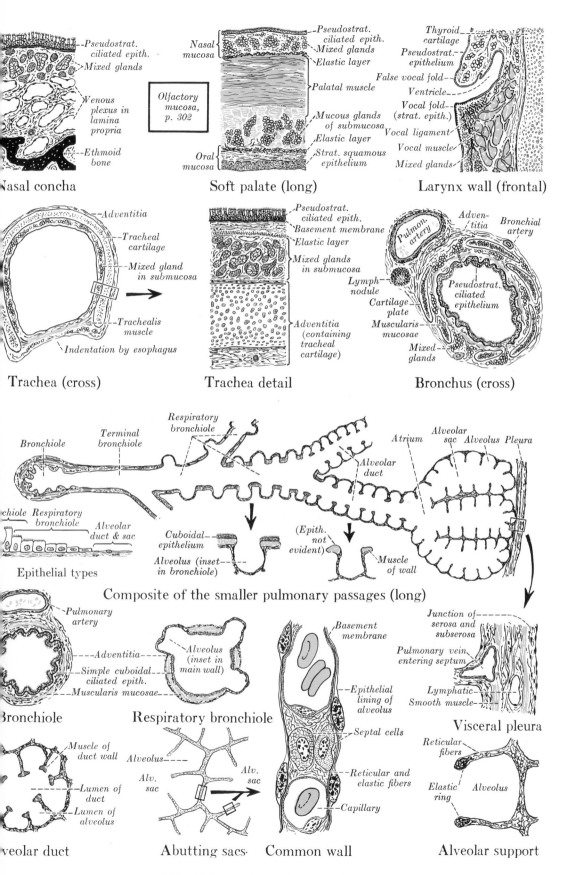

THE RESPIRATORY ORGANS

A. STRUCTURAL PLAN:

Each lung subdivides into nearly separate *lobes,* and these into indistinct *lobules.*
The lung is attached at the *hilus,* where a chief bronchus and vessels enter.
> Here the two portions of the pleura become continuous.
>> The *parietal pleura* lines the thoracic wall.
>> The *visceral pleura* is reflected so as to enclose the lung.
> The pleurae are typical serous membranes, moistened by fluid.
The system of branching air tubes is divided into conducting and respiratory divisions.
> The *conducting tubes* include branches of the *bronchi* and all ordinary *bronchioles.*
>> They correspond to the excretory ducts of a gland.
> The *respiratory tubes* consist of *respiratory bronchioles, alveolar ducts, atria* and, terminally, *alveolar sacs;* all contain at least some air cells, or *alveoli.*
>> They correspond to the smaller ducts and alveoli of a gland.
The smaller subdivisions of this system are closely crowded and displaced.
> Hence sections of a collapsed lung give a poor picture of the true spatial relations.
> Accompanying the air passages are fibrous tissue, smooth muscle, vessels and nerves.
The lung is organized into rather poorly defined primary and secondary *lobules.*
> The larger, or secondary, lobules are bounded by *interlobular septa.*

B. LOBULATION:

The right lung is divided into three major *lobes,* the left lung into two lobes.
Internally there can be recognized small, poorly defined *lobules.*
> It is commonly considered that an ordinary bronchiole and all branching passages beyond it constitute a pulmonary lobule; this is often called a *secondary lobule.*
> It makes a pyramidal mass, whose basal-size may equal a 25-cent coin.
>> Such bases can be seen marked off on the surface of the lung.
>> They show well in the fetus or when outlined by pigment in the septa.
> The sides of such a lobule are bounded by incomplete *interlobular septa.*
Some authorities recognize a much smaller unit as the *primary lobule.*
> It consists of an alveolar duct and all of its terminal subdivisions.
Many of these primary lobules associate to constitute a secondary lobule.

C. DETAILED STRUCTURE:

1. Framework.

Each lobed lung is intimately invested with a fibro-elastic membrane.
> This is the deep layer of the *visceral pleura* that also contains smooth muscle.
Extending inward are *interlobular septa* that enclose *secondary lobules* fairly well.
> At the apex of a lobule they join the connective tissue that surrounds bronchi.
The lobules of the lung are permeated with *reticular networks* and *elastic networks.*
> These support the bronchioles, smaller air tubes and alveolar sacs.

2. Conducting Tubes.

The several named tubes that lie within the lungs have distinctive characteristics.
A. BRONCHUS.
> The *epithelium* gradually reduces in thickness and layering.
>> The larger bronchi within the lungs have *pseudostratified epithelium.*
>>> Cilia and goblet cells occur, as in the chief bronchi and trachea.
>> In the smallest bronchi the epithelium becomes *simple columnar.*
>>> Cilia are still abundant, and goblet cells are numerous.

A *muscularis mucosae* encircles the thin *lamina propria* as interlacing spirals.
It gradually replaces the elastic layer of the trachea and chief bronchi.
Its contraction causes the mucosa to appear folded.
Nevertheless, some elastic tissue is retained even in the smallest tubes.
The *submucosa* contains mixed, *sero-mucous glands*.
These glands also project into the spaces between the cartilages.
They decrease in number and size as the bronchi grow smaller.
Solitary *lymph nodules*, when present, lie outside the muscular layer.
The *adventitia* contains separate *cartilaginous plates* instead of C-shaped rings.
They overlap in the larger bronchi, but are scarce in the smaller divisions.
Some *lymph nodes* may occur in the adventitia of the largest bronchi.

B. BRONCHIOLE.

The largest bronchioles are about 1 mm. in diameter; the smallest, 0.5 mm.
The latter (*terminal bronchioles*) number 50 to 80 in each secondary lobule.
The *epithelium* is reduced to a simple columnar or cuboidal type, both ciliated.
Goblet cells become progressively infrequent and disappear.
The *muscularis mucosae* is relatively heavier than elsewhere in the tubular system.
It forms a network of spiraling fibers that dominates the *lamina propria*.
Many elastic fibers intermingle with the smooth muscle, as in bronchi.
An *adventitia* remains; but cartilage, glands and lymph nodules no longer occur.
In this loss of firm support, the mucosa is thrown into longitudinal folds.

3. Respiratory Tubes.

A. RESPIRATORY BRONCHIOLE.

This conduit is a short branching tubule, 0.5 mm. or less in diameter.
About two arise from each terminal bronchiole; each subdivides once or twice
Structurally it is transitional between a conducting and respiratory tube.
The *epithelium* ranges from a low columnar type to a low cuboidal layer.
Goblet cells do not occur, but cilia are still present in the larger tubes.
The thin *supporting wall* consists primarily of collagenous fibers.
It contains an interlacing network of smooth muscle and elastic fibers.
Alveoli appear as little outpouchings that interrupt the main wall at intervals.
They project beyond the ordinary wall as still thinner, box-like insets.
Alveoli increase in number progressively at lower levels of the bronchiole.

B. ALVEOLAR DUCT.

Each respiratory bronchiole gives rise to several branching *alveolar ducts*.
They are relatively long, thin-walled, fibro-elastic tubes.
There is no plainly distinguishable epithelial lining.
Scattering spirals of smooth muscle occur in the main wall between alveoli.
The duct is thickly beset with single alveoli.
Also clusters of alveoli (*alveolar sacs*) open into its lumen.
These are the most abundant and conspicuous feature of the alveolar duct.

C. ATRIUM.

This is a sort of antechamber between an alveolar duct and several air sacs.
From 3 to 6 atria branch off from the end of each alveolar duct.
The 'atrium' is regarded by some authorities as only a terminal alveolar duct.
Under this interpretation it would not receive a special name.

D. ALVEOLAR SACS AND ALVEOLI.

From 2 to 5 single or compound *alveolar sacs* open off from each atrium.
Each sac is composed of a variable number of thin-walled, minor compartments.

These latter are primary *alveoli*, all opening into the main lumen of the sac.
The total number of alveoli runs into hundreds of millions.
An individual alveolus, or air cell, is like a hexagonal box with its top open.
Thus the interior of an alveolar sac has a honeycombed appearance.
Both the sacs and their component alveoli are packed as snugly as possible.
Histological relations are identical in any membrane that separates cavities.
That is, a side wall (*septum*) separating two alveoli of the same sac is identical
with the common floor serving abutting alveoli of different sacs.
It will be noted that such a septum is always a common partition.
It is like a common wall that separates adjoining rooms in a house.
The framework of a septum is a dense network of fibers.
Most abundant are reticular fibers, but there are elastic fibers also.
A ring of elastic fibers encircles the mouth of each alveolar sac.
Smooth muscle fibers are entirely lacking.
Weaving through the spaces in this fibrous, septal mesh are capillaries.
These anastomose into a very closely spaced *capillary net*.
In all, they constitute by far the bulkiest part of the septum.
Regions of a septum, not occupied by capillaries and fibers, contain cells.
Most abundant are pale, rounded *septal cells* of undetermined origin and use.
Also present are macrophages and some fibroblasts.
A long dispute concerning the tissue at the free surface of alveoli has ended.
One claim favored endothelium and connective tissue, exposed directly to air.
The electron microscope, however, demonstrates a true *epithelial lining*.
This layer is too thin (0.2 μ) to be resolved well with light microscopes.
A very thin *basement membrane* separates epithelium from capillary epithelium.
Such approximation facilitates gaseous interchanges between air and blood.
It is now agreed that some adjacent alveoli communicate by *alveolar pores*.
These are true apertures that perforate the floor common to both sacs.

4. Pleura.

The visceral reflection of the *pleura* covers the lung and follows its lobes.
Like all serous membranes, it is surfaced with *mesothelium*.
The underlying *fibro-elastic tissue* becomes coarser-meshed at deeper levels.
This stroma contains plates of *smooth muscle*.
At deep levels are veins and lymphatic vessels.
At the boundaries of lobules the deep tissue blends with interlobular septa.
The parietal and visceral pleurae are normally in contact, surface to surface.
Only a film of *pleural fluid* intervenes between the two.

5. Vessels and Nerves.

A. BLOOD VESSELS.

There are two sets: one is for respiration; the other nourishes the air tubes.
The pulmonary arteries and veins carry blood that participates in respiration.
The *pulmonary artery* follows branching air ducts as it conveys impure blood.
It lies on, or is attached to, the wall of the bronchus and bronchioles.
It ends in capillary networks wherever pulmonary alveoli exist.
Pulmonary veins collect purified blood from alveoli, and from the pleura.
For a considerable distance they run in the septa between lobules.
Here they pursue solitary courses, and this is a distinctive feature.

They ultimately join the bronchi and are attached to their walls.

A vein is situated opposite to the similarly attached pulmonary arter

Bronchial arteries nourish the air tubes and accompanying pulmonary arteries.

They are much smaller than the pulmonary arteries and veins.

They differ by coursing within the walls of the air tubes and arteries.

Such vessels do not extend peripherally beyond the respiratory bronchioles.

Here anastomoses are made with capillaries from the pulmonary arteri

The bronchial arteries supply also the interlobular septa and pleura.

This blood is returned by the pulmonary veins.

True *bronchial veins* are said to occur only at the hilus of the lung.

B. LYMPHATICS.

A profuse superficial *pleural network* receives lymph from interlobular septa.

Valves prevent backflow, and draining trunks conduct the lymph to the hilu

A *deep set* of lymphatics accompanies the air tubes and pulmonary artery.

It begins with the alveolar ducts and drains toward the hilus of the lung.

C. NERVES.

The *vagus nerve* and *sympathetic system* supply the air tubes and blood vessels.

There are constrictor (vagal) and dilator (sympathetic) fibers to the tubes.

Some sensory endings are described in relation to muscle and epithelium.

D. BIRTH CHANGES:

The fetal lung has a compact, glandular appearance, unlike the fully expanded organ.

Even at birth, alveoli are small and the lung does not fill its pleural cavity.

With breathing, the air passages dilate greatly and the whole lung expands.

Such a lung will float in water, whereas the lung of a still-born sinks.

The lung has finished its progressive branching by the end of pregnancy.

Two months after birth, alveoli first appear in the alveolar ducts.

Also terminal bronchioles bud off alveoli and become respiratory bronchioles.

E. REGENERATIVE ABILITY:

Loss of the mucosa in the trachea and bronchi is repaired by cell migration and mitosis.

The new epithelium differentiates ciliated cells and gland cells.

After tissue destruction in the lung, by surgery or disease, healing is by scar tissue.

There is no evidence of a capacity of pulmonary tissue to regenerate as such.

F. DIAGNOSTIC FEATURES:

Bronchi within the lungs show several cartilage-plates in the adventitia.

These decrease in size in the smaller divisions and become scarcer.

The mucosa differs from that of the trachea in two particulars.

It is folded and possesses a muscularis mucosae.

Hence separate cartilage-plates and a muscularis mucosae securely identify these tubes

The presence of adjacent lung tissue can be expected.

Ordinary *bronchioles* possess a simple columnar to cuboidal, ciliated epithelium.

Cartilage and glands are lacking; goblet cells are sparse or absent.

The muscularis mucosae is well developed in relation to the size of the tube.

Alveoli, with a chick-netting appearance, always surround the bronchiole.

Respiratory bronchioles differ from the terminal bronchioles in an important respect.

They have thin alveoli that protrude here and there through gaps in the main wall.

Sections that miss these alveoli can be mistaken for the smallest bronchioles.

Alveolar ducts differ from respiratory bronchioles by an increased number of alveoli.

These alveolar interruptions in the wall make a continuous series.

Smooth muscle is reduced to tiny, local knobs in what remains of the main wall.

Such a knob, surmounting a septal wall between two alveoli, resembles a drumstick.

No epithelial lining is recognizable in this tube or its alveoli.

A longitudinal section can be likened to rows of doorless rooms opening off a hallway.

Alveolar sacs consist of box-like alveoli arranged about a main, central lumen.

The walls between alveoli show no easily determinable structure.

A differential characteristic over alveolar ducts is the absence of muscular knobs.

Sections cutting across the central lumen of an alveolar sac (or alveolar duct) resemble a circle of doorless rooms opening off a central rotunda.

Tangential sections that miss the central lumen cut through several alveoli.

These show as a thin network about polygonal spaces, like chick netting.

. FUNCTIONAL CORRELATIONS:

The primary purpose of the lungs is to serve as the seat of *respiratory exchanges*.

This is accomplished through the breathing of air.

The smooth pleural surfaces are kept moist with a serous fluid.

This fluid-film enables the lungs to glide without friction during breathing.

During *inspiration* the conducting system of air tubes increases in length and diameter.

As the chest expands, the lungs also increase in size and draw in air.

This is the consequence of negative pressure developing in the pleural cavities.

The lung, in expanding, stretches elastic tissues everywhere within the organ.

If the pleural cavity is opened, pressures equalize and the lung collapses.

This shrinkage is the result of elastic recoil.

Such retraction is the condition seen in ordinary sections of the uninflated lung.

During *inspiration*, the respiratory division of the pulmonary tubes also expands.

Probably the volume increase is due to elongation and distention of alveolar ducts.

Seemingly the alveoli change volume but little, although they do change shape.

During *expiration*, it is the elastic tissue that provides for recoil in both the conducting and respiratory divisions; muscular force is used only in hard breathing.

There is a double spiral of muscle in bronchi, bronchioles and alveolar ducts.

This arrangement both contracts these tubes and shortens them.

The relatively heaviest concentration of muscle is in the bronchioles.

As might be expected, these tubes are subject to strongest asthmatic spasms.

The lungs act as intermediaries in respiratory *gaseous exchanges*.

These exchanges take place through a film of fluid, and a very thin layer of tissue.

The transfers probably are accomplished by processes involving physical diffusion.

Oxygen is given to the blood, and carbon dioxide is removed from it.

Nearly a quart of water is also eliminated through the lungs daily.

The total respiratory surface of the alveoli is estimated at 125 to 500 square yards.

At rest, however, only 5 per cent of this surface is actually being used.

The *air-filtering* service of the respiratory system is a significant activity.

Inspired particulate matter adheres to the lining of respiratory tubes.

In the conducting tubes this foreign material is removed in a mass movement.

Here (and in respiratory bronchioles) cilia are present and beat upward.

They force mucus and its entrapped particles upward, whence it is expelled.

In so doing, mucus is also kept from accumulating and occluding the air ducts.

Alveolar ducts and alveolar sacs lack cilia to move and expel foreign particles.

Instead, macrophages (known as *alveolar phagocytes* and *dust cells*) become active.

They enter the alveoli and engulf the particles of dust, smoke or bacteria.

Some cells deposit this material in the septa, lymphoid tissue and lymph nodes
In this way the lungs of a city dweller, in particular, become blackened
Other dust cells move upward to the respiratory bronchioles.
Thence cilia or coughing bring them to the pharynx.
In certain types of heart disease they contain broken-down hemoglobi
(hemosiderin) and are called 'heart-failure cells.'

Chapter *XXII*. THE URINARY SYSTEM

The *urinary system* consists of the *kidneys* and the urinary passages leading away from them.
>The latter include the *calyces, renal pelvis* and *ureter* in relation to each kidney.
>Additional parts are the *urinary bladder* and its drainage duct, the *urethra*.

I. THE KIDNEY

The *kidney* is a compound tubular gland, adapted to filtering wastes from the blood.
>It is located in the lumbar region, just outside the dorsal peritoneum.

STRUCTURAL PLAN:
>The *kidney* is a flattened, bean-shaped organ, about 4.5 in. long.
>It is surrounded by a thin, fibrous *capsule*, which is weakly attached.
>The *hilus* is a slit-like orifice, opening into a more expanded *renal sinus*.
>>The sinus is a flattened cavity, filled with various things.
>>>Chief in importance is the *renal pelvis*, or expanded ureter, and its branches.
>>>Other components are connective tissue, fat, vessels and nerves.
>The renal pelvis subdivides into 2 to 3 *major calyces*, and these into 7 to 10 *minor calyces*.
>>Each cup-shaped minor calyx fits over a conical eminence, or *papilla* of the kidney.
>The interior of the kidney is almost wholly *parenchyma*.
>>Trabeculae or other gross supporting tissue are replaced by delicate *reticulum*.
>The parenchyma consists of many long, tortuous secretory canals (*nephrons*).
>>These join *excretory ducts* whose common trunks empty into the minor calyces.
>>A nephron and its excretory duct, together, comprise a *uriniferous tubule*.
>The parenchyma is plainly divisible into a cortex and a more centrally located medulla.
>>The *medulla* is gray in fresh material.
>>>It usually consists of 10 to 15 *pyramids*, whose apices point toward the hilus.
>>>>Two or three pyramids commonly fuse and end in one common *papilla*.
>>>>Hence there are fewer papillae (6 to 14) than pyramids.
>>>The pyramids have a radially striate appearance as they diverge from papillae.
>>>>This is because the tubules and vessels in them are straight.
>>>The tip of a pyramid bears 10 to 25 pits where the main excretory ducts of tubules open.
>>The *cortex*, brownish in life, has an irregular inner border (next to the medulla).
>>>It overlies the bases of the pyramids and dips down between them.
>>>>These latter, displaced portions of cortex invade the medullary territory.
>>>>They constitute the *renal columns* (of Bertin).
>>>A magnifying lens shows that the cortex is not uniform in texture.
>>>>It is subdivided into alternating radial tracts.
>>>The lighter tracts are radially striate (*pars radiata*).
>>>>They are continuous with the striate medulla and hence were long called 'medullary rays'; *cortical rays* is a better name.

The darker tracts have a granular appearance when cut and viewed with a lens.
  This is because the convoluted tubules, which compose it, are cut irregularly.
  Hence this part is called the *pars convoluta*, or labyrinth.
  Among fresh tubules, bright red points are seen.
      These are globular vascular tufts, or *glomeruli*, at the blind ends of tubules.

B. LOBULATION:

A *lobe* consists of a pyramid, together with the cortex overlying it.
  Their boundaries (up to 20) are prominent on the surface of a fetal kidney.
  However, they become blurred and fused in the adults of many mammals (including man).
  They are not outlined by trabeculae or other obvious landmarks.
  Yet such external lobation is permanent in reptiles, birds, the ox and bear.
  In fact, the kidney of most mammals has a single pyramid, and hence but one lobe.
  Example: rodents; cat; monkey.
A *lobule* is a smaller unit than the lobe; it is a natural functional unit.
  It consists of a cortical ray, plus those nearer parts of the adjoining labyrinths whose nephrons drain into that particular ray.
  Hence each ray is the core of its particular lobule.
  The drainage-territory comprises approximately one-third of each adjacent labyrinth.
Such lobules are marked off by interlobular blood vessels, coursing radially (p. 263).
  Like the functional 'portal lobule' of the liver, it is not a well outlined unit.
  It is best visualized when blood vessels have been injected with colored fluid.
The continuation of a cortical ray into its medullary pyramid is not clearly defined.
  Yet this continuation can be considered as a part of the lobule.
  It extends and completes the functional secretory and drainage unit.

C. DETAILED STRUCTURE:

1. Framework.

The thin, firm, weakly attached *capsule* consists mostly of collagenous fibers.
The *interstitial connective tissue* is extremely scanty, especially in the cortex.
  It consists almost wholly of reticular tissue.
  Some collagenous fibers do occur, but their distribution is limited.
      They surround blood vessels, glomerular capsules and large papillary ducts.
  Each uriniferous tubule is enclosed throughout its length by a *basement membrane*.
      This is composed of reticular fibers, embedded in amorphous ground substance.

2. Uriniferous Tubule.

The kidney is a compound tubular gland; the tubules are very long and closely packed.
A complete *uriniferous tubule* consists of two component parts.
  These components have separate embryonic origins, but become linked secondarily.
  The *secretory tubule*, or *nephron*, is unbranched and about 35 mm. long.
      Some portions of it are straight, while other portions are convoluted.
  There are about 1,300,000 tubules in each kidney.
      Their combined length in each kidney totals some 38 miles.
  The *collecting tubule* belongs to a branched, tree-like system of excretory ducts.
      These ducts are all straight; the total length of each drainage path is 21 mm.
  Their main stems are named *papillary ducts;* 10 to 25 open on a papilla.

All uriniferous tubules have the same general form, composition and relations.

Some minor differences depend on the position of a nephron in the cortex (p. 260).

Nevertheless, to know one tubule and its blood supply is to know the entire kidney.

Since the tubules intermingle so intimately, simple inspection of sections does not identify surely all of the portions that belong to any particular nephron.

Each nephron, however, is a compact mass, except for a long, looped portion.

Maceration and teasing methods have isolated complete nephrons successfully.

3. Subdivisions of a Tubule.

A total *uriniferous tubule* consists of a number of consecutive portions or segments.

These differ structurally and, for the most part, functionally as well.

It is customary to designate these distinctive segments as 'tubules.'

Usage makes the term *proximal* indicate 'nearer the glomerulus.'

Similarly, *distal* indicates 'nearer the papilla.'

Beginning at the blind, proximal end these parts are, in order, as follows:

A. SECRETORY PORTION.

Glomerular capsule (of Bowman).

Neck.

Proximal convoluted tubule.

Straight portion of proximal convoluted tubule.

This is the first (thick, descending) segment of Henle's loop.

Thin segment of Henle's loop (second segment of Henle's loop).

Thick, ascending segment of Henle's loop (third segment of Henle's loop).

Distal convoluted tubule.

B. EXCRETORY (OR DUCT) PORTION.

Arched collecting tubule (or junctional tubule).

Straight collecting tubule.

Papillary duct (of Bellini).

4. Locations of Tubule Segments.

All uriniferous tubules have their component segments distributed similarly.

The locations of these 'tubules' are constant and in definite, recognizable regions.

There are three chief topographical regions in the kidney, each easily identified.

These are: (1) cortical labyrinth; (2) cortical ray; (3) medulla.

In each region, three different tubular segments can be recognized easily.

These prominent and important tubules are marked by asterisks in the lists:

A. CORTICAL LABYRINTH.

*Glomerular capsule (of Bowman).

Neck.

*Proximal convoluted tubule.

Thick, ascending segment of Henle's loop.

*Distal convoluted tubule.

Arched collecting tubule.

B. CORTICAL RAY.

*Straight portion of proximal tubule (thick, descending segment of loop).

*Thick ascending segment of Henle's loop.

*Straight collecting tubule.

C. MEDULLA.

Straight portion of proximal tubule (thick, descending segment of loop).

(Limited to the boundary zone, next to the cortex.)

*Thin segment of Henle's loop.

*Thick, ascending segment of Henle's loop.
*Straight collecting tubule; papillary duct (of Bellini).

5. Nephron Variations Correlated with Position.

The chief variation is in Henle's loop—its length, position and composition.
Nephrons located *high in the cortex* have short Henle's loops.
That is, the loop does not dip far into the medulla.
The thin segment does not extend down to the apex of the loop.
Nephrons located *near the medulla* have long Henle's loops.
That is, the loop dips far down into the pyramid.
The thin segment passes around the apex and part way up the ascending limb
All intergrades between these two extreme types naturally occur.
Tubules with short loops are much more numerous (7:1, it is said).

6. Tubule Characteristics.

The *epithelium* is specific for each segment of a secretory tubule (nephron).
By contrast, the epithelium of all excretory ducts is of one structural type.
The epithelium of the entire uriniferous tubule rests on a *basement membrane*.
This membrane is not particularly distinct without special staining.

A. RENAL (OR MALPIGHIAN) CORPUSCLE.

This is a spheroidal body, about 0.2 mm. wide, associated with a tubule.
It consists of a vascular *glomerulus*, nearly enveloped by a double-walled cup.
The thin cup is an indented epithelial sac, named the *glomerular capsule*.
In development the corpuscle arises from a knot of blood vessels that become
grown around by the expanded, blind end of the secretory tubule.

1. GLOMERULUS.

This is a *rete mirabile* (p. 123), interrupting an arteriole in its course.
It is lobulated and contains tangled vessels, resembling capillaries.
The *afferent arteriole* subdivides into many loops, which anastomose somewhat
Each loop is tortuous, and their combined length is about 1 inch.
Their total length in each kidney is some 16 miles, while the total free
surface of the glomeruli is said to be more than 1 square yard.
The *efferent arteriole* is formed when the loops reunite as a single vessel.
This vessel is smaller than the afferent arteriole.
The points of entry and exit of the arterioles are close together.
This region is often called the *vascular pole* of the corpuscle.
The *endothelium* is extremely thin (0.04 μ), except where nuclei occur.
Hence little of these cells can be seen with a light microscope.
Electron micrographs show many perforations, 0.04 to 0.08 μ wide.
The capillary loops are partially invested by a much-folded basement
membrane.
The tunica media of the afferent arteriole, near its entrance, is modified.
The smooth muscle cells are large, pale-staining and lack myofibrils.
The epithelioid cells contain granules subject to variation in number
This myo-epithelioid cuff is the *juxtaglomerular apparatus*.
It is closely associated with the *macula densa* of the ascending limb.

2. GLOMERULAR CAPSULE.

Another name for this double-walled, epithelial cup is *Bowman's capsule*.
There is a parietal and a visceral layer, separated by a narrow space.
The two components are continuous where the arterioles join the glo
merulus.
Here is the rim where the visceral layer reflects over the glomerulus

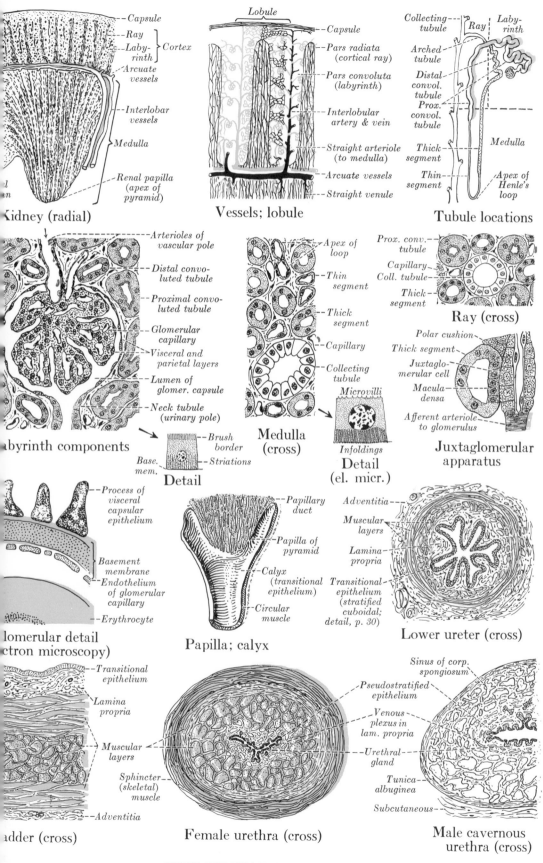

Kidney (radial)

- Capsule
- Ray
- Laby-rinth } Cortex
- Arcuate vessels
- Interlobar vessels
- Medulla
- Renal papilla (apex of pyramid)

Vessels; lobule

Lobule

- Capsule
- Pars radiata (cortical ray)
- Pars convoluta (labyrinth)
- Interlobular artery & vein
- Straight arteriole (to medulla)
- Arcuate vessels
- Straight venule

Tubule locations

- Collecting tubule
- Ray
- Laby-rinth
- Arched tubule
- Distal convol. tubule
- Prox. convol. tubule
- Medulla
- Thick segment
- Thin segment
- Apex of Henle's loop

Labyrinth components

- Arterioles of vascular pole
- Distal convoluted tubule
- Proximal convoluted tubule
- Glomerular capillary
- Visceral and parietal layers
- Lumen of glomer. capsule
- Neck tubule (urinary pole)

Detail

- Brush border
- Base. mem.
- Striations

Medulla (cross)

- Apex of loop
- Thin segment
- Thick segment
- Capillary
- Collecting tubule

Detail (el. micr.)

- Microvilli
- Infoldings

Ray (cross)

- Prox. conv. tubule
- Capillary
- Coll. tubule
- Thick segment

Juxtaglomerular apparatus

- Polar cushion
- Thick segment
- Juxtaglomerular cell
- Macula densa
- Afferent arteriole to glomerulus

Glomerular detail (electron microscopy)

- Process of visceral capsular epithelium
- Basement membrane
- Endothelium of glomerular capillary
- Erythrocyte

Papilla; calyx

- Papillary duct
- Papilla of pyramid
- Calyx (transitional epithelium)
- Circular muscle

Lower ureter (cross)

- Adventitia
- Muscular layers
- Lamina propria
- Transitional epithelium (stratified cuboidal; detail, p. 30)

Bladder (cross)

- Transitional epithelium
- Lamina propria
- Muscular layers
- Sphincter (skeletal) muscle
- Adventitia

Female urethra (cross)

Male cavernous urethra (cross)

- Sinus of corp. spongiosum
- Pseudostratified epithelium
- Venous plexus in lam. propria
- Urethral gland
- Tunica albuginea
- Subcutaneous

THE URINARY ORGANS

Both layers are squamous epithelium; only the parietal layer is easily seen.

The *parietal layer* forms a smooth external capsule, spheroidal in shape.

Cell boundaries and a thin basement membrane are demonstrable.

Cells of the *visceral layer* branch into complicated, feather-shaped arms.

Tiny end-processes come into contact with the basement membrane.

A common basement membrane separates these endings from endothelium.

Where endothelial pores occur, blood bathes this membrane directly.

B. NECK.

The parietal layer opens into the *neck* of the nephron at the *urinary pole*.

This pole of the corpuscle is almost directly opposite the vascular pole.

The neck is a very short segment of rapid epithelial transition.

The flat, capsular cells elevate to a cuboidal and then low columnar cell-type.

C. PROXIMAL CONVOLUTED TUBULE.

This is the longest (14 mm.) and broadest (60 μ) segment of the nephron.

It constitutes most of the bulk of the pars convoluta of the cortex.

The *proximal tubule* is remarkably contorted throughout most of its length.

Hence it is cut very irregularly in sections.

The tubule loops about in the immediate vicinity of its renal corpuscle.

Finally the tubule enters a ray and passes downward in it to the medulla.

Within the ray it pursues first a wavy, then a straight course.

It is often called the *straight portion* of the proximal tubule.

This tubule comprises the *thick descending segment* of Henle's loop.

The component *cells* of a tubule are low columnar (actually pyramidal) in shape.

Freshly obtained cells appear opaque and granular.

They disintegrate rapidly and are difficult to preserve faithfully.

Cell limits usually are not plain, owing to the presence of fluted edges.

These margins interlock complexly with neighboring cells.

The *nuclei* are large, pale and spheroidal.

Only 3 to 4 nuclei show in a transverse section at any level.

The *cytoplasm* stains deeply with acid dyes.

The basal part, when well fixed, shows vertical striations.

Such represent mitochondria and infoldings of the plasma membrane.

The free surface bears a prominent *brush border* (for resorptive activities).

It may appear homogeneous if the fixation is poor, or may even be lost.

In the latter instance the cell appears shorter, with a ragged top.

The appearance of a cell varies with its state of rest or activity.

Active cells become shorter; their lumen, wider; their brush border, taller.

D. THIN SEGMENT OF LOOP.

In the boundary zone of the medulla there is a sudden transition from the straight proximal tubule to a slender segment 2 to 10 mm. long and only 15 μ wide.

This *thin segment* runs a direct, radial course in the medulla.

If it extends past the apex of Henle's loop, it makes a sharp hair-pin bend.

It may be short, or long and recurved, as explained in topic 5 on p. 260.

(It resembles a capillary somewhat, but is larger and thicker-walled.)

The interlocking *cells* are squamous, with a pale staining cytoplasm.

An obvious *brush border* is lacking from this level onward in the nephron.

Nevertheless, electron micrographs reveal the presence of microvilli.

The somewhat flattened *nuclei* cause local bulgings into the lumen.

E. APEX OF LOOP.

This sharply recurved bend varies in composition, correlated with its location.

If the loop dips deep into the medulla, a long thin limb makes the loop.

If the loop lies high in the medulla, the thick ascending segment is involved.

F. THICK, ASCENDING SEGMENT OF LOOP.

This straight, radial tubule is about 9 mm. long and 30 μ in diameter.

There is an abrupt transition from the thin limb into cuboidal epithelium.

The component *cells* stain more deeply acidophilic than those of the thin limb.

They resemble those of the distal convoluted tubules, and significantly so.

This segment can be considered a straight portion of the distal tubule.

(The relation is comparable to the proximal tubule and its straight segment.)

Entering a ray the thick segment ascends, and then passes into the labyrinth.

It ends close to the afferent arteriole of its glomerulus.

The portion in contact with the juxtaglomerular apparatus is specialized

This *macula densa* is an elliptical cluster of taller, crowded cells.

G. DISTAL CONVOLUTED TUBULE.

This segment is short (5 mm.) in comparison to the proximal convoluted tubule.

It is narrower and less convoluted; its width is variable (20 to 50 μ).

Most of its convolutions occur near Bowman's capsule.

Several characteristics distinguish the distal from the proximal tubule.

The *epithelium* is lower (cuboidal) and the lumen is larger.

Cells are smaller and their boundaries more distinct.

Hence 5 to 8 *nuclei* show in a transverse section, instead of 3 to 4.

The *cytoplasm* stains less intensely with acid dyes.

Basal striations are faint, and an obvious brush border is lacking.

(Yet basal infoldings of the plasma membrane are extensive.)

H. ARCHED COLLECTING TUBULE.

This short, junctional segment connects the nephron with the excretory duct.

It is somewhat difficult to locate in sections, except in fortunate cuts.

From 7 to 10 arched tubules join a single, straight collecting tubule.

Hence there are far fewer collecting tubules than nephrons in the kidney.

I. COLLECTING TUBULE.

In a ray and the outer zone of the medulla, the collecting tubules run straight radial courses, without fusions with each other.

In the inner zone of the medulla they unite with other, similar ducts.

This produces large straight tubes, the *papillary ducts* (of Bellini).

From 10 to 25 papillary ducts open on a papilla.

The diameter of ducts in the tree-like system ranges from 40 to 200 μ.

Transverse sections show an even, nearly circular external outline.

The *epithelium* is very different from that of secretory tubules in the nephron.

The cells are cuboidal to tall columnar in shape, and regularly arranged.

Cell boundaries are distinct, and the tops tend to bulge into the lumen.

Nuclei are dark staining and located at one level, toward the base.

The *cytoplasm* is pale and clear, never staining deeply.

7. Blood Vessels.

The blood supply is rich; one-fifth of all blood traverses the kidney each minute.

The various vessels, with special names, are successive portions of vascular trees.

A. ARTERIES.

Interlobar arteries branch off the renal artery and pass up between pyramids.

Each becomes an *arcuate artery* as it bends horizontally to form a short arch.

These lie in the plane of junction of cortex and medulla.

Each gives off vertical branches, named *interlobular arteries.*

An *interlobular artery* ascends radially in the axis of each labyrinth.

These vessels serve to stake off the edges of functional renal lobules.

Some terminal branches supply the capsule, and the cortex just beneath.

Most of the interlobular twigs become *glomerular arterioles* (afferent; efferent).

Afferent and efferent vessels are connected by several *capillary loops.*

Actually these anastomosing loops comprise a rete mirabile (p. 123), rather than typical capillaries.

The *efferent arteriole* vascularizes the tubules of the cortex nearby.

Arteriolae rectae arise from glomerular efferents, located near the medulla.

They dip into the medulla and vascularize it.

Renal arteries tend to be 'end arteries,' the sole supply of regions served.

If occluded, such an affected region suffers acutely from lack of blood.

B. CAPILLARIES.

Capillary plexuses surround the tubules of both the cortex and medulla.

Their supply is from the efferent arterioles of glomeruli.

All blood to the glandular tissue has first passed through glomeruli.

Probably each set of convoluted tubules receives the blood that just previously passed through its own glomerulus.

In the cortical rays the blood comes from the nearest glomerular efferents.

The pyramids are supplied by the arteriolae rectae.

C. VEINS.

Stellate veins lie beneath the capsule and drain into interlobular veins.

Interlobular veins course medullaward in company with interlobular arteries.

They receive blood from the capillary bed of the cortex in general.

Arcuate veins parallel the course of corresponding arteries.

They receive the interlobular veins.

Venulae rectae drain the medulla and join the arcuate veins directly.

Hence these vessels have relations quite different from arteriolae rectae.

Interlobar veins make their exits alongside the pyramids, as do also arteries.

8. Lymphatics.

There are networks in the capsule that join those of adjacent organs.

Another set is related to the uriniferous tubules and associated blood vessels.

These lymphatics accompany the vessels and leave the kidney at the hilus.

9. Nerves.

Both sensory and motor fibers accompany the blood vessels and innervate them.

Fibers to the tubules have also been described by some workers.

). REGENERATIVE ABILITY:

Renal epithelium, especially that of the proximal convoluted tubule, can repair injuries.

After bichloride poisoning, multinucleate masses of cytoplasm appear in this tubule.

Within ten more days, normal structure and function are restored.

Regeneration is restricted to the replacement of cells dying by disease or aging.

Parts of nephrons can be replaced by new cells, but no new nephrons are formed.

Total nephron loss is compensated for effectively by the hypertrophy of other tubules.

Cells enlarge and become highly efficient in increasing functional activity.

E. DIAGNOSTIC FEATURES:

    The kidney is the only compound gland highly deficient in connective-tissue.

        The *renal corpuscle* is a specific diagnostic feature, easily recognized.

    Regions of a kidney, cut in any *radial plane*, show cortex and medulla.

        The *cortex* contains alternate, parallel regions that differ in appearance.

            The convoluted portion has renal corpuscles and irregularly cut tubules.

            The rays consist of parallel tubules, cut lengthwise.

        The *medulla* contains parallel tubules throughout its extent.

            These show a fan-shaped spreading from the papilla of a pyramid to its base.

            All the tubules are cut nearly lengthwise.

    Regions cut *transversely* (*i.e.*, tangential to kidney curvature) have two appearances.

        They show either cortex or medulla, depending on the level of section.

        The *cortex* contains two different kinds of lesser regions.

            A convoluted area is a continuous field of renal corpuscles and irregular tubule

            The rays are groups of tubules, cut transversely, surrounded by a convoluted fiel

        The *medulla* contains tubules, all cut transversely; collecting tubules are prominent.

    Because of the curvature a total section may show regional differences.

        Centrally the plane is transverse; peripherally it is somewhat radial.

    The component segments of tubules separate, by locations, into three groups (p. 259).

        Tubule segments in each territory are then diagnosed by epithelial characteristics.

F. FUNCTIONAL CORRELATIONS:

    The kidney does not secrete like other glands, but serves more as a filter.

        This helps to maintain the composition, pH, and osmotic pressure of blood.

        It does not elaborate urinary products to any degree (ammonia ? hippuric acid ?).

        The chief function is to eliminate body wastes and foreign matter from the blood.

            A notable exception is carbon dioxide, which is eliminated mostly from the lung

    Regional differences in nephron structure reflect differences in function.

        At present, however, such correlations are incompletely determined.

    The collecting tubules are practically inert conducting canals; slight water resorption?

1. Capsular Filtration.

    The *renal corpuscle* is a filtration apparatus that rests at intervals.

        Blood pressure in glomerular capillaries provides the required filtration-energy.

    Capsular urine is essentially identical with plasma, less its proteins and fats.

    The method of filtration is usually held to be a physical process.

        About 150 quarts of fluid pass daily into the Bowman's capsules.

        This is about 10 per cent of the amount of blood that flows through the kidneys.

    The *final urine* in mammals is far more concentrated than the capsular urine.

        There are also significant quantitative differences.

            For example, urea increases more in concentration than do salts.

            Also glucose, which served as a vehicle during filtration, disappears.

        These quantitative changes are accomplished largely by resorption by the tubul

            Yet a minor factor is secretion into the tubule-segments distal to the capsul

2. Resorption.

    Various constituents of the dilute capsular urine are recovered by the tubule proper.

        For the most part this is due to vital cell activity rather than simple diffusion.

    The *proximal convoluted tubule* is more active in resorption than other segments.

Glucose, amino acids, proteins and most of the water are recovered.

There is evidence that this tubule does not perform identically at all its levels.

The *thin segment* is not well understood, but apparently resorbs some water.

The *distal tubule* resorbs electrolytes from the provisional urine.

It also is believed to adjust the final volume and concentration of urine.

Only about 0.6 per cent of the water of provisional capsular urine is retained.

The final product is obtained far less efficiently than would have occurred had the urinary wastes been eliminated from the blood by direct secretion.

3. Secretion.

Concentration and changes in the proportions of specific constituents are also aided by some *differential secretion* (or, better, excretion).

Creatinine, hippuric acid and potassium are known to be eliminated through the *proximal convoluted tubule*.

Ammonia is probably synthesized in the *distal convoluted tubule* and excreted there.

Activities of the juxtaglomerular apparatus and macula densa are not well understood.

Their relation to *renin*, an extractive inducing hypertension, is disputed.

II. THE RENAL PELVIS, URETER AND URINARY BLADDER

A. STRUCTURAL PLAN:

Each renal pyramid is capped at its apex by a *minor calyx* (7 to 10 in all).

The calyx is a double-walled cup whose inner wall has been reflected so that it fits around the projecting tip of the pyramid.

The epithelium of the inner wall is continuous with that of the papillary ducts.

Several minor calyces open into a *major calyx*, and the latter into the *renal pelvis*.

The calyx-pelvis system is merely an expansion of the ureter.

The *ureters* are paired tubes, about 12 inches long, that course behind the peritoneum.

They connect the renal pelvis with the *urinary bladder*, also retroperitoneal.

All of these parts are conventionally constructed, hollow organs.

They have much the same basic structure and can be treated as a unit.

Quantitatively their walls increase in thickness from above downward.

Along with the urethra, they serve as excretory passages to the exterior.

B. DETAILED STRUCTURE:

1. Mucosa.

The lining *epithelium* is of the transitional stratified type.

In the calyx its cells make 2 to 3 layers; in the ureter, 4 to 5; in the bladder, 6 to 8.

The exact appearance and thickness vary with stretching, due to organ-distention.

In an empty bladder the 6 to 8 layers of cells range from rounded to club-shape.

Under distention the cells become thin, through stretching; the number of layers can reduce to 2 to 3, apparently through cells 'slipping by.'

In general, *glands* are lacking except in the vicinity of the urethral orifice.

Here occur some small ingrowths, resembling urethral glands (see beyond).

There is no *basement membrane* beneath the transitional epithelium.

Because of this, capillaries often indent the lower epithelial surface.

The *lamina propria* consists of thin fibers, mostly collagenous.

Papillae do not indent the epithelium, as occurs in highly stratified types.

Hence the junction between epithelium and lamina propria is even.
Diffuse lymphoid tissue and occasional *solitary nodules* may be encountered.

2. Submucosa.

A clearly demarcated *submucosal layer*, like that of various organs, does not exist.
For this reason many refuse to recognize the presence of a submucosa.
Yet the deeper layers are looser, more elastic and could be so considered.
This laxity permits longitudinal *folding* of the lamina propria of the ureter-bladder.
In the *ureter* about five major and minor folds are characteristic.
This gives a regular, stellate pattern to the transversely-cut lumen.
In the relaxed *bladder* the mucosa is thrown into thick, irregular folds.

3. Muscularis.

The *muscular tunic* contains 2 to 3 loosely arranged layers, rather than compact sheet.
The smooth muscle occurs in discrete *bundles*, separated by connective tissue.
The inner layer is arranged longitudinally; the layer next outside, circularly.
In addition, the lower third of the *ureter* and all of the *bladder* have a third, outer
most coat whose muscle is arranged longitudinally.
In the *pelvis* and *calyces* the muscle is thin and largely circular.
About each papilla there is a sort of sphincter.
In the *bladder* the muscular coat is robust and the bundles interlace.
The three layers are not sharply separable as such; the middle layer is thickest.
At the urethral orifice the circular muscle is densely arranged in thin bundles.
This constitutes the *internal sphincter* of the bladder.

4. Adventitia.

The fibrous, external tunic blends with the surrounding connective tissue.
In the *renal pelvis* it becomes continuous with the capsule of the kidney.
The *ureter* lies outside the peritoneum.
The superior surface only of the *bladder* is covered with peritoneum.
Hence the outer tunic becomes a *serosa* in this restricted region.

5. Vessels and Nerves.

Blood vessels run in the adventitia; they supply the muscularis, form a plexus in th
submucosa and another plexus beneath the epithelium.
Lymphatics also gather into plexuses in the submucosa and muscularis.
In the bladder they are said to occur in the muscularis only.
Nerves form a plexus, with ganglia, in the adventitia.
Motor nerves supply the muscularis.
Sensory nerves extend through the mucosa and into the epithelium.
(This general pattern of vessels and nerves holds for the urethra and genital ducts; onl
special features will be mentioned hereafter.)

C. REGENERATIVE ABILITY:

Gaps in the epithelial lining heal readily from the edges of the wound.
Injury-defects in the muscle are replaced by scar tissue.

D. DIAGNOSTIC FEATURES:

Transitional epithelium is a specific feature of the pelvis, ureter and bladder.
Glands are lacking, except a few at the bladder outlet.

The *muscular layers* consist of bundles, rather than closely knit sheets.

The innermost layer is longitudinal smooth muscle.

Next there is a circular layer of smooth muscle.

An outermost, longitudinal layer occurs in the lower ureter and bladder.

The *ureter* is a small tube with a rather symmetrical, stellate lumen.

The radial arms of the lumen usually branch at their ends.

The *bladder* is a large organ, and only sections from sample blocks are seen.

It has a thick wall, heavy muscularis and an irregularly folded mucosa.

E. FUNCTIONAL CORRELATIONS:

Urine comes from the papillary ducts at the rate of 15 drops a minute.

The *calyces* show milking movements, apparently to aid the passage of urine.

Similarly, the ureter exhibits rhythmically peristaltic movements, downward.

The *ureters* pierce the wall of the bladder obliquely, pursuing an intramural course.

Their lumina in these regions tend to be closed by pressure of the bladder contents.

This prevents backflow of urine.

Also a flanking fold of the bladder mucosa acts as a guarding valve.

Epithelium and longitudinal muscle constitute the only wall of the intramural ureter.

Contraction of this muscle opens the lumen of the ureter.

The *bladder* is a reservoir for temporary urinary storage; its normal capacity is one pint.

There is little evidence of absorption, except for bloating of the superficial cells.

A stratified epithelium serves as a barrier against the hypertonic urine.

This prevents further exchanges between the urine and blood.

The plastic and elastic transitional epithelium is well adapted to changing demands.

III. THE URETHRA

A. FEMALE URETHRA:

This terminal segment of the urinary tract is a short duct, about 1.5 in. long.

It extends from the bladder to its outlet in the vestibule.

1. Mucosa.

The *epithelium* near the bladder is transitional stratified.

Next comes a relatively long segment with areas varying in epithelial type.

Some areas are pseudostratified epithelium; others are stratified columnar.

Finally, near the outlet, is stratified squamous epithelium.

Occasional nests of mucous cells occur within the epithelium.

Also there are some small diverticula containing mucous cells.

These *urethral glands* are more numerous in the male urethra (see beyond).

The epithelium rests upon an inconspicuous *basement membrane*.

The *lamina propria* lacks papillae, but is folded longitudinally.

This gives the lumen an irregular, crescentic shape.

2. Submucosa.

A deeper stratum, rich in elastic fibers and veins, could be considered a *submucosa*.

Many, however, interpret this layer as belonging to the lamina propria.

The veins constitute a plexus of prominent, thin-walled channels.

They represent a sort of spongy, *semi-erectile tissue*.

3. Muscularis.

There is a rather thick coat of *smooth muscle*.

The inner layer is arranged longitudinally.

There is considerable intermingling with the venous plexuses of the submucosa

The outer layer is arranged circularly.

At the neck of the bladder it condenses, forming an *involuntary sphincter*.

Bundles of circular *skeletal fibers* occur outside the smooth fibers.

This voluntary muscle is the *constrictor urethrae*.

It is deficient on the posterior surface (next the vagina).

At the lower end of the urethra it forms a *voluntary sphincter*.

4. Adventitia.

This coat is indefinite because of fusions with surrounding structures.

Dorsally there is merging with the fibrous coat of the vagina.

Elsewhere the muscular coat and neighboring constrictor urethrae muscle adjoin.

B. MALE URETHRA:

This tube is 8 inches long; only its stem is homologous to the female urethra.

That is, below the urethral crest it serves also as a genital duct.

This corresponds to the primitive urogenital sinus (permanent vestibule of females).

It has three regional segments, with different neighboring relations.

The *prostatic urethra*, next to the bladder, is only 1.5 inches long.

It bears the elevated urethral crest on its posterior wall.

The prostatic utricle and paired ejaculatory ducts open onto this crest.

The *prostate gland* surrounds and discharges into this segment of the urethra.

The *membranous urethra*, between the prostate and penis, is 0.5 inch long.

It is surrounded by muscles and other components of the urogenital diaphragm.

The *cavernous urethra* extends for 6 inches through the penis.

1. Mucosa.

The *epithelium* varies regionally; also the distribution shows individual variations.

Near the bladder it is transitional in type.

Most of the remainder is variably stratified columnar or pseudostratified.

Near the meatus it becomes stratified squamous.

Intra-epithelial *glands* (*i.e.*, nests of mucous cells) are common.

The epithelium rests on a thin *basement membrane*.

The *lamina propria* resembles that of the female urethra, already described.

Branching mucous tubules extend into the lamina propria, and even deeper.

They are *urethral glands* (of Littré), best developed in the cavernous urethra.

Their ducts contain intra-epithelial nests or pockets of mucous cells.

They open into local recesses of the lumen, produced by epithelial pocketings

2. Submucosa.

A well-defined *submucosa* is not distinguishable as such.

As in the female, there is a deeper layer containing many veins.

The entire cavernous urethra is ensheathed by true *erectile tissue*.

This is the *corpus cavernosum urethrae* (or corpus spongiosum).

It is customarily considered as a part of the penis proper.

That is, it is not a specialized submucosa of the urethra.

3. Muscularis.

A *muscular tunic* occurs chiefly in the prostatic and membraneous segments.

The inner layer of smooth muscle is arranged longitudinally.

The outer layer of smooth muscle is arranged circularly.

It is best developed at the neck of the bladder, forming a *sphincter* there.

Except proximally, the cavernous segment lacks typical smooth muscle layers.

(Instead, longitudinal muscle is distributed in the true erectile tissue.)

4. Adventitia.

There is no typical *adventitial tunic*.

The prostatic urethra is surrounded by the tissue of the prostate gland.

The membranous urethra is encircled by a sphincter of skeletal muscle belonging to the deep transverse perineal muscle.

The cavernous urethra is surrounded by erectile tissue and a dense outer sheath.

Neither is considered as belonging to the urethra itself.

C. DIAGNOSTIC FEATURES:

The *epithelium* changes from level to level, and is variable at some levels.

Represented are transitional, pseudostratified, stratified columnar and -squamous.

Diverticula with mucous cells (urethral glands) are characteristic features.

The *lamina propria* is notable for its prominent venous spaces.

The *muscle arrangement* is: inner layer, longitudinal; outer layer, circular.

The male cavernous urethra lacks muscle layers, as such.

The *female urethra* throughout has a heavier musculature than the male.

It can be confused only with the male membranous urethra (see below).

The male *prostatic urethra* is surrounded by that gland, and hence is distinctive.

The projecting urethral crest gives the lumen a crescentic shape.

The male *membranous urethra* resembles the female urethra closely.

However, its lumen tends to be stellate, not crescentic as in the female.

Both abut peripherally on adjacent skeletal muscle.

The male *cavernous urethra* is surrounded by cavernous erectile tissue.

This segment of the urethra is included within the penis as a component of that organ.

D. FUNCTIONAL CORRELATIONS:

The *female urethra* is exclusively a urinary drainage duct from the bladder.

Only the stem of the *male urethra* is an exclusive urinary duct.

The remainder, therefore, is a joint urinary and genital canal.

It is a permanent retention of the embryonic urogenital sinus.

The secretion of the urethral glands is lubricative only.

Chapter XXIII.   THE MALE REPRODUCTIVE SYSTEM

The male reproductive organs include the following parts:
> The *testes*, or male sex glands.
> The *ducts* of the testes, and the auxiliary glands associated with them.
> The *penis*, or copulative organ.

I. THE TESTIS

The *testis* is functionally a double gland.
> Its exocrine product is chiefly the sex cells; hence it is a *cytogenic gland*.
> An internal secretion is elaborated by certain cells; hence it is also an *endocrine gland*.

A. STRUCTURAL PLAN:

> The *testis* is an ovoid gland, about 1.8 inches long.
> It is surrounded by a thick capsule, the *tunica albuginea*.
>> Along the posterior border the capsule projects inward, like a ridge.
>> This thickened, inturned crest is named the *mediastinum testis*.
> Thin, fibrous partitions (*septula*) radiate from the mediastinum to the capsule proper.
>> The compartments, thus formed, are pyramidal lobules (*lobuli testis*).
> Within the lobules are located the contorted *seminiferous tubules*.
>> These lie in a bed of loose connective tissue, containing groups of *interstitial cells*.

B. DETAILED STRUCTURE:
1. Framework.
> The *tunica albuginea* is a thick, tough capsule that encases the testis.
>> It is composed of dense fibro-elastic tissue, and appears white in life.
>> The innermost layer is the *tunica vasculosa;* it is looser and more vascular.
> Along the posterior margin of the testis is the thickened *mediastinum testis*.
>> It corresponds to a hilus region; ducts, vessels and nerves connect here.
> The *septula testis* are thin fibrous partitions, incomplete and branching.
>> These radiate from the crest-like mediastinum to the inner surface of the capsule.
>> They divide the testis into about 250 compartments, or *testis lobules*.
>>> Each lobule is a pyramidal space, with its apex toward the mediastinum.
>>> Since the septula are incomplete partitions, the lobules communicate in places.
>>> (Within the lobules are seminiferous tubules, embedded in a fibrous stroma.)
> Each seminiferous tubule is surrounded by a *layered sheath* of fibrous tissue.
>> This is a local condensation of the general connective tissue within a lobule.
> The connective-tissue *stroma* occupies the spaces between tubules.
>> This material is a loose soft tissue, containing fine collagenous fibers.
>> It also contains vessels, nerves and several types of cells.
>> Most interesting are the specific *interstitial cells*, or 'cells of Leydig.'
>>> These are large irregular-shaped cells, usually occurring in groups.

Their rounded, chromatic nucleus contains one or two prominent nucleoli.
The cytoplasm is rich in inclusions, such as fat, pigment, etc.
Many cells also contain peculiar rod-shaped *crystalloids.*
These are albuminous bodies, characteristic of the human testis.
The interstitial cells are important because of their endocrine role (p. 274).

2. Seminiferous Tubules.

Each lobule of the testis contains 1 to 4 highly contorted *seminiferous tubules.*
A tubule is 1 to 3 ft. long and about 0.2 mm. wide.
Their combined length in some 500 tubules of a human testis is about 275 yards.
A tubule rarely shows blind side-branches or a blind ending.
Instead, simple or branched tubules join with other tubules into arched loops.
They may even unite, by lateral branches, with tubules of adjoining lobules.
At the apex of a lobule each seminiferous tubule (tubulus contortus) loses its
convolutions and becomes a *straight tubule* (tubulus rectus).
A contorted, seminiferous tubule is lined with a specialized, stratified epithelium.
This is known as the *germinal* or *seminiferous epithelium.*
Most of its cells are sex cells; others are auxiliary, supporting elements.
The epithelium rests upon a *basement membrane* whose thickness varies with age, etc.
The tubular membrane is surrounded by a *layered sheath* of fibrous tissue.
Centrally the epithelium borders upon an axial lumen.
Not until the time of puberty do the 'tubules' acquire a definite, central canal.
Some atrophic tubules begin to appear in the third decade of life.

a. Sustentacular Cells.

These elements (also called *Sertoli cells*) are supporting and nutritive cells.
Relatively few in number, they are spaced at fairly regular intervals.
Their shape is tall and pillar-like.
The base rests on the basement membrane of the tubule.
The free end extends in a radial direction toward the lumen.
The sex cells are crowded between the Sertoli cells and indent them.
As a result, their sides bear branching, winged processes.
The cell outline is so irregular and indistinct that it is hard to trace.
The *nucleus* is located some distance above the base of the cell.
It is ovoid, pale and radially oriented; its surface is often grooved.
The nucleolus is prominent and of a peculiar, compound type.
The *cytoplasm* has a reticular appearance in fixed preparations.
It contains fibrils, lipoid droplets and a tapering crystalloid body.
Spermatids attach to Sertoli cells during their transformation period.
Apparently these supporting elements also serve as nurse cells at this time.
They successfully withstand various influences that destroy the sex cells.

b. Sex Cells.

The *germ cells* (or sex cells) make up a stratified layer 4 to 8 cells deep.
The cells differentiate progressively, from periphery to lumen, in the tubule.
Proliferation (never amitotic) pushes cells toward the lumen.
Those nearest the lumen transform into spermatozoa and detach as motile
cells.
This sequence of events is known as *spermatogenesis.*
Well-defined cyclic waves do not pass up the tubules of man.
Yet not every stage is seen at the same time at a given level.
Probably the time taken in producing a spermatozoön is 2 to 3 weeks.

1. SPERMATOGONIA.

    These cells lie adjacent to the basement membrane.

    They are the only sex cells present until the time of puberty.

    Human spermatogonia contain 23 pairs of chromosomes (*i.e.*, a double-set).

        This number replaces the former, erroneous count of 48.

    During mitosis each of the 46 chromosomes splits lengthwise.

        Hence every daughter cell also contains the full double-set of 23 pairs.

2. PRIMARY SPERMATOCYTES.

    These represent the terminal stage of full-grown spermatogonia.

        They are the largest germ cells seen (18 μ).

    Division of the primary and secondary spermatocytes is by a modified mitosis.

        This peculiar type of cell division is named *meiosis*.

        Its characteristic feature is the reduction of the double set of chromosomes,
            present in the young primary spermatocyte, to a single set.

        A further peculiarity is the premature splitting of each member of each
            chromosome pair, even before the first division is well begun.

            This makes a group of four, a *tetrad*, out of each chromosome pair.

            In this way preparations are completed for two rapid divisions.

    On dividing, individual members of each chromosome-pair separate bodily

        That is, a group of 23 chromosomes passes into each daughter cell.

        As a result of this reduction, the chromosome-number is halved (46 to 23).

            Yet the single set contains one of each kind originally present.

            (An exception occurs in the unequal sex-determining pair; see be-
                yond.)

        Each chromosome of the 'single set' in a daughter cell is really double.

            This is because it had already split before this division began.

3. SECONDARY SPERMATOCYTES.

    These are daughter cells of the primary spermatocytes.

    They are about half the size of the primaries and lie nearer the lumen.

        Almost as soon as they are formed, they divide and produce *spermatids*.

        Hence few of them are seen in a section of a tubule.

    This cell division is much like an ordinary mitosis.

        The split halves of each chromosome pass into the two daughter cells.

        Thus a complete single set of 23 chromosomes is maintained in each.

4. SPERMATIDS.

    These are daughter cells of the secondary spermatocytes.

        They are about half the size of the latter and lie close to the lumen.

    No mitoses occur among them, but each spermatid is transformed by a re-
        modeling process (*spermiogenesis*) into a functional spermatozoön.

    The nucleus furnishes most of the sperm *head*.

        Part of the Golgi apparatus becomes the *acrosome* at the apex of the head.

    The cytoplasm supplies a thin investment, the *head-cap*, about the head.

        Most of it, however, extends along the neck, body and tail as a *sheath*.

        The excess of unused cytoplasm is sloughed off.

    One *centriole* locates in the *neck*, just below the head.

        The other centriole becomes ring-shaped and moves tailward.

            It halts at the lower end of the *body* (also called the middle piece).

        From the anterior centriole an *axial filament* extends through the tail.

            Near its tip-end this thread is not ensheathed with cytoplasm.

            The filament is a cluster of finer threads, like all cilia (p. 32).

Mitochondria segregate in the body; they become arranged as a *spiral thread*.

5. SPERMATOZOA.

Groups of nearly mature *spermatozoa* still attach to Sertoli cells.

Free, detached spermatozoa in the lumen are not commonly seen.

This is because they are carried into the ducts as fast as formed.

Human spermatozoa have a total length of about 60 μ.

The *head* (5 μ) is pear-shaped and flattened.

The short *neck* and longer *body* (5 μ) interconnect the head and tail.

The *tail* (50 μ) is long, extremely slender and vibratile.

3. Vessels and Nerves.

Blood vessels enter the testis at the mediastinum.

Some follow the septula inward, and form networks about the tubules.

Others supply the tunica vasculosa.

Lymphatics drain the interstitial tissue.

Nerves follow the blood vessels, but endings within the tubules seem doubtful.

C. REGENERATIVE ABILITY:

The testes are incompetent to repair wounds other than by producing scar tissue.

The interstitial cells, nevertheless, can proliferate when the occasion requires.

Sex cells are highly susceptible when subjected to certain environmental conditions.

For example, slightly elevated temperature causes widespread decline and destruction.

Yet recovery can follow severe depletion if normal temperature is restored.

D. DIAGNOSTIC FEATURES:

There are *epithelial tubules*, surrounded by distinct connective-tissue sheaths and embedded in a more or less *cellular stroma*.

The irregularly sectioned tubules take a multiplicity of shapes (O, C, J, S, etc.).

The *epithelium*, 4 to 8 cells deep, is a specialized stratified cuboidal type.

Actually, the cells are rounded to polyhedral in shape.

Some, next to the lumen, may show transformation stages into spermatozoa.

Prepuberal 'tubules' are mostly solid; sustentacular (Sertoli) cells dominate the field.

Senile tubules vary, but typically show atrophy and a reduction or loss of sex cells.

Yet some individuals may have quite normal appearing testes in the eighth decade.

E. FUNCTIONAL CORRELATIONS:

The *exocrine function* of the testis is to produce male sex cells.

For this reason it is a type of cytogenic gland.

The development of spermatozoa depends on several factors.

A *hormone* (*FSH*) of the hypophysis is a stimulating, necessary agent.

Vitamins (especially E) are also indispensable.

A suitable *temperature* is critical; such is furnished by the scrotum.

This has to be slightly lower than that in the abdominal cavity.

In man, *spermatogenesis* is a continuous process, various stages showing at any level.

It may continue even into old age.

Local regions of the testis may revert, temporarily or not, to the prepuberal state.

Furthermore, in illness there are regressive changes.

Spermatozoa are adapted to swimming and penetration of the relatively huge egg.

The nucleus has been condensed to the limit imposed by close chromosome packing.

Cytoplasm has been reduced to the minimum consistent with flagellate swimming.

The locomotor apparatus is 92 per cent of the total length of the cell.

The effective contribution to a new individual is thus limited to chromosomes and seemingly, the centrosome.

The *sex-determining role* of spermatozoa is correlated with the types that are produced.

Half of the secondary spermatocytes acquire a female-determining chromosome (X)

An equal number acquire a male-determining chromosome (Y).

(A single sex chromosome [X or Y] then continues into daughter spermatids and spermatozoa.)

This is the only instance in which the members of a chromosome pair are unlike.

The chief *endocrine secretion* of the testis is a steroid hormone, *testosterone*.

The weight of evidence favors the interstitial cells as the source of this hormone.

Testosterone controls secondary sex characters, the sex impulse and the proper maintenance of the genital ducts and accessory glands.

Its production depends on stimulation by the LH (or ICSH) hormone of the hypophysis

Castration before puberty results in a retention of *infantilism*.

Castration after puberty results in retrograde changes (*eunuchism*).

II. THE SCROTUM

The *scrotum* is a divided pouch of the integument that contains the testes.

It was invaded by the testes, which migrated from an original abdominal position.

1. Structure.

The *scrotum* is specialized integument, somewhat modified from ordinary skin.

The *epidermis* is changeably thick, and more pigmented than that of the body in general.

The *dermis* contains sparse hair follicles and large sebaceous and sweat glands.

The *subcutaneous* has a thick layer of smooth muscle that comprises the *dartos tunic*.

It also is notable for the absence of fat cells.

The twin cavities of the scrotum were produced by the invasion of two peritoneal sacs.

These serosal extensions pushed into the subcutaneous tissue in late fetal life.

They then detached from the general peritoneum and became closed sacs.

Such a serosal sac is named the *tunica vaginalis*.

Its *parietal layer* makes a lining to the scrotum.

Its *visceral layer* is reflected over three-fourths of the testis and epididymis.

The surface mesothelium corresponds to the germinal epithelium of embryonic glands.

Both layers meet along the posterior, attached border of the testis.

2. Diagnostic Features.

The scrotum, penis and areola mammae have integument of the same specialized type.

Differences in pigmentation, glands and muscle content are largely quantitative only.

3. Functional Correlations.

Each vaginal sac contains enough serous fluid to afford its walls frictionless play.

The tissue anchoring the testis still allows it considerable freedom of movement.

The muscle-content of the scrotal wall responds to temperature conditions.

The scrotum contracts when cold and relaxes when warm.

This makes the testes hug the body closely or become pendulous, respectively.

The scrotum acts as a thermoregulator, which is an adaptation, since sex cells are susceptible to injury by a temperature equaling that of the interior body.

The muscular dartos tunic is responsible for the *dartos reflex*.
This is a writhing movement of the general scrotal wall when stroked locally.

III. THE MALE GENITAL DUCTS

The *male ducts* differ structurally at seven levels along their course.
For this reason they have been given different regional names.

A. TUBULI RECTI:

At the apex of a lobule each seminiferous tubule becomes a single, short *straight tubule*.
The diameter of the duct narrows to about 25 μ.
Only the sustentacular (Sertoli) cells remain, arranged as a simple epithelium.
The component cells are columnar or cuboidal elements with fatty inclusions.

B. RETE TESTIS:

The straight ducts open into a network of canals within the mediastinum.
These are irregular, anastomosing channels of variable breadth.
Their lining is a *simple epithelium*, cuboidal to columnar in shape.
Some cells bear a single flagellum.
There is a delicate *basement membrane*, but no specific lamina propria.
That is, the epithelium lines clefts in the fibrous stroma of the mediastinum.

C. DUCTULI EFFERENTES:

About 10 to 15 *efferent ductules* emerge from the upper part of the rete testis.
Each forms a spirally wound *lobule of the epididymis*, conical in shape.
Each ductule is about 3 in. long, when straightened, and 0.2 to 0.4 mm. in diameter.
The several lobules comprise a mass named the *head of the epididymis*.
The individual tubules are embedded in connective tissue, and are surrounded by a very
thin layer of smooth muscle fibers, circularly arranged.
The *epithelium* is mostly simple columnar, but it is variable in a characteristic pattern.
Externally the tubule has a fairly smooth contour.
Internally it is indented by closely spaced pits.
This is owing to the presence of much shorter cells in these local areas.
Some of the tall cells are ciliated; others are not.
The finely granular cytoplasm is acidophilic.
It contains fat droplets and pigment granules.
The shorter cells form cup-like pits; these are *intra-epithelial glands*.
The cytoplasm is clear, pale and contains pigment granules.
Some of these cells may bear cilia also.
The *cilia* of both cell-types beat toward the epididymis and move spermatozoa along.
These are the only motile cilia in the entire duct system.
Both the nonciliated tall and short cells are said to be *secretory*.
Blebs of secretion sometimes adhere to their free surfaces.
In addition, there are a few rounded, basal cells that do not reach the lumen.
The epithelium rests upon a distinct *basement membrane*.
The winding tubules, at their ends, change gradually into the epithelium of the epi-
didymis and join individually with that duct.

D. DUCTUS EPIDIDYMIDIS:

A compact mass, the *epididymis*, stretches along the posterior side of the testis.

Its middle and lower regions ('body' and 'tail') consist of a single coiled duct.

This *duct of the epididymis*, by itself, is often incorrectly called the epididymis.

It is a highly tortuous duct, nearly 20 ft. long and about 0.4 mm. wide.

The duct has a smooth cylindrical outline, inside and out.

The *epithelium* is thicker than in the efferent ductules, and is uniform in thickness.

The duct is surrounded by a definite *basement membrane* and a thin layer of circular *smooth muscle;* it lies embedded in a fibrous stroma.

The *epithelium* is pseudostratified; it contains basal cells and tall columnar cells.

The rounded basal cells contain fatty droplets.

The tall cells contain secretion droplets, granules, vacuoles and pigment.

At the surface there is a pencil of nonmotile, clumped cilia (*stereocilia*).

The secretion passes out through this fibrillated cytoplasm.

E. DUCTUS DEFERENS:

The duct of the epididymis enlarges into the *deferent duct*, which soon straightens.

It traverses the inguinal canal and courses behind the peritoneum toward the urethra

This is a typically organized tubular organ, about 18 in. long and 2 to 3 mm. wide.

The wall is relatively very thick and the lumen relatively narrow.

In the scrotum and inguinal canal the ductus deferens courses within the *spermatic cord*.

It is easily palpable through the scrotum and the soft cord.

Other contents of the spermatic cord are the following:

Testicular artery and the pampiniform system of veins.

Lymph vessels and nerves of the testis and epididymis.

Fascias and the *cremaster muscle* enclose the spermatic cord.

The muscle is responsible for the *cremasteric reflex*.

Leaving the cord, the duct courses behind the pelvic peritoneum toward the urethra.

It ends in a short, dilated segment, known as the *ampulla*.

1. Mucosa.

The *epithelium* is pseudostratified; many of the tall cells bear *stereocilia*.

There is a delicate *basement membrane* and a thin *lamina propria*.

The latter contains many elastic fibers.

The mucosa is thrown into 4 to 6 longitudinal folds.

In transverse section the lumen is, therefore, stellate.

2. Submucosa.

There is no definite *submucosal layer*, although the deeper level of the lamina propria contains numerous blood vessels.

3. Muscularis.

The *muscular coat* is very heavy and gives the duct a cord-like feel.

It is thickest in the pelvic part of its course.

The inner layer is a relatively thin sheet of longitudinal smooth muscle.

The middle, circular layer is strongly developed.

It is loosely arranged, and longitudinal bundles intermingle with it.

This layer is especially well represented in the pelvic course of the duct.

The outer longitudinal layer is also robust.

4. Adventitia.

The fibrous *external tunic* is typical, blending with adjoining tissues.

F. AMPULLA OF DUCTUS DEFERENS:

Terminally the duct dilates into an irregular spindle-shaped tube, the *ampulla*.

Here the lumen is larger and the mucosa much more folded.

Thin *mucosal folds* branch and anastomose, thereby producing pocket-like *recesses*.

From these recesses, occasional outpocketings invade the muscularis.

The appearance resembles somewhat the arrangement in the seminal vesicle (p. 278).

The simple columnar *epithelium* gives indications of secretion.

The *muscularis* shows much interlacing of circular and longitudinal bundles.

It is the external longitudinal layer that retains its identity best.

G. EJACULATORY DUCT:

This is the short (0.8 in.), slender, terminal segment of each male genital duct.

It appears as if it were formed by the union of the ampulla and seminal vesicle.

The duct pierces the prostate gland and opens into the urethra on the urethral crest.

The *mucosa* is highly folded, much like that of the ampulla.

The simple columnar to pseudostratified *epithelium* is apparently secretory.

Some mucosal outpocketings occur, like those from the recesses of the ampulla.

Except at the upper end, the *supporting wall* consists of fibrous tissue alone.

In the terminal portion cavernous vascular spaces occur, as in the urethra.

H. VESSELS AND NERVES:

These auxiliaries are distributed according to the general plan described on p. 266.

I. DIAGNOSTIC FEATURES:

The rete testis, efferent ductules and epididymis are all embedded in a fibrous stroma.

None has a conspicuous muscular layer.

The *rete testis* appears as a localized set of irregular-calibered, *communicating channels*.

The channels are well-spaced in a bed of dense fibrous tissue.

Their *epithelium* varies from simple cuboidal to a columnar type.

The *efferent ductules* are tortuous tubules that become sectioned in various planes.

They are characterized by a unique type of *epithelium*.

Externally the cell bases produce a fairly even contour.

Internally the contour is uneven, making a scalloped lumen.

These *crests* and *troughs* are produced by alternate groups of tall and short cells.

Some cells are ciliated; others show secretory blebs.

The *epididymis* is a fatter, winding duct, sectioned many times and in various planes.

Its epithelium is not folded, and its external and internal contour are both even.

Transverse sections show as regular, *washer-shaped bands*.

The *epithelium* consists of tall, ciliated cells and rounded basal cells.

The half of the epithelial cells bordering the lumen is free of nuclei.

Stored spermatozoa can be expected in the lumen of normal postpuberal ducts.

The *ductus deferens* has a wall that is very thick in comparison to lumen-size.

The *epithelium* resembles that of the epididymis.

However, it is folded so as to produce a stellate lumen (in transverse section).

The muscular coat is exceptionally thick, showing three layers.

The inner and outer layers are longitudinal; the middle layer, circular.

The *ampulla* of the ductus deferens has complicated, thin mucosal folds.

The epithelium is simple columnar.

Its thick muscularis shows a markedly irregular arrangement.

Longitudinal and circular bundles intermingle.

The *ejaculatory duct* has a mucosa resembling that of the ampulla.
> The tube lacks a muscular coat and is supported by fibrous tissue alone.
> It lies within prostatic tissue.

J. FUNCTIONAL CORRELATIONS:

This system of ducts *transports* and *stores* spermatozoa.
How nonmotile spermatozoa pass through the *straight tubules* and *rete testis* is not known.
> Perhaps secreted fluid washes them along, since cilia are lacking.
> In any event they pass quickly; they are seen rarely in sections.

The cilia of the *efferent ductules* are functional.
> Presumably they aid in moving spermatozoa to the epididymis.

The *epididymis* is a long storage duct, through which spermatozoa pass slowly.
> The journey may take as long as six weeks.
> Here, also, spermatozoa ripen and acquire optimal fertilizability.
>> At the same time, they become capable of motility.
> The thick, viscid secretion supplies nutritive substance to be used by spermatozoa.

The *ductus deferens*, its ampulla and the ejaculatory duct are primarily for transport.
Powerful contractions of the epididymis, ductus deferens and urethra forcibly expel spermatozoa under the stimulus of climactic sexual excitement.
Efferent ductules, epididymis, ampulla and ejaculatory ducts give evidence of secretion.
> Their functional maintenance depends on stimulation by the testicular hormone.

The efferent ductules and upper epididymis can absorb fluid, and probably do so normally.

IV. THE AUXILIARY GENITAL GLANDS

These organs are the paired *seminal vesicles*, and the *prostate* and *bulbo-urethral glands*.

A. SEMINAL VESICLE:

Each *vesicle* is a diverticulum off the adjacent ductus deferens, just below the ampulla.
> It is a convoluted *glandular sac*, about 2 in. long and 0.7 in. wide.
>> If straightened, it would be a tube more than twice this length.
> The lumen is irregular and highly recessed throughout; there are some side bays.

Some mammals (insectivores; carnivores; etc.) lack seminal vesicles.

1. Mucosa.

The *lining membrane* is remarkably folded into an intricate system of elevations.
> High primary *folds* branch into secondary and tertiary folds.
>> The thin folds project far into the lumen and frequently merge with others.
>> As a result, the internal surface appears honeycombed.
> The *recesses* are of different sizes, and all communicate with the lumen.
>> There are no true glandular alveoli, but only these chambers between folds.

The capacious lumen regularly contains stored *secretion*.
> It is a yellowish, gelatinous, sticky, mucoid, weakly alkaline fluid.
> It contains rounded, acidophilic masses; fixation coagulates the fluid.

A. EPITHELIUM.

The *epithelium* may be simple columnar; but it is usually pseudostratified.
> Besides low columnar cells, there are rounded basal elements.
>> Cell height varies with secretion-storage, age, and other influences.

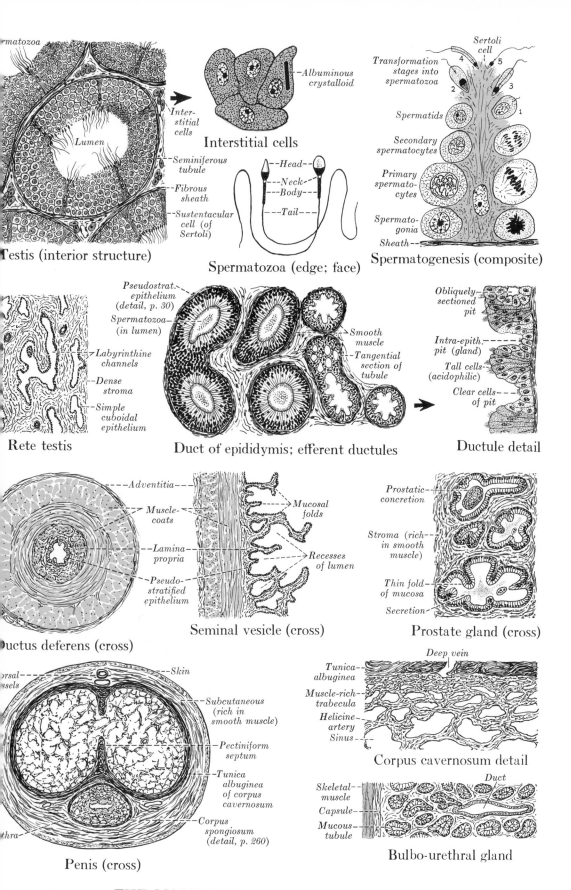

Testis (interior structure)

Spermatozoa
—Albuminous crystalloid
—Interstitial cells

Interstitial cells

Lumen
—Seminiferous tubule
—Fibrous sheath
—Sustentacular cell (of Sertoli)

--Head--
--Neck--
--Body--
--Tail--

Spermatozoa (edge; face)

Sertoli cell
Transformation stages into spermatozoa
Spermatids
Secondary spermatocytes
Primary spermatocytes
Spermatogonia
Sheath--

Spermatogenesis (composite)

Pseudostrat. epithelium (detail, p. 30)
Spermatozoa (in lumen)
→Smooth muscle
—Tangential section of tubule

Labyrinthine channels
—Dense stroma
—Simple cuboidal epithelium

Rete testis

Duct of epididymis; efferent ductules

Obliquely sectioned pit
Intra-epith. pit (gland)
Tall cells (acidophilic)
Clear cells of pit

Ductule detail

—Adventitia—
—Muscle coats
→Mucosal folds
—Lamina propria
→Recesses of lumen
—Pseudo-stratified epithelium

Seminal vesicle (cross)

Prostatic concretion
Stroma (rich in smooth muscle)
Thin fold of mucosa
Secretion

Prostate gland (cross)

Ductus deferens (cross)

Deep vein
Tunica albuginea
Muscle-rich trabecula
Helicine artery
Sinus

Corpus cavernosum detail

—Skin
—Subcutaneous (rich in smooth muscle)
—Pectiniform septum
—Tunica albuginea of corpus cavernosum
—Corpus spongiosum (detail, p. 260)

Dorsal vessels
thra

Penis (cross)

Skeletal muscle
Capsule
Mucous tubule
Duct

Bulbo-urethral gland

THE MALE REPRODUCTIVE ORGANS

The cells contain *secretory granules* and yellow, lipoidal *pigment*.

   The pigment first appears after puberty; it colors the fresh mucosa.

Some cells show blebs of secretion on their free surface.

B. LAMINA PROPRIA.

This *lamina* is a thin layer of richly elastic connective tissue.

Thin extensions from it serve as supports for the epithelial folds.

There is no recognizable *basement membrane*, and no *submucosa*.

2. Muscularis.

The *muscular coat* is relatively less heavy than that of the ductus deferens.

Internally, there are circular and oblique bundles of smooth muscle.

   These bundles interlace considerably.

Externally there is a longitudinal layer of smooth muscle.

3. Adventitia.

The *external tunic* is thin and composed mostly of elastic fibers.

   It blends with the surrounding connective tissue.

Many blood vessels and some autonomic ganglia occupy this layer.

4. Vessels and Nerves.

The distribution follows the plan described on p. 266.

5. Diagnostic Features.

The *seminal vesicle* is an elongate, saccular organ, folded upon itself.

   A typical section through it appears to contain several separate compartments.

The *mucosa* forms high, thin folds that branch and anastomose.

   Small, open recesses and obliquely sectioned, enclosed cavities are seen.

   T- and L-shaped folds are common; between such large folds occur smaller ones.

   Looping arches often bound cavities and enclose minor folds.

      These are obliquely sectioned recesses.

The *epithelium* is mostly pseudostratified, but may be simple in some regions.

The capacious *lumen* of the adult constantly contains *secretion*.

   It commonly appears as a deeply staining, acidophilic, net-like coagulum.

   It may contain small acidophilic masses, but fixation often destroys them.

   Some spermatozoa are usually seen in the lumen of specimens taken after death.

A well-developed *muscular coat* surrounds the organ.

   Yet this is far less imposing than in the ampulla of the ductus deferens.

6. Functional Correlations.

The *epithelium* of the seminal vesicles (and prostate) depends on hormonal support.

   It is the male hormone, *testosterone*, that exerts this direct influence.

   Castration before puberty results in underdevelopment and secretory failure.

   Castration after puberty is followed by involution and loss of secretory power.

      Administration of testis extract promptly restores the cells to function.

The seminal vesicle functions primarily as a gland with a voluminous lumen (4 ml.).

   It secretes and stores the viscid component of seminal fluid.

   Folding of the mucosa increases the secretory surface and aids distention.

Storage of spermatozoa is seemingly incidental and inconstant.

   They probably enter incidentally, as the result of backflow.

This may occur during sexual excitement without ejaculation, or after death. In some mammals spermatozoa are never found in these organs.

B. PROSTATE GLAND:

This gland, about 1.5 in. in diameter, surrounds the urethra as it leaves the bladder.

It is really an aggregate of 30 to 50 tubulo-alveolar glands, grouped in five *lobes*.

These empty into the prostatic urethra by 15 to 30 ducts.

The glands are not fully developed until puberty.

1. Capsule and Stroma.

The whole gland is surrounded by a fibro-elastic *capsule*.

Its inner zone, in particular, is rich in smooth muscle.

A dense, very abundant *stroma* embeds the alveoli in a compact mass.

The stroma is arranged as septum-like bands which join the capsule.

It constitutes one-fourth of the volume of the organ.

The fibro-elastic stroma contains a rich intermixture of *smooth-muscle* strands.

There is no specialization into a *basement membrane*.

2. Parenchyma.

The elongate *alveoli* and *tubules* vary greatly in size and shape.

They are irregular, varicose and branching; some become cystic.

Both these secretory portions and their ducts have relatively wide lumina.

The *epithelium* is remarkably folded into large and small folds.

These festoons are supported by thin extensions of the fibro-muscular septa.

The *epithelial cells* are cuboidal to columnar in shape.

They contain *secretion granules* and yellowish, *lipoidal droplets*.

Some cells show cytoplasmic protrusions that seemingly detach, apocrine style.

In some places, basal cells occur also.

The *ducts* have an irregular lumen, the smaller ones resembling secretory tubules.

Terminal excretory ducts, near the urethra, have pseudostratified epithelium.

In them are patches of secretory cells.

3. Secretion.

Secretion is said to be continuous, but especially active during coitus.

The *prostatic secretion* is thin, milky and faintly acid; its odor is distinctive.

The secretory product makes up most of the bulk of the seminal fluid.

Yet removal of the gland does not necessarily incur reproductive incapacity.

Fixation coagulates the fluid into an acidophilic, granular mass.

The secretion frequently contains ovoid *prostatic concretions* (corpora amylacea).

Many of these acidophilic secretion-condensations are lamellated.

Their size is extremely variable, even up to 2 mm. or more.

Concretions first appear in adult life.

They become more abundant with advancing age (since discharge is less frequent?).

Large concretions are often retained, and may calcify into *calculi*.

4. Vessels and Nerves.

Blood vessels, *lymphatics*, *nerves*, ganglia and sensory corpuscles are abundant.

They are found in the capsule and stroma, and are abundant alongside the organ

5. Diagnostic Features.
>There are many long, wide-lumened *alveoli*, not closely spaced.
>Alveoli are embedded in a dense, abundant, fibro-muscular *stroma*.
>>The stroma has a rich content of *smooth muscle* that shows on staining.
>The *columnar epithelium* forms many thin folds within alveoli.
>>Each is supported by a notably thin plate of stromal tissue.
>>Tangential sections of folds often appear as isolated tissue-islands.
>The *secretion* makes an acidophilic, granular mass in fixed preparations.
>>It may contain acidophilic *concretions*, usually lamellated.

6. Functional Correlations.
>The gland contributes an important component to the seminal fluid (p. 282).
>Dependence on hormonal support parallels the behavior of the seminal vesicle (p. 279).

BULBO-URETHRAL GLAND:
These paired bodies, also called *Cowper's glands*, lie behind the membranous urethra.
Each is a compound tubulo-alveolar gland, the size of a pea.
>It is a special, larger type of urethral gland (p. 268).

1. Capsule and Stroma.
>Each is surrounded by skeletal muscle and invested with a thin *capsule*.
>Connective-tissue *septa* subdivide the organ into *lobules*.
>>These septa contain considerable skeletal muscle and some smooth muscle fibers.
>>Within the lobules the *stroma* may contain some smooth muscle fibers locally.
>*Basement membranes* surround the secretory tubules and ducts.

2. Parenchyma.
>The *secretory end pieces* of the gland are variable in size and form.
>>They may be tubular, alveolar or somewhat saccular.
>>These end-pieces either terminate blindly or connect by anastomoses.
>The *epithelium* is variable in appearance.
>>Most alveoli consist of cuboidal to columnar, pale epithelium.
>>>Some of them are dilated and lined with flattened epithelium.
>>>The cytoplasm contains *mucigen droplets* and colloid spherules.
>>>>It also contains acidophilic, spindle-shaped inclusions.
>>>The *nuclei* are flattened and basally located.
>>Other darker-staining alveoli, with rounded nuclei, are at rest functionally.
>>>They resemble somewhat serous alveoli.

3. Secretion.
>The *secretory product* is clear, viscid, glairy and stringy.
>>It is a mucoid substance, differing somewhat from true mucus.
>Fixation precipitates the secretion into angular masses.
>>These stain brightly with acid dyes.

4. Ducts.
>Within most lobules there are definite *ducts*, and these may be dilated locally.
>>In some regions the ducts are also secretory and appear as glandular tubules.
>Also, the *main excretory ducts* contain patches of mucous cells, and even alveoli.
>>These ducts are 3 to 4 cm. long and open into the cavernous urethra.

They are surrounded by thin rings of smooth muscle.
Their epithelium is simple, but becomes stratified columnar near the outlet.

5. Diagnostic Features.

The bulbo-urethral gland is a lobulated mucous gland, surrounded by skeletal musc[
A minority of the alveoli may resemble a group of serous cells.
Some regions may lack recognizable intralobular ducts.
Elsewhere the intralobular ducts are large and often dilated.
The main excretory ducts are equipped with some circular muscle.
They often contain mucous areas of epithelium, or even mucous diverticula.
The secretion shows angular masses, staining brightly with eosin.

6. Functional Correlations.

The gland supplies a small amount of mucus under erotic stimulation (see beyond).
The spindle-shaped inclusions are said to dissolve in the mucus after discharge.

D. REGENERATIVE ABILITY:

Repair, leading to the replacement of specific cells, is limited in these glands.
Yet hypertrophy and hyperplasia occur with aging.
These responses also occur in response to hormonal stimulation.

E. SEMINAL FLUID AND EJACULATION:

1. Semen.

Seminal fluid (semen) consists of spermatozoa suspended in a thick fluid.
The auxiliary genital glands furnish most of the fluid-bulk by far.
A minor amount is supplied by the system of genital ducts.
Semen is a whitish, opaque, gelatinous fluid, with a characteristic odor.
The ejaculate (3.5 ml.) contains some 350,000,000 spermatozoa.
Liberated spermatozoa are motile; they swim about 1.5 mm. per minute.

2. Ejaculation.

The forcible discharge of seminal fluid is the chief feature of the *orgasm*.
Its events are said to occur in a definite sequential series.
The *bulbo-urethral glands* discharge their product during erection.
Mucus, accumulated in the ducts and sacs, is expelled.
Perhaps additional secretion occurs during the orgasm.
The discharged mucus serves to lubricate the urethra.
The *prostate* is supposed to discharge first during actual ejaculation.
Its nearly alkaline fluid reduces the acidity of the urine-bathed urethra.
(Spermatozoa are highly susceptible to an acid environment.)
It also dilutes the thicker constituents of semen and augments sperm motility.
The *spermatozoa* are next forced down the seminal ducts.
Some of the supply, stored and ripening in the epididymis, is forced out.
This is accomplished by contractions of the muscle in that duct.
Passage through the ductus deferens is speeded by its massive muscle.
Lastly the *seminal vesicle* adds its thick secretion to the composite mass.
The spermatozoa are said to be pushed along by it, thus clearing the urethra.
It also has a nutritive value to spermatozoa; there is a rich content of fructose.
These several components enter the urethra and mix with the mucus already there.
Semen is forced to the outside by the *bulbo-cavernosus muscle*.
It acts by compressing the bulb of the urethra.

V. THE PENIS

The *penis* serves both as a urinary outlet and as a copulatory organ.

A. STRUCTURAL PLAN:

The *penis* contains three cylinders of erectile tissue and the cavernous urethra.

One of the cylinders is the *corpus cavernosum urethrae*, or corpus spongiosum.

    This unpaired column encloses the *cavernous urethra*.

    The spongy mass enlarges terminally into the *glans penis*.

Parallel and dorsal are two larger cylinders, the *corpora cavernosa penis*.

    However, they extend distad only to the region of the glans.

    They are united by a common median partition, the *pectiniform septum*.

Each corpus is enclosed by a fibrous sheath, the *tunica albuginea*.

    Internally each corpus is a mass of unique erectile tissue.

All three cylinders are surrounded by muscular *subcutaneous tissue* and by thin *skin*.

    Terminally the skin reduplicates in a fold named the *prepuce*.

    It continues over the surface of the glans and blends with the urethral outlet.

B. DETAILED STRUCTURE:

1. Skin.

The *skin* enveloping the penis is thin and soft, with tall papillae.

    It has only lanugo-type hairs (except at base), and small sweat glands only.

A thick *subcutaneous layer* attaches the skin to the erectile cylinders.

    This subcutaneous tissue is unusual in two regards.

        It has no fat, but contains considerable *smooth muscle*.

The *glans penis* is surrounded by the *prepuce*, a cylindrical fold of skin.

    The epithelium of the glans is united firmly to the fibrous tissue beneath.

        It becomes continuous with urethral epithelium at the urinary orifice.

    On the glans and facing prepuce, the skin is moist like a mucous membrane.

        Sebaceous glands, usually described as present, are probably inconstant and rare.

    The odoriferous *smegma* consists mostly of cheesy, epithelial debris.

2. Corpora Cavernosa Penis.

These begin as *crura* and run side by side, dorsally, to conical endings at the glans.

Each cylinder is enclosed by a robust fibrous sheath, the *tunica albuginea*.

    It has an inner circular and outer longitudinal layer of collagenous fibers.

    The common median wall, between the two corpora, is the *pectiniform septum*.

        Distally it has slit-like openings through which the blood sinuses communicate.

Trabeculae, continuous with the fibrous sheath, form a dense, internal framework.

    They carry blood vessels and intervene between the labyrinthine sinuses.

The erectile *blood sinuses* are a prominent system of cavernous spaces (see beyond).

3. Corpus Cavernosum Urethrae.

This cylinder occupies a groove on the under-surface of the corpora cavernosa penis.

It is traversed axially by the *cavernous urethra*, already described (p. 268).

Terminally it expands into the conical, hood-like *glans penis*.

    This consists of dense connective tissue and plexuses of veins.

The external covering (*tunica albuginea*) is thin and contains many elastic fibers.

Hence it resists expansion feebly during erection.

Its inner layer contains smooth muscle fibers, circularly arranged.

Trabeculae are thinner and more elastic than those of the corpora cavernosa penis.

They also contain less smooth muscle.

The cavernous *sinuses* grade into the smaller venous spaces about the urethra.

4. Erectile Tissue.

This is a labyrinth of *blood sinuses*, best developed in the corpora cavernosa penis.

They are supplied by capillaries and special arterioles, and drained by venules.

In the corpora cavernosa penis the central sinuses are larger than peripheral ones.

In the corpus cavernosum urethrae the sinuses are nearly uniform in size.

The sinuses of the *flaccid penis* remain collapsed through tonic muscular compression.

Hence they then appear as mere clefts, virtually bloodless.

During *erection* the sinuses become large cavities, engorged with blood.

The *trabeculae* of erectile tissue are the common partitions between adjacent sinuses.

They consist of *collagenous fibers, elastic networks* and strands of *smooth muscle*.

Their surfaces are covered with the *endothelial lining* of the sinuses.

This endothelium is continuous with that of the communicating vessels.

These vessels both supply (capillaries; arterioles) and drain (venules).

5. Blood Supply.

During the *flaccid state*, the *dorsal artery* of the penis provides circulating blood.

It supplies the tunica albuginea and larger trabeculae.

Here the arterial twigs break down into capillaries.

Their small amount of blood enters the sinuses and drains into the venules.

During *erection*, a *deep artery*, traversing each of the three corpora, is paramount.

These arteries give off trabecular branches that are called *helicine arteries*.

They are spiraling arterioles, many of which open directly into the sinuses.

The convolutions provide 'slack' to be taken up during erection.

The media is thick and the intima bears a longitudinal ridge of muscle.

Muscular tone causes these projecting ridges to plug the lumen.

Only when the muscle relaxes does blood pass through and flood the sinuses.

Venules occur plentifully on the inner surface of the tunica albuginea of each corpus.

They drain the spongy venous sinuses and join into somewhat larger vessels.

These radicles pierce the albuginea and unite as the deep *dorsal vein*.

The large central sinuses of the corpora cavernosa penis connect with special veins.

These have funnel-shaped valves that allow blood to leave but slowly.

6. Lymphatics and Nerves.

A superficial *lymphatic plexus* occurs in the skin.

A deep network in the erectile tissue is also described.

Sensory nerve fibers terminate in a variety of sensory end-organs, many encapsulated.

Some (including genital corpuscles) are in skin and others in the urethra.

Motor nerve fibers supply the smooth muscle of blood vessels and trabeculae.

Still others supply the skeletal fibers of the bulbo-cavernosus muscle.

C. REGENERATIVE ABILITY:

Skin regenerates as elsewhere, except for the deep muscular layer which is indolent.

The *corpora cavernosa* heal defects by filling-in of scar tissue.

). DIAGNOSTIC FEATURES:

The *penis* is covered with skin; it contains the urethra and cavernous bodies.

The thin *skin* has only very fine hairs, except at the base of the organ.

The abundant *subcutaneous layer* is without fat, but contains smooth muscle.

The urethra is surrounded by a prominent cylinder of spongy *erectile tissue.*

Overlying this *spongiosum* are the even larger, paired *corpora cavernosa penis.*

They are enclosed by a thick, fibrous sheath and separated by a median septum.

The interior consists of *erectile sinuses*, separated by fibro-muscular trabeculae.

The *glans* is surfaced with moist skin; highly vascular fibrous tissue envelops the urethra.

Transverse sections vary in appearance, according to the level cut through.

The prepuce may or may not surround the glans.

The glans may overlap the tapered ends of the corpora cavernosa penis.

. FUNCTIONAL CORRELATIONS:

The urinary function of the *penis* is incidental to the incorporation of the urethra in it.

The penis arose primarily as a *copulative organ;* it is a seat of erotic excitation.

Its evolution among mammals has paralleled that of the vagina and uterus.

In some mammals a *penile bone* is a feature in addition to erectile tissue.

By contrast, the requisite rigidity in most mammals depends wholly on erectile tissue.

Hence functional correlations pertain chiefly to the mechanism of erection.

In the *flaccid penis,* some blood passes from trabecular capillaries into the sinuses.

It is drained by the plexus of venules in the tunica albuginea.

During erection arterioles are the active agents; venules are passive.

Erection is almost wholly a function of the *corpora cavernosa penis.*

It begins with the relaxation of muscular tone in arteries and trabeculae.

Blood is then able to force its way through the straightening helicine arterioles.

The cavernous sinuses begin to fill, the large central ones first.

This compresses the periphery, where venules underlie the firm tunica albuginea.

The result is that venous drainage is severely hampered.

By these means the sinuses are filled and put under pressure.

Turgidity results because the fibrous tunica albuginea resists distention.

In the *corpus cavernosum urethrae*, rigidity is less marked.

This is partly because the central and peripheral sinuses are about the same size.

As a result, blood is not so well retained, and this tissue is less turgid.

In addition, the tunica albuginea is thinner and more elastic.

This permits distention and prevents the compression of peripheral veins.

The glans contains only convoluted venules, and never attains significant rigidity.

At the termination of sexual excitement flaccidity is regained through *detumescence.*

The arteries soon recover their muscular tone as the nervous control is regained.

As a result, the blood supply to the sinuses is shut off.

Flaccidity is resumed slowly because of the compression of peripheral venules.

It is said that the central sinuses drain first through their valved veins.

This results in a reduction in pressure peripherally where veins have been squeezed.

The ordinary route of peripheral venous drainage is then restored.

The residual blood content of the sinuses is pressed out by the muscular trabeculae.

Chapter *XXIV*. THE FEMALE REPRODUCTIVE SYSTEM

The female reproductive system includes the *ovaries* and a set of tubular organs.
  The latter are the *uterine tubes, uterus, vagina* and *external genitalia*.
    These organs have other functions than serving merely as a system of ducts.
The female organs are in a fully developed, functional condition for about thirty years.

I. THE OVARY

An *ovary* lies on each side of the uterus on the lateral wall of the pelvic cavity.

A. STRUCTURAL PLAN:
  The *ovary* is an ovoid exocrine (cytogenic) and endocrine gland about 1.5 in. long.
    It is surfaced with a specialized layer of reflected peritoneum (*germinal epithelium*).
  One margin receives a mesentery (the *mesovarium*), which attaches to the *broad ligament*.
    This attached, ovarian border is the *hilus* where blood vessels enter.
  The ovary consists of a cortex and medulla, not sharply delimited.
    The *cortex* is a compact layer, interrupted at the hilus.
      It contains *eggs*, in *follicles* of various sizes and degrees of development.
      It also contains transformed, discharged follicles (*corpora lutea*) and degenerating
        atretic follicles.
    The *medulla* is a vascular and fibrous core, looser than the cortex.
      It reaches the 'surface' only at the hilus where it merges with the mesovarium.

B. DETAILED STRUCTURE:
  #### 1. Medulla.
    The interior of the ovary, or *medulla* is a core of rather loose fibro-elastic tissue.
    Abundant *blood vessels* enter at the hilus, and then take spiral courses inward.
    The *stroma* contains scattered strands of smooth muscle (especially at the hilus).
    Enlarging ovarian follicles encroach upon the medulla each month.

  #### 2. Cortex.
    The *cortical zone* consists of a dense *stroma* that contains *follicles* with eggs.
      In a functional ovary many follicles are quiescent, or practically so.
        Others are undergoing progressive or regressive development.
    The exact condition, however, depends upon the age of the ovary.
      Before *puberty* the ovary shows, with few exceptions, only *primitive follicles*.
      Sexual maturity is characterized by the presence of *growing* (and *ripe*) *follicles*.
        Also their end-products (*corpora lutea; atretic follicles*) occur.
      In the later reproductive years the ova progressively decrease in number.
        After the menopause they disappear completely.
      The *senile cortex* becomes a narrowed zone of ordinary fibrous tissue.
    All of the descriptions that follow refer to the mature, functional ovary.

A. GERMINAL EPITHELIUM.

This surface layer is a specialized portion of the *peritoneal epithelium*.

Its cuboidal cells do not rest upon a definite *basement membrane*.

Hence the epithelium detaches easily and is commonly lost from sections.

B. STROMA.

The connective-tissue *stroma* is peculiar; it is much like an embryonic type.

It is compact, rich in cells and relatively poor in fibers.

The *cells* are spindle-shaped with elongate nuclei, somewhat like smooth muscle.

They have more potentialities than ordinary fibroblasts possess.

The *fibers* are thin, reticular threads that form a meshwork between the cells.

They are fine elements, like thin collagenous fibers but argyrophilic.

The *tunica albuginea* is a zone directly beneath the germinal epithelium.

It is less cellular, less vascular and more compact than the general stroma.

About the follicles the stroma specializes into distinctive envelopes (*thecae*).

They are characteristic of growing follicles and will be described with them.

C. OVA.

All of the egg cells are large, spherical elements.

The most immature ova (technically *oögonia*) are about 20 μ in diameter.

When fully grown, they are six times this size; volume increase is 200 times.

Such a stage, at the completion of growth, bears the name *primary oöcyte*.

The *nucleus* is large and vesicular; the nucleolus, prominent and dark staining.

The *cytoplasm* is opaque and granular, especially centrally.

The larger granules are particles of nutritive substance (*yolk*).

A definite *cell membrane* is lacking; there is only a delicate cytoplasmic border.

As the egg grows, it becomes surrounded by a thick, tough, refractile membrane.

This *zona pellucida* is usually held to be a product of the follicle cells.

D. PRIMARY FOLLICLES.

The greatest number of follicles occurs in the fetal ovary (200,000 or more).

Progressive destruction continues until none is left at about 50 years.

After puberty some of these follicles grow periodically and release eggs.

Apparently the germinal epithelium does not produce 'fresh' eggs.

A primitive ovum, before growth begins, is enclosed by a single layer of cells.

These flat elements, products of the germinal epithelium, are *follicle cells*.

Such a *primary follicle* measures 30 to 40 μ in diameter.

E. GROWING, SOLID FOLLICLES.

In more advanced stages both ovum and follicle have increased in size.

The *zona pellucida* organizes, and *yolk granules* appear.

The *follicle cells* become first cuboidal, and then columnar.

Proliferation next produces a stratified, cellular ensheathment of the egg.

This phase of growth is a self-contained, ovarian function.

F. GROWING VESICULAR FOLLICLES.

These hollow sacs (also called *Graafian follicles*) occur in mammals alone.

Follicles about 0.2 mm. in diameter begin to collect pools of fluid.

This follicular fluid (*liquor folliculi*) is secreted by the follicle cells.

It comes to occupy a single cavity, the *antrum*, within the follicular layer.

The fluid crowds the ovum, and its neighboring follicle cells, to one side.

This eccentric, cellular mound constitutes the *cumulus oöphorus*.

A peripheral shell of cuboidal follicle cells then surrounds the antrum.

It is several layers deep and is named the *stratum granulosum*.

Meanwhile adjacent stroma has organized into a double-layered capsule, the *theca*

The *theca interna* is vascular and cellular in composition.

Between it and the stratum granulosum is a basement or *glassy membrane*

The *theca externa* is a denser and more fibrous layer.

Follicles of 0.5 mm. begin to expand toward the ovarian surface.

A *mature follicle* is probably completed 10 to 14 days after growth begins.

Although large (1 cm.), it bulges but little beyond the ovarian surface.

It occupies the full breadth of the cortex and indents the medulla.

The production of vesicular follicles is induced by a hypophyseal hormone (FSH)

3. Maturation and Ovulation.

The full-grown 'egg' is actually still a *primary oöcyte*, and technically immature.

Before it is liberated from the follicle, an unequal cell division occurs.

The daughter cells are a *secondary oöcyte* and the tiny, first *polar body*.

The chromosome assortment in each is reduced to a single set of 23 chromosomes

This reduction is the result of meiosis, as in spermatogenesis (p. 272).

At about this time the large follicle, covered with thinned cortex, ruptures.

This is *ovulation;* it is, in part, the result of simple overdistention by fluid.

The follicular fluid oozes out, carrying the loosened ovum with it.

Some follicle cells adhere to the ovum and comprise the *corona radiata*.

Ovulation occurs at about 28-day intervals, and roughly in alternate ovaries.

The time is about midway between two menstrual onsets.

Usually only one ovum becomes fully grown and set free in each cycle.

The free oöcyte probably remains fertilizable for something less than one day.

If fertilized by a spermatozoön, the oöcyte undergoes a second maturation division.

This results in a *mature ovum* (oötid) and a tiny, *second polar body*.

The ripe ovum still possesses a complete single set of chromosomes (*cf.* p. 272).

Thus, only one daughter cell of a primary oöcyte becomes functional.

This is a sacrifice in number, to insure adequate size to one functional egg.

4. Corpus Luteum.

The collapsed follicle becomes prominently folded and heals its rupture.

The cavity is filled with transuded serum and unexpelled follicular fluid.

There is sometimes a little bleeding within the cavity of the follicle.

More often, significant bleeding follows later vascularization.

The follicular wall transforms into a temporary glandular body, the *corpus luteum*.

It is called a *corpus luteum of ovulation* if pregnancy does not follow.

It is called a *corpus luteum of pregnancy* if pregnancy ensues.

(Corpus luteum spurium and corpus luteum verum are other terms used, re
spectively.)

There is no essential difference between the two, except size and length of life.

In pregnancy the glandular mass grows to a larger size and lasts longer.

The epithelial cells of the stratum granulosum are the ones chiefly concerned.

They transform directly into a cell type different in structure and function.

These cells enlarge greatly into spheroidal elements, but they rarely divide.

The transformed granulosa cells are called *granulosa lutein cells*.

Their abundant cytoplasm is clear; it increasingly acquires lipid droplets.

Lutein cells become arranged in cords, separated by capillaries.

The theca interna also produces epithelioid elements called *theca lutein cells*.

These have less cytoplasm and are easily distinguishable.

They aggregate peripherally, especially where the wall is indented by folding.
They are smaller, stain more intensely and have smaller, darker nuclei.
Capillary sprouts and spindle-shaped cells of the theca interna invade the main mass.
Some fibroblasts organize a delicate *reticulum* throughout the corpus luteum.
Other fibroblasts reach the internal surface of the luteal wall and spread along it.
Here they form a fibro-gelatinous lining about the central cavity.
They also organize the central coagulum and absorb it.
The *corpus luteum of ovulation* attains its highest development at the ninth day.
At this same time the involution of this ordinary corpus luteum begins.
The former rich and intimate vascularization of the granulosa mass declines.
Granulosa lutein cells undergo fatty degeneration; lipochrome pigment increases.
The corpus luteum now first assumes a bright yellow color.
Theca lutein cells also become less numerous and gradually disappear.
Regression is well advanced after 2 weeks, but continues for several months.
Hence several stages, from different cycles, are always found in an ovary.
There is gradual reduction to a hyaline scar named the *corpus albicans*.
The *corpus luteum of pregnancy* is large because its cells continue to grow.
In the second month it attains a diameter of 2 to 3 cm., but is relatively pale.
Involution begins promptly and slowly reduces the mass to a fibrous scar.
After pregnancy the final decline and replacement proceeds at a rapid rate.
Yet the resulting corpus albicans is large and quite persistent.

5. Atresia of Follicles.

The process of *atresia* is a characteristic feature in immature and mature ovaries.
This process is one of degeneration (involution) of ovarian follicles.
It occurs abundantly between fetal life and puberty.
It also continues, less actively, throughout the functional sexual years.
The duration of the active sexual span in woman is 30 to 35 years.
Only about 400 follicles reach full maturity during this time.
Yet follicles are seen constantly at various stages of growth.
All unsuccessful follicles (many thousands) involute and disappear.
The depletion is nearly complete at the time of the menopause.
Within 3 to 4 years thereafter all residual follicles have succumbed.
Atresia may attack follicles when they are young, growing or practically mature.
The *ovum* is primarily attacked, but the causative factors are unknown.
The ensuing process is a reaction that brings about the absorption of dead material.
Atresia in *primary follicles* involves first a degeneration of the *ovum*.
This is followed by similar changes in the *follicular cells*.
The empty space, at the end of the process, is then filled-in with stromal tissue.
Atresia in *vesicular follicles* introduces more complicated changes.
The first degenerative signs tend to appear in the *ovum*, as in primary follicles.
After this the follicular epithelium (granulosa) undergoes fatty degeneration.
Cells of the *theca interna* develop much like those in a corpus luteum.
They become epithelioid cells, arranged in vascularized, radial cords.
The appearance of a well advanced stage is much like a corpus luteum.
But there is (or was) a degenerating ovum in the interior of the follicle.
The *zona pellucida* swells, stains deeply and may persist by itself for a long time.
The *glassy membrane* may likewise thicken, fold, hyalinize and persist.
Eventually connective tissue penetrates it and replaces interior residues.

The final fate of such a follicle is fibrosis and shrinkage.
The scar-tissue mass looks like a corpus albicans, but is smaller.

6. Interstitial Cells.

Groups of epithelioid cells sometimes show in the ovarian stroma of mammals.
The cytoplasm of such spheroidal cells contains fine lipoidal droplets.
They are best seen in rodents, where they constitute the '*interstitial gland.*'
In the adult, human ovary they are either absent or very poorly represented.
All such cells derive from the internal theca of follicles undergoing atresia.
Accordingly, they are most abundant when atresia is commonest.
In the human this is the first year of life.
These elements are lingering products of atresia, dispersed by growth processes.
They are not comparable to the interstitial cells of the testis.

7. Vessels and Nerves.

Blood vessels from the hilus spiral through the medulla to the cortex.
Capillary networks are abundant in the theca interna of follicles.
Lymph capillaries begin in the theca externa of follicles and unite into larger vessels.
Such collecting vessels enter the medulla and leave at the hilus.
Nerve fibers follow the blood vessels and supply their muscular coat.
Other fibers form plexuses about the follicular epithelium.
Some sensory fibers and lamellar (Pacinian) corpuscles occur in the stroma.

C. REGENERATIVE ABILITY:

Ovaries are notoriously incompetent in effecting repair beyond healing by scar tissue.

D. DIAGNOSTIC FEATURES:

The ovary has a cortex and thicker medulla, different structurally.
The *medulla* is fibrous and contains prominent blood vessels.
The *cortex* is bounded by a cuboidal to flattened *epithelium*.
This layer, however, is commonly lacking in sections from preserved ovaries.
The cortical *stroma* is highly cellular and deficient in obvious fibers.
Its spindle-shaped cells resemble somewhat swirling groups of smooth muscle.
Follicles, before puberty, are mostly primordial, with a single epithelial layer.
Between puberty and the menopause, *follicles* of all sizes can be expected.
Also a *corpus luteum* (at some stage) and *corpora albicantia* are commonly seen.
The cell columns of the c. luteum resemble somewhat those of suprarenal cortex.
Atretic follicles are encountered in almost every section.
After the menopause, follicles disappear and the ovary shrinks.
The thinned cortex is replaced by fibrous tissue.

E. FUNCTIONAL CORRELATIONS:

As an *exocrine gland* the ovary produces eggs; it is a *cytogenic gland*.
The production of a large egg, with much cytoplasm, is an adaptive specialization.
It must furnish the actual building material for the body of a new individual.
Endocrine synthesis produces two important hormones.
Estrogen is apparently elaborated by the cells of the theca interna.
This occurs during the growth of vesicular follicles and also of the corpus luteum.
At puberty it is responsible for the development of the genital tract and breasts.
It also brings out the secondary sexual characters and the sex drive.

After menstruation it directs the proliferative repair of the uterine mucosa.

During pregnancy it is dominant in influencing the growth of the mammary glands.

Progesterone is produced by the corpus luteum.

It brings the estrogen-primed uterine mucosa to a condition fit for pregnancy.

During pregnancy it preserves the uterine mucosa and embryo.

It probably aids in producing growth of the mammary gland.

The ovary, itself, is activated and governed by *hypophyseal hormones* (p. 178).

II. THE UTERINE TUBE

The egg-conducting *uterine tube* is also called the *oviduct* and the *Fallopian tube*.

It extends from the ovary to the uterus in a fold of peritoneum.

This mesentery (*mesosalpinx*) attaches to the broad ligament.

The tube is 4 to 5 inches long, and is unique in not uniting directly with its gland.

The uterine tube shows four regional divisions:

The *infundibulum* flares and opens trumpet-fashion; it bears fringed folds (*fimbriae*).

The *ampulla* is a dilated region, comprising two-thirds of the length of the tube.

The *isthmus*, slender and narrowed, connects with the uterus.

A continuation of the canal through the uterine wall is called the *intramural portion*.

The wall of the uterine tube thickens progressively toward the uterus.

Conversely, the lumen diminishes remarkably in this direction (from 8 mm. to 1 mm.).

1. Mucosa.

The *epithelium* is mostly simple columnar, but sometimes has basal cells.

Some cells are *ciliated*, the direction of their stroke being downward.

Other cells contain granules and secrete a *mucoid substance*.

However, no true glands are present in the uterine tube.

Both cell-types are probably functional variants of one cell.

Slight changes in height occur, co-ordinated with the cyclic changes of the uterus.

The *lamina propria* is highly cellular; there is no definite *basement membrane*.

The *cells* are spindle-shaped or angular, separated by thin fibers.

The whole mucosal lining is thrown into characteristic longitudinal *folds*.

Next to the uterus the folds are few (3 to 4), low and simple.

Toward the ovarian end the thin folds are many, high and intricate.

The primary folds branch and interconnect, lengthwise.

They also give rise to subordinate folds in a most complicated manner.

This system of folds subdivides the *lumen* into a labyrinth of narrow clefts.

At the rim of the flaring tube, close to the ovary, the mucosal lining of the tube and
the peritoneal mesothelium of the serosa become continuous.

2. Submucosa.

The lamina propria extends without change all the way to the muscular coat.

Hence there is no recognizable *submucosa*.

3. Muscularis.

This tunic of smooth muscle becomes progressively thicker toward the uterus.

The *inner layer*, circularly arranged, is well developed.

The *outer layer* is thin and loosely distributed in longitudinal bundles.

It does not make a closed layer, but is best developed near the uterus.

There is no distinct boundary between the two muscle coats.

4. Serosa.

The uterine tube is loosely invested with a *serosal fold* of reflected peritoneum.

This is continuous into that portion of the broad ligament called the *mesosalpinx*.

The muscle-bundles of the longitudinal coat are embedded in this relatively thick layer.

5. Vessels and Nerves.

The distribution follows the plan described on p. 266.

6. Diagnostic Features.

The *uterine tube* is a specialized duct, with characteristic features.

The *epithelium* is simple columnar.

Cilia occur on some cells, but routine sections often fail to show them.

The *lamina propria* is characterized by its highly cellular composition.

(The uterus is the only hollow organ sharing this type of tissue.)

A *circular muscle layer* is complete and clearly seen.

The outer, *longitudinal layer* is arranged in scattered bundles.

Only close to the uterus does it approximate a closed layer.

The *serosa* is loosely applied; its deeper levels contain the longitudinal muscle.

Wide quantitative variations are seen at different levels of the duct.

Toward the *ovarian end*, the tube is much larger.

Its muscularis is thin and the lumen wide.

The mucosa is remarkably folded into a complex series of thin plates.

The lumen is thereby reduced to a labyrinth of narrow spaces.

Toward the *uterine end*, the tube is much smaller.

Its muscularis is thicker, and the lumen is greatly reduced.

The mucosal folds become fewer, lower and simpler.

7. Functional Correlations.

The uterine tube receives the ovum and transports it to the uterus.

Reception may be accomplished by cilia, which wave the egg inward.

This is aided by the fimbriae, which become turgid and sweep over the ovary.

Downward *transportation* is probably the result of muscular activity.

The tube serves as a meeting place for the egg and sperm.

Tubal contraction, rather than swimming ability, force spermatozoa up the tube.

Fertilization occurs usually in the ampullary region.

The mucoid secretion is lubricative; it possibly nourishes eggs in transit.

The open, fimbriated end of the tube is always a potentially dangerous feature.

It provides an avenue for the passage of infection into the peritoneal cavity.

III. THE UTERUS

The *uterus* lies between the bladder and rectum; it occupies a midregion in the broad ligament.

It is a hollow, pear-shaped organ, about 3 in. long, with a thick muscular wall.

It receives the uterine tubes and opens into the vagina.

Regional divisions into *fundus*, *corpus* and *cervix* are recognized.

A transitional zone, between corpus and cervix, is designated the *isthmus*.

The cervix projects for a short distance into the vaginal cavity.

Structurally the fundus and corpus are alike; hence only two regions demand consideration.

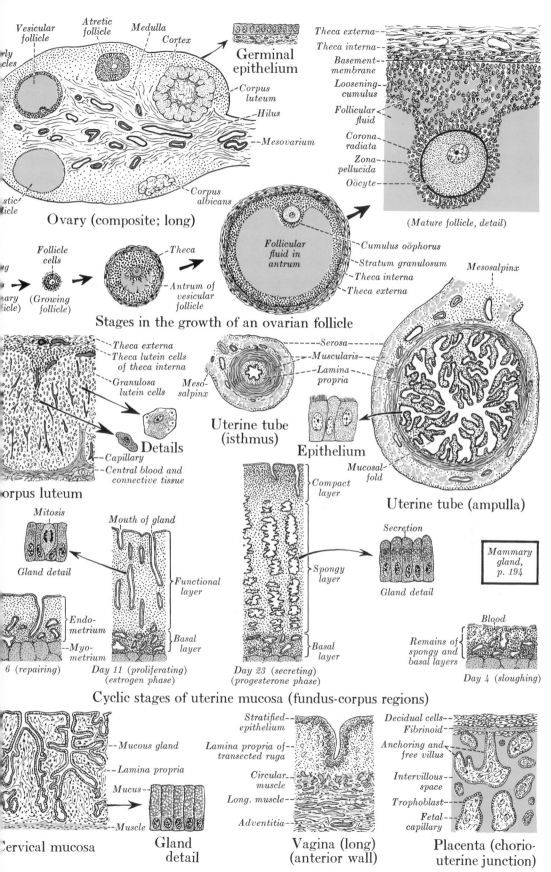

Ovary (composite; long)

Vesicular follicle — *Atretic follicle* — *Medulla* — *Cortex*

Germinal epithelium

Corpus luteum
Hilus
Mesovarium
Corpus albicans

ly cles — *stic icle*

(Mature follicle, detail)

Theca externa — *Theca interna* — *Basement membrane* — *Loosening cumulus* — *Follicular fluid* — *Corona radiata* — *Zona pellucida* — *Oöcyte*

Stages in the growth of an ovarian follicle

Follicle cells — *Theca* — *Antrum of vesicular follicle*

(Growing follicle)

ary icle — *g*

Follicular fluid in antrum

Cumulus oöphorus — *Stratum granulosum* — *Theca interna* — *Theca externa*

Mesosalpinx

Corpus luteum

Theca externa — *Theca lutein cells of theca interna* — *Granulosa lutein cells* — *Meso salpinx*

Details

Capillary — *Central blood and connective tissue*

Uterine tube (isthmus)

Serosa — *Muscularis* — *Lamina propria*

Epithelium

Uterine tube (ampulla)

Mucosal fold

Cyclic stages of uterine mucosa (fundus-corpus regions)

Mitosis — Gland detail — *Mouth of gland*

Functional layer

Endo- metrium — *Myo- metrium*

Basal layer

6 (repairing) — Day 11 (proliferating) (estrogen phase)

Compact layer

Spongy layer

Basal layer

Day 23 (secreting) (progesterone phase)

Secretion

Gland detail

Mammary gland, p. 194

Blood

Remains of spongy and basal layers

Day 4 (sloughing)

Mucous gland — *Lamina propria* — *Mucus* — *Muscle*

Cervical mucosa

Gland detail

Stratified epithelium — *Lamina propria of transected ruga* — *Circular muscle* — *Long. muscle* — *Adventitia*

Vagina (long) (anterior wall)

Decidual cells — *Fibrinoid* — *Anchoring and free villus* — *Intervillous space* — *Trophoblast* — *Fetal capillary*

Placenta (chorio- uterine junction)

THE FEMALE REPRODUCTIVE ORGANS

A. STRUCTURAL PLAN:

The *uterus* is organized according to the general plan for hollow organs.

The several tunics are represented as in the oviduct, but they receive special names.

These are: *endometrium* (mucosa); *myometrium* (muscularis); *perimetrium* (serosa).

The endometrium is notable for its *cyclic changes*, ending in extensive destruction.

The entire wall participates in the changes and enlargement entailed by pregnancy.

B. DETAILED STRUCTURE:

1. Endometrium.

This layer, elsewhere called a *mucosa*, abuts directly against the muscular coat.

Its thickness and structure in the fundus-corpus vary cyclically month by month.

It is simplest to describe first the general condition, as at the middle of the cycle.

At this time the total thickness is about 2 to 3 mm.

A. SURFACE EPITHELIUM.

In the *fundus-corpus* it is a simple columnar layer, with groups of ciliated cells.

In the *cervix* the cells are taller and have basally located nuclei.

A few are ciliated, but most contain much mucus in the free end.

B. GLANDS.

The *uterine glands* extend through the full thickness of the mucosa.

They are spaced apart by a distance about four times the breadth of a gland.

There are two regional types: in the fundus-corpus; and in the cervix.

1. FUNDUS AND CORPUS.

This region embraces the upper two-thirds of the uterus.

The slightly tortuous *fundic glands* make a vertical palisade of tubules.

Usually called simple tubular, they often branch toward their basal ends.

The component *cells* (some ciliated) are like those on the surface.

They undergo periodic changes in a monthly secretory cycle (see beyond).

Their secretion is *mucoid*, gaining in *glycogen* as the changes advance.

2. CERVIX.

This region corresponds to the lower one-third of the uterus.

Cervical glands, consisting of tall *mucous cells*, are highly branched.

These glands sometimes become occluded and dilate with secretion.

Such cysts are called *Nabothian follicles*, or ovules of Naboth.

Cervical glands do not participate in the events of the menstrual cycle.

However, the secretion of mucus does vary somewhat during the cycle.

In pregnancy the cervical glands both enlarge and proliferate.

C. LAMINA PROPRIA.

The framework is *reticular fibers*, which also condense into a *basement membrane*.

The *stromal cells* are very abundant, occupying the spaces of the mesh.

They are small, angular cells with a large ovoid nucleus.

Wandering lymphoid cells and other leucocytes also are to be seen.

There is a superficial resemblance to lymphoid tissue in this cellular layer.

In the *cervix* the stroma is firmer, more fibrous and less cellular.

Longitudinal folds, the *plicae palmatae*, are produced.

2. Myometrium.

The *muscularis* is a relatively massive coat of smooth muscle, 0.6 in. thick.

It is arranged in bundles, separated by connective tissue.

The muscle fibers are large, varying cyclically between 40 and 90 μ in length.

In pregnancy the muscle fibers become relatively huge elements, 600 to 800 μ long.

They also increase in number; old fibers divide and new fibers differentiate.

There are three layers of muscle, somewhat blended due to interconnecting bundles.

The *inner layer*, mostly longitudinal, is the so-called *stratum submucosum*.

The *middle layer*, the thickest coat, is arranged obliquely circular.

Many large vessels give it a spongy texture; it is the *stratum vasculare*.

The thin *outer layer*, mostly longitudinal, is the *stratum supravasculare*.

The muscle of the *cervix* is relatively deficient and is arranged in irregular bundles.

Intermixed white and elastic fibers produce a firm consistency.

An outer, more longitudinal layer continues into the vagina.

3. Perimetrium.

This is a typical *serosa*, continued from the peritoneum of the broad ligament.

It is lacking caudally on the anterior wall, where the bladder abuts.

4. Vessels and Nerves.

Blood vessels from the broad ligament penetrate to the middle layer of the myometrium.

One set of *arterial extensions* supplies the basal part of the endometrium.

Another set, specialized as *coiled arteries*, extends to higher levels.

Here each branches into a terminal tuft.

Veins in the endometrium are thin-walled, forming a varicose meshwork.

A plexus of larger vessels occurs in the vascular stratum of the myometrium.

Lymphatics form plexuses in the mucous, muscular and serous coats.

They are extremely abundant, yet are wholly absent in the superficial mucosa.

Unmyelinated *nerve fibers* supply blood vessels and muscle bundles.

Myelinated fibers enter the mucosa, but their endings are obscure.

C. CYCLIC CHANGES:

During the potential child-bearing years the endometrium undergoes periodic changes.

The entire lining, except that of the cervix, is involved in this *menstrual cycle*.

There is a building-up, followed by marked destruction and repair.

Hence the appearance of the mucosa varies from day to day.

A complete cycle consumes 21 to 35 days; the average is 28 days.

The first day of flow is numbered as day one of the cycle.

Five *stages* can be recognized in a continuous cycle of events.

These stages do not start and stop abruptly, but each passes insensibly into the next.

The times given for the following stages represent averages based on a 28-day cycle.

1. Resurfacing (day 5 or 6).

Even before all bleeding has ceased, *repair* begins to get under way.

Epithelial cells leave the surviving remnants of torn glands.

These remnants are located in the basal and deepest spongy layer of the membrane.

Cells glide over the denuded surface and epithelize it anew.

(Such spreading, without mitosis, characterizes early wound healing in general.)

2. Follicular Stage (days 7 to 15).

This phase is also commonly called the *proliferative stage*.

It extends and completes the postmenstrual repair; it is a period of growth.

It coincides with the growth of ovarian follicles and is induced by estrogen.

It is variable in duration, correlated with the length of the cycle.

The mucosa increases from 1 mm. (or less) in thickness to 2 mm. (or more).

The *glands* proliferate, lengthen rapidly and finally become wavy.

Glycogen accumulates in the cells; only a thin mucoid secretion is given off.

Connective-tissue cells also multiply and rebuild the lamina propria.

They produce a new meshwork of *reticular fibers* as the restoration advances.

Coiled arteries are regrowing laggardly into the otherwise regenerated mucosa.

3. Luteal Stage (days 16 to 27).

Other terms are the *progravid* or *secretory stage*; uterine competence is attained.

The time lapse between its start and the onset of bleeding tends to be 14 days.

This period is quite uniform, regardless of the length of the total cycle.

The glands no longer proliferate, but they swell and secrete abundantly.

Throughout a middle region, saccular ('baggy') outpocketings appear.

These are distended with a thicker *mucoid secretion*, rich in glycogen.

Such changes are induced by progesterone, secreted by the corpus luteum.

The *coiled arteries* spiral much more tightly and extend nearly to the surface.

By the end of this period, the endometrium is from 4 to 6 mm. thick.

This increase is due largely to the swelling of tissues and the accumulation of secretion and tissue fluid.

Three horizontal zones of the endometrium are given special names.

Nearest the surface is the *compact layer*, containing the straight necks of glands.

It is also characterized by enlarged stromal cells, of connective-tissue origin.

These are identical with the still larger *decidual cells* of pregnancy.

Deeper is the thick *spongy layer*, featured by the dilated portions of glands.

The compact and spongy layers are often called the *functional layer*.

Deepest of all is the thin *basal layer*, containing the blind ends of glands.

It does not participate to any extent in the cyclic changes.

4. Ischemia (day 28).

One day or more before bleeding starts, the *coiled arteries* constrict intermittently.

The interruption of blood-flow continues for periods of several hours.

The functional layer becomes pale and shrinks.

It lacks blood, and loses glandular secretion and tissue fluid.

5. Menstruation (days 1 to 5).

The functional layer next undergoes necrosis and sloughs away.

Blood cells slip through the walls of intact capillaries.

At times the *coiled arterioles* relax locally and blood escapes from bursting vessels.

It also escapes from the injured capillaries whose blood supply has failed.

Pools of uncoagulated blood are thus formed in the lamina propria.

Patches of blood-soaked tissue separate off and are lost.

This exposes torn glands, arteries and veins.

Blood oozes (by reflux) from veins so opened.

The *discharge* contains blood, disintegrated epithelial and stromal cells, glandular secretions, and sometimes tissue fragments.

The compactum and some, at least, of the spongiosum are lost, leaving a raw surface.

The surviving stratum remains intact, although it has shrunk down considerably.

The straight arteries to the basal endometrium do not constrict during the cycle.

Hence the blood supply to this zone is good at all times.

D. PREGNANCY CHANGES:

1. Structural Features.

An important organ, the *placenta*, features the period of pregnancy.

It is a composite organ produced partly by the uterus and partly by fetal tissue.

The *maternal component* is endometrium, continued even beyond the secretory stage
The *fetal component* is supplied by the chorionic sac that encloses the embryo.
Actually this is not fetal tissue proper, but rather auxiliary fetal tissue.
The maternal contribution, or *decidua basalis*, is not a complete endometrial thickness
It lacks the superficial portion of the compact layer of the endometrium.
That is, it includes only the endometrium beneath the implanted chorionic sac
A characteristic feature, in the first half of pregnancy, is the *decidual cells*.
These are enlarged, connective-tissue cells of uncertain significance.
The fetal contribution consists of a *chorionic plate* and its branching *villi*.
The *chorionic plate* is merely a portion of the chorionic sac about the embryo.
It is that local region of the membrane that lies deepest in the decidua.
Chorionic villi extend from the chorion, like branching trees.
Many end freely, but some fuse with the decidua as anchoring elements.
Both the chorionic plate and the villi have the same essential structure.
A *villus* contains a fibro-muscular core, embedding extensions of fetal blood vessels.
Its surface-covering is an epithelial tissue, named *trophoblast*.
In the first half of pregnancy two trophoblastic layers are recognizable.
The inner layer is composed of separate cuboidal cells, arranged one cell deep
It is called the *cellular trophoblast* (cytotrophoblast).
The outer layer is without cell boundaries, and hence is *syncytial trophoblast*
It shows a *brush border* and has its nuclei spaced fairly evenly in one row
It arises by cells of the inner layer merging into a common mass.
In the last half of pregnancy the cellular trophoblast gradually disappears
It finally ceases to proliferate, and its cells add to the syncytial layer.
The syncytial layer is mostly thin, but scattered clumps of nuclei occur in it
These make local bulges called *syncytial knots*.
Where syncytium overlies capillaries, it is an especially thin layer.
Degenerative changes produce patches of *fibrinoid substance*.
In addition to the trophoblast, maternal blood is also involved.
The enlargement of myometrial *smooth-muscle fibers* during pregnancy is notable.
They increase in length ten times, and also increase in number.
The *cervical glands* become larger and secrete mucus abundantly.
This forms a mucous plug that seals up the cervical canal.

2. Circulatory Relations.

The fetal and maternal bloods follow wholly independent courses, without mixing.
The *fetal vessels* comprise a closed circuit of small vessels and capillaries.
Uterine arterioles open by tiny nozzles into a labyrinthine *intervillous space*.
Veins drain the intermittently spurted blood away from this space.
The *intervillous space* was created at the expense of eroded decidual tissue.
It is carpeted everywhere with a continuous sheet of trophoblast.
That is, trophoblast covers the chorionic plate, villi and decidua basalis.
The space and its lining are unique as a corridor for the passage of blood.
Hence all interchanges between the two circulations must cross a protoplasmic barrier

E. REGENERATIVE ABILITY:

The *endometrium* is highly efficient in repairing injuries even when severe.
The course after delivery, curettage or other destruction is like postmenstrual repair.

F. DIAGNOSTIC FEATURES:

The *uterus* is a thick-walled organ with a distinctive mucosa (*endometrium*).

Its *epithelium* is simple columnar; some ciliated cells show if preservation is good.

The *glands* of the fundus and corpus are vertical tubules, not plainly branching.

They are not crowded, but are rather liberally spaced.

Their length, tortuosity and distention vary throughout the cycle.

The tubular *cervical glands* are obviously branched; they are mucus-secreting.

The gland cell (like the surface cell) is tall and pale, with a basal nucleus.

This type does not participate significantly in the cyclic changes.

The *lamina propria* is rich in cells and poor in fibers, like the uterine tube.

These cells enlarge in pregnancy into so-called decidual cells.

The *muscularis* is heavy and contains three layers, not sharply delimited.

Each layer shows interlacing bundles.

Sections through the *placenta* are featured by myriads of tissue-islands in a blood space.

These are sectioned *villi*, containing small vessels and bordered by epithelium.

The association of cuboidal cells and a syncytium is safely diagnostic of pregnancy.

In the last half of pregnancy, cuboidal cells lack; the syncytium collects in *knots*.

G. FUNCTIONAL CORRELATIONS:

The *uterus* is specialized toward receiving and rearing an egg within its mucosa.

It nourishes and protects the embryo, and expels it at the proper time.

At *puberty* the uterus is brought into functional condition by ovarian hormones.

In *childhood* it is small, and the mucosa is thin; growth is controlled by estrogen.

After the *menopause* the uterus undergoes marked atrophy.

The same is true of the uterine tubes and vagina; estrogen-decline is responsible.

The significance of the *menstrual cycle* is that it anticipates each month the possibility of pregnancy and prepares a bed suitable for the fertilized ovum.

Postmenstrual, proliferative changes are directed by the follicular hormone (*estrogen*).

Postovulatory, secretory changes are governed by the luteal hormone (*progesterone*).

If pregnancy occurs, the egg implants during this favorable stage of upbuilding.

If *pregnancy fails*, the corpus luteum declines and its hormonal influence wanes.

The mucosa then is unstable; it collapses and sloughs from lack of hormonal support.

Sporadically *ovulation fails* and there is no corpus luteum to secrete progesterone.

In this instance the endometrium collapses at the end of the proliferative stage.

Such an atypical course is called an *anovulatory cycle*.

If *pregnancy supervenes*, the progravid changes continue under progesterone influence.

Hormone is supplied first by the persisting corpus luteum and later by the placenta.

The hormonally-supported mucosa thereby becomes the *decidua* of pregnancy.

The stromal cells become the *decidual cells* of pregnancy.

Part of the decidua becomes the maternal portion of the placenta.

The placenta serves the fetus as a lung, intestinal-absorptive apparatus and kidney.

Among its syntheses is a *chorionic gonadatropin* (by its cellular trophoblast).

The presence of this hormone in urine makes possible simple tests for pregnancy.

It also secretes *estrogen* and *progesterone* (probably a synthesis by the syncytium).

The placenta acts as a *barrier* against particulate matter, such as micro-organisms.

Only chemical substances under a certain molecular size can pass through.

Hence fat and various blood proteins first break down into simpler products.

IV. THE VAGINA

The *vagina* is a fibro-muscular sheath, lined with a transversely folded mucosa.

Its upper end is continuous with the uterine cervix.

The lower end is bounded by the *hymen*, a transverse, annular fold of the mucosa.
It separates vagina from vestibule; stratified squamous epithelium covers both surfaces.

1. Mucosa.

This is continuous, by reflection, onto the outer wall of the protruding uterine cervix.
The thick *epithelium* is of the stratified squamous type.
It is uncornified and lacks glands; lubricative mucus comes from the cervix.
Transition into the simple epithelium of the cervical canal is abrupt.
The *lamina propria* is a thick feltwork of fine fibers, including an elastic network.
Lymphocytes and occasional *lymph nodules* occur.
Many lymphocytes invade the epithelium.
Papillae indent the epithelium; these are tall on the posterior wall.
Transverse ridges are responsible for the mucosal folds (*rugae*) of the vagina.

2. Submucosa.

A deeper, looser and more vascular layer exists, but is rather indefinite.

3. Muscularis.

Smooth muscle is arranged in interlacing bundles that do not occupy well-defined layers.
The *inner portion* is thin and contains more circular or spiral bundles.
The thicker, *outer portion* is preponderantly longitudinal; it continues onto the uterus.
At the entrance of the vagina there is a *sphincter* of skeletal muscle.

4. Adventitia.

A thin layer of dense, fibrous tissue merges into looser, adjoining connective tissue.
In front and behind, it blends with adventitia of the bladder and rectum, respectively.
It is rich in large blood vessels.

5. Vessels and Nerves.

These follow the general plan described on p. 266.

6. Diagnostic Features.

The vagina is lined with an uncornified, stratified squamous *epithelium*.
Papillae indent the epithelium; in the posterior wall they are tall.
The *lamina propria* is a thick, connective-tissue network.
A *muscularis mucosae* and glands are missing (unlike the condition in the esophagus).
The *muscular coat* consists of smooth muscle, mostly longitudinal.
On its inner surface, a thin circular layer occurs.
The *adventitia* blends in much of its extent with that of other organs.

7. Functional Correlations.

The vagina serves as a distensible *copulatory receptacle* and *birth canal*.
The epithelium contains a variable amount of glycogen.
Its abundance is dependent on the periodic increase of *estrogen* prior to ovulation.
Consequently, its fermentation to lactic acid in vaginal fluid is greatest then.
Midway of the cycle, keratohyalin granules accumulate in the more superficial layers.
Superficial cells, then cast off, are faintly acidophilic and have small, dark nuclei.

In some mammals the *estrous cycle* is accompanied by definite changes in the types and
proportions of epithelial cells and leucocytes found free in the vaginal lumen.
The exact stage can be determined by examining vaginal smears.
In man, less clearly marked cyclic changes occur at ovulation.
Yet smears will indicate the presence or absence of effective estrogen production.

V. THE EXTERNAL GENITALIA

The parts of the external genitalia are known collectively as the *vulva.*
Its lateral boundaries are formed by the *greater lips*, within which are *lesser lips.*
The *vestibule* is a shallow cavity into which the urethra and vagina open.
The *vestibular glands* also discharge into it, and the *clitoris* protrudes here.

1. Clitoris.

The *clitoris* is a rudimentary and incomplete counterpart of the penis.
It has two cavernous, *erectile bodies* and a rudimentary *glans* and *prepuce.*
It lacks a urethra and corpus cavernosum urethrae.
The whole organ is surrounded with thin, stratified squamous epithelium.
It contains specialized sensory *nerve endings* of several types.

2. Vestibular Glands.

The *major vestibular glands* are also known as the glands of Bartholin.
They are two bodies, located in the lateral walls of the vestibule.
Each is about 0.5 in. long; its duct opens at the base of the hymen.
These glands correspond to the bulbo-urethral glands in the male (p. 281).
They are *tubulo-alveolar glands*, structurally like those of the male.
A lubricative *mucus* is discharged during sexual excitement.
The *minor vestibular glands* are several small mucous glands located around the urethral
opening and near the clitoris.
They resemble the *urethral glands* (of Littré) of the urethra (p. 268).

3. Labia Minora.

These *lesser lips* form the lateral walls of the vestibule.
Each is a long, high but relatively thin fold of mucous membrane.
Tall connective-tissue *papillae* indent the stratified squamous epithelium.
The basal layer of the epithelium contains *pigment granules.*
Sebaceous glands occur on both surfaces of the fold.
Neither hair follicles nor fat cells are found in the labia minora.

4. Labia Majora.

These *greater lips* are folds of skin that cover the labia minora.
Within each fold there is a considerable amount of *fat.*
The *inner surface* is soft, smooth and hairless.
Its mucosa is much like that of the labia minora.
The *outer surface* is covered with cornified epidermis and bears coarse hairs.
Both surfaces are supplied with sebaceous glands and sweat glands.

5. Diagnostic Features.

The *clitoris* has two erectile columns, but lacks a urethra and surrounding spongiosum.

The *major vestibular glands* are essentially like the male bulbo-urethral glands (p. 281).

Each *labium minus* is a simple mucosal fold, clothed with stratified squamous epithelium.
Sebaceous glands on both surfaces are a distinctive characteristic.

Each *labium majus* is a thicker fold, containing fat and having unlike surfaces.
One surface is hairy skin; the other surface is soft mucous membrane.
Both surfaces contain sebaceous glands and sweat glands.

6. Functional Correlations.

The *vestibule* is a shallow urogenital sinus, corresponding to much of the male urethra.

The *clitoris* is an erectile organ and a receptor for erotic sensation.

The *labia minora* correspond to the under surface of the penis, but remain ununited.

The *labia majora* correspond to the halves of the scrotum, but remain ununited.
Both sets of lips serve as guards to the shallow vestibule.

Chapter XXV. THE SENSE ORGANS

The peripheral endings of sensory nerve fibers are functional *dendrons* (sensory receptors).
The sheaths end somewhat proximal to the terminations of the fibers themselves.
Each fiber branches near its end; the final naked twigs may bear berry-like swellings.
Sensory receptors can be classified in different ways.
One classification is based on the source of stimuli exciting the receptive endings.
Exteroceptors are affected by stimuli external to the body itself.
Example: touch; pressure; cutaneous pain and temperatures; smell; sight; hearing.
Proprioceptors are affected by stimuli arising within the body wall.
Information is given concerning position and muscular tension.
Example: excitation from muscles, tendons, joints and the ear.
Interoceptors are affected by stimuli arising within the various visceral organs.
Example: excitation from activities such as digestion, excretion and circulation.
Another classification is based on the widespread or limited location of the receptors.
General sensibility collects information from the body as a whole.
Example: touch; pressure; pain; temperature; visceral sense; position; movement.
Special sensibility is related to sense organs in definite portions of the head.
Example: smell; taste; sight; hearing; balancing.

I. ORGANS OF GENERAL SENSIBILITY

These endings are simple structurally and are distributed widely throughout the body.
They can be classified on the basis of whether or not the terminal fibers are *encapsulated*.
Another grouping is based on the *kind of tissue* in which the sensory fibers end.
A combination of both sets of criteria will be used in the descriptions that follow.

A. ENDINGS IN EPITHELIUM:

1. Free Endings.
The innervated epithelium may be external (epidermis) or internal (mucous membranes).
Nerve fibers, resolving into simple branches, terminate among the cells.
Of special note are the *peritrichial endings* activated by movements of the hairs.
The outer root sheath of a hair follicle is encircled by nerve fibers.
Some fibers ascend in a palisade; endings are made on the glassy membrane.

2. Terminal Disks.
Somewhat more specialized are the networks at the ends of certain nerve twigs.
Each saucer-like plexus comes in contact with a single, modified epithelial cell.
Such a receptive cell and its fiber are called a *tactile cell* and *-disk* (of Merkel).
They occur in deep epidermis, in hair follicles and in the hard palate.

B. ENDINGS IN CONNECTIVE TISSUE:

1. Free Endings.

A nerve fiber ends in bush-like *branchings*, in an interlacing *network*, or in a knot-lik
skein (*glomerulus*).

Example: skin; serous and mucous membranes; periosteum; sclera.

2. Encapsulated Endings.

This group is characterized by a *fibrous capsule* of varying thickness.

The capsule is continuous with the endoneurium of the nerve fiber.

A. GLOMERULI.

Branching nerve fibers form a tightly interlacing and anastomosing skein.

This spheroidal mass is enclosed by a thin, layered capsule.

Such corpuscles occur in the skin, mucous membranes, conjunctiva and heart.

Examples: *terminal cylinders* (of Ruffini); *end bulbs* (of Krause); *genital co*
puscles.

B. TACTILE CORPUSCLES.

This ellipsoidal receptor is also known as *Meissner's corpuscle*.

The commonest location is the skin of the palm, sole and the tips of digits.

They occur prominently in many of the papillae that indent the epidermis.

The largest corpuscles measure from 40 to 180 μ in length.

There is a fibrous capsule, and a core of flattened tactile cells.

The cells lie transversely, interspersed with horizontal fibrous shelves.

One or more nerve fibers enter and course upward, spiraling.

Branches end in net-like skeins in relation to the tactile cells.

C. LAMELLAR CORPUSCLES.

The commonest type is also known as a *Pacinian corpuscle* (or Vater-Pacinian).

Similar ones, but smaller and simpler, receive still other names.

They occur both in superficial and in deep locations in the body.

Lamellar corpuscles are macroscopic; the largest measure 2 x 4 mm.

Structurally this is the most complex type of sensory ending.

The *core* is a slender, protoplasmic cylinder, of semifluid consistency.

A single nerve fiber enters at one end and runs axially through it.

The fiber gives off lateral twigs and ends in a fibrillated knob.

The fibrous *capsule* is very thick and consists of many layers (up to 60).

These dense lamellae are arranged concentrically, like an onion.

C. ENDINGS IN MUSCLE AND TENDON:

1. Ordinary Endings.

Some are simple *branchings;* others are *encapsulated endings*.

They lie between or on the fibers of muscle or tendon.

2. Neuromuscular Spindles.

These are slender bundles that occur in a muscle, and mostly near its tendon.

They are oriented parallel to the long axis of the muscle.

A *spindle* is usually 2 to 4 mm. long and consists of 3 to 10 skeletal muscle fibers.

These fibers are of the 'red' type (p. 96) and are notably thin.

The cluster of fibers is encapsulated with layered fibrous tissue.

Nerve fibers enter, branch and frequently spiral about the muscle fibers.

They come into close apposition with the sarcolemma-sheaths.

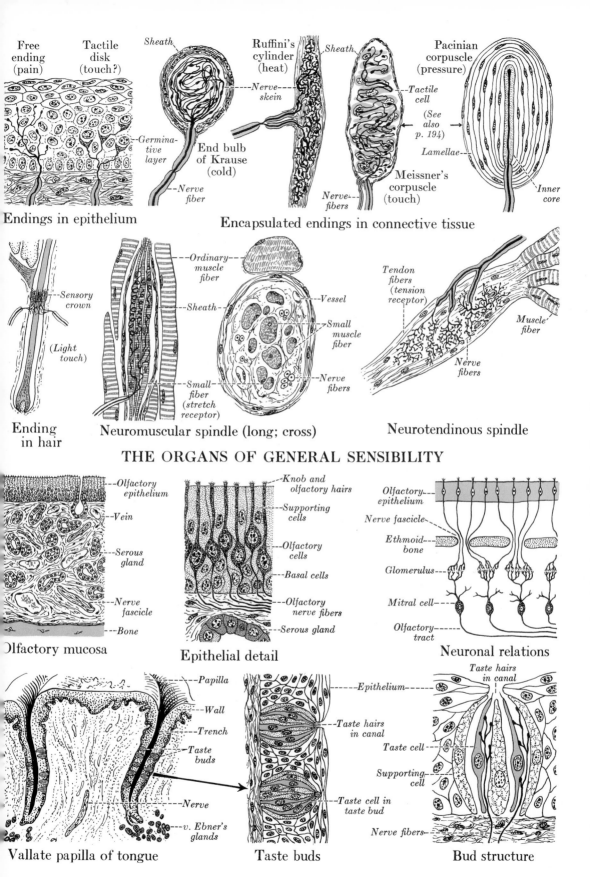

Free ending (pain) · Tactile disk (touch?)

Endings in epithelium

Sheath · Nerve-skein · End bulb of Krause (cold)

Ruffini's cylinder (heat) · Sheath

Tactile cell (See also p. 194) · Lamellae · Meissner's corpuscle (touch) · Nerve-fibers

Pacinian corpuscle (pressure) · Inner core

Germinative layer · Nerve fiber

Encapsulated endings in connective tissue

Sensory crown · (Light touch)

Ending in hair

Ordinary muscle fiber · Sheath · Small fiber (stretch receptor)

Vessel · Small muscle fiber · Nerve fibers

Neuromuscular spindle (long; cross)

Tendon fibers (tension receptor) · Nerve fibers · Muscle fiber

Neurotendinous spindle

THE ORGANS OF GENERAL SENSIBILITY

Olfactory epithelium · Vein · Serous gland · Nerve fascicle · Bone

Olfactory mucosa

Knob and olfactory hairs · Supporting cells · Olfactory cells · Basal cells · Olfactory nerve fibers · Serous gland

Epithelial detail

Olfactory epithelium · Nerve fascicle · Ethmoid bone · Glomerulus · Mitral cell · Olfactory tract

Neuronal relations

Papilla · Wall · Trench · Taste buds · Nerve · v. Ebner's glands

Vallate papilla of tongue

Epithelium · Taste hairs in canal · Taste cell in taste bud

Taste buds

Taste hairs in canal · Taste cell · Supporting cell · Nerve fibers

Bud structure

THE ORGANS OF SMELL AND TASTE

3. Neurotendinous Spindles.

Several groups of tendon fibers, near their junction with muscle, are involved.

The spindle-shaped bundle measures up to 3 mm. in length.

It is thinly encapsulated with connective tissue.

Nerve fibers enter, branch freely and end in clubbed enlargements on fibers.

D. REGENERATIVE ABILITY:

Free endings degenerate and regenerate as do peripheral nerve fibers in general (p. 116).

Information concerning encapsulated endings seems to be unknown, or at least unrecorded.

This lack includes data on their behavior after denervation and nerve regeneration.

Of interest would be data on their possible new formation in regenerated skin.

E. APPEARANCE IN SECTIONS:

Arborizations in epithelium and connective tissue are not seen after ordinary staining.

Special techniques (silver; methylene blue) demonstrate them satisfactorily.

Some of the *encapsulated endings* are readily recognizable.

Meissner's *tactile corpuscles* are identifiable in some dermal papillae of the skin.

Their location is limited to hairless surfaces (palm; sole; nipple; etc.).

Both the fibrous framework of the ellipsoidal corpuscle and the contained cells are ordinarily demonstrable.

Lamellar corpuscles are conspicuous near the junction of the dermis and subcutaneous.

Occasionally they are encountered in deep internal organs.

Example: pancreas; prostate; serous membranes.

The thick, concentric onion-layered arrangement is unmistakable.

Glomeruli have a thin, layered capsule and a relatively voluminous, granular interior.

A *neuromuscular spindle* is seen but rarely, and then in a chance section.

Its encapsulation and contained, thin skeletal fibers are points of recognition.

Neurotendinous spindles are scarcely to be expected in ordinary sections.

Their site is not at locations where tissue samples are commonly taken.

F. FUNCTIONAL CORRELATIONS:

The stimulation of any receptor merely activates a conducted, nervous impulse.

The translation of the impulse into a conscious sensation is accomplished in the brain.

1. Endings in Epithelium.

Diffuse arborizations mediate the sensation of *pain;* (also touch, heat and cold?).

Peritrichial endings are *touch receptors* for hairy regions of the skin.

Terminal disks presumably mediate the sensation of *light touch.*

2. Endings in Connective Tissue.

Free endings, like those in epithelium, are concerned with *pain reception*, at least.

Functions of all the varied encapsulated endings are incompletely assigned.

Krause's end bulbs are *cold receptors*, for some regions at least.

Ruffini's terminal cylinders seemingly mediate the sensation of *warmth.*

Meissner's tactile corpuscles are point *touch receptors* for the hairless surfaces.

Pacinian lamellar corpuscles are thought to be concerned with *pressure sensibility.*

3. Endings in Muscle and Tendon.

These receptors furnish information concerning *movements* and *positions* of the limbs and other parts of the body.

Neuromuscular spindles become *stretch receptors* when pulled upon.
They are extended when the muscle elongates passively during relaxation.
Neurotendinous spindles are *tension receptors*, responding to any pull.
This force may be due to active muscle contraction as well as to passive stretch.

II. THE SPECIAL SENSE ORGANS

i. The Olfactory Organ

Combining the olfactory organ with the respiratory intake was introduced by lung fishes.
All higher vertebrates retained this feature, and some improved on it by evolving a palate.

A. STRUCTURAL PLAN:

The *olfactory region* of a nasal cavity includes a narrow roof and the adjacent mucosa.
The latter covers the superior concha and an equal extent on the nasal septum.
The area on each lateral and medial wall is about the size of a dime.
The olfactory organ is merely a highly specialized mucous membrane, brownish in color.
The receptive cells, within the epithelium, are bipolar ganglion cells.
They are the only ones to retain a primitive location in a surface epithelium.
Extensions of the olfactory cells become *nerve fibers* that pass to the brain.
The olfactory cell, with its fiber-process, is a neuron of the first order.
Other cells of the epithelium are insensitive *supporting elements*.

B. DETAILED STRUCTURE:

1. Olfactory Epithelium.

The thick *epithelium* is a pseudostratified type, without goblet cells.
The *olfactory cells* are spindle-shaped elements, with round nuclei.
These nuclei occupy a broad middle- to deep zone in the epithelial layer.
The *distal part* of the cell is slender; it serves as a dendron.
It ends in a bulbous knob that bears 6 to 8 *olfactory hairs*.
These hairs are the actual receptive elements.
The *proximal part* of the cell is drawn out into a thin axon-process.
This is the *olfactory nerve fiber* that makes connections within the brain.
It is an unmyelinated fiber that continues through the lamina propria.
Here it gains a neurolemma sheath.
Hence the total olfactory cell is a peculiar bipolar neuron.
The chief *supporting cells* are tall, columnar and nonciliated.
Their free surfaces elaborate a striated border (*olfactory limiting membrane*).
The proximal half of each cell is much narrower than the distal half.
In addition there are some angular, low *basal cells*.
Both cell-types have an ovoid nucleus and contain a yellowish pigment.
These nuclei are nearer the cell top, or base, than those of olfactory cells.
Yet there is a prominent zone, free of nuclei, near the free surface.

2. Lamina Propria.

There is no definite *basement membrane*.
Superficially the lamina is delicately fibrous and contains many cellular elements.
Through it pass myriads of olfactory *nerve fibers* gathered in small clusters.
It contains the *olfactory glands* (of Bowman), which secrete continuously.
These are branched, tubulo-alveolar glands with a serous secretion.
Ducts convey the watery secretion to the surface of the mucous membrane.

More deeply the lamina is coarsely fibrous and fuses with the underlying periosteum.
In it occur about 20 prominent *fascicles* of nerve fibers.
These represent gatherings of the smaller clusters at higher levels.
Each bundle passes through an opening in the ethmoid bone to reach the brain.

C. REGENERATIVE ABILITY:

After destruction of olfactory mucosa, the ability to detect some odors may return.
This is probably owing to the survival of intact fragments of the original mucosa.
At least, the formation of new olfactory cells in the restored membrane is not known.

D. DIAGNOSTIC FEATURES:

The olfactory mucosa is surfaced with a thick, *pseudostratified epithelium*.
Ordinary cilia are not seen, but short *sensory hairs* may show on olfactory cells.
Nuclei are densely packed in a thick layer; goblet cells are lacking.
The lamina propria contains *serous glands*, and *nerve bundles* occur at a deep level.
This level lacks the venous plexuses, so prominent in the nasal respiratory region.
The mucous membrane lies upon bone.

E. FUNCTIONAL CORRELATIONS:

Olfactory stimulation is caused by gaseous, odoriferous substances in solution.
To this end the serous glands of the membrane bathe the surface with a watery fluid.
Continuous secretion serves also to freshen the fluid-film.
This prevents the retention of dissolved odors and lingering stimulation by them.
The actual receptive instruments are short olfactory hairs exposed at the surface.
No known differences in structure among olfactory cells are correlated with the discrimination of different kinds of odors.

ii. The Gustatory Organ

In fishes the organs of taste are widespread, occurring even on the gills, body and tail.
All higher vertebrates restrict them to the cavity of the mouth.

A. STRUCTURAL PLAN:

The *organ of taste* consists of numerous ovoid *taste buds*, about 70 μ tall.
They are most plentiful, in the adult, on the *vallate papillae* of the tongue.
Such a papilla bears about 200 taste buds on its sides.
The wall of the trench, opposite the papilla, bears about 50 buds.
These numbers are highly variable, and they decrease progressively with aging.
Taste buds are also plentiful in the middle folds of the series of *foliate papillae*.
These papillae, however, are often regressive or rudimentary.
A few buds occur on the fungiform papillae, soft palate, pharynx and epiglottis.
In general, they are more numerous and widespread in the newborn than later.
A *taste bud* is a paler, ovoid specialization within a stratified squamous epithelium.
It contains *neuro-epithelial cells* and *supporting cells*.
It communicates with the free surface by a tiny *taste canal* opening by a *taste pore*.

B. DETAILED STRUCTURE:

A *taste bud* extends vertically from the basement membrane almost to the free surface of the stratified squamous epithelium.
The overlying layers of the general epithelium are pierced by a *taste canal*.
The shape of a bud is somewhat like a barrel, but is often narrower at the top.

Two cell types comprise a taste bud.

The *taste cells*, 4 to 20 in number, are slender, spindle-shaped elements.

The elongate nucleus occupies a middle position.

The free end of the cell bears several cytoplasmic processes (*taste hairs*).

These project freely into the *taste canal* even to its *external taste pore*.

The *supporting cells* are tall pale elements, with rounder light nuclei.

Most of these are at the periphery; they resemble thick barrel staves.

Some gustatory *nerve fibers* enter the bud, branch and make knobbed endings.

These endings touch the surface of the taste cells, and also the 'supporting cells.'

Other fibers end in twigs about the exterior of the taste bud.

C. REGENERATIVE ABILITY:

Taste buds are stable only when their innervation is intact.

Interference with the nerve supply leads to degeneration; removal is aided by phagocytes.

Immediate replacement is by ordinary epithelial cells, following local proliferation.

On reinnervation, after nerve regeneration, the buds differentiate anew.

D. DIAGNOSTIC FEATURES:

A paler, barrel-shaped *cluster of cells* lies vertically in a stratified squamous epithelium.

The commonest location in an adult is on the sides of a vallate papilla.

Smaller numbers occur in the wall surrounding the trench.

From the top of a bud a slender *canal* leads to the free surface of the epithelium.

Slanting sections may transect this canal variously, or fail to include it.

In well-preserved specimens, *taste hairs* can be seen within the canal.

E. FUNCTIONAL CORRELATIONS:

Various substances stimulate the taste hairs and educe the sensations of taste.

Such substances are effective only when in solution.

It is possible that the so-called supporting cells are inexactly named.

Primarily they may be replacing elements for the gustatory cells.

At least, transitional stages between the two extremes are demonstrable.

Moreover, the sensation of taste is not restricted to regions containing taste buds.

Actually, all of the lingual mucosa innervated by gustatory nerves is responsive.

Sensitivity to the four taste modalities is different regionally in the tongue.

Even individual papillae may respond only to sweet, sour, salt or bitter.

Yet no recognizable differences occur in the structure of individual taste buds.

iii. The Eye

The visual organ consists primarily of the *eyeball* and *optic nerve*.

But it also includes various accessories (*extrinsic muscles; eyelids; tear apparatus*).

The several components of the visual organ are sheltered within the bony *orbit*.

A. STRUCTURAL PLAN:

The spheroidal *eyeball* consists of three *coats* that enclose certain *refractive media*.

The outer coat is the tough, fibrous *tunica fibrosa*.

Most of it is the opaque *sclera*, but anteriorly it becomes the transparent *cornea*.

The middle coat is the vascular and pigmented *tunica vasculosa* (or uvea).

Most of it is the relatively unspecialized *chorioid*.

Near the front it becomes the muscular *ciliary body* and the *iris*.

The iris ends about a circular opening, the *pupil*.

The innermost coat is the *tunica interna,* or *retina.*

Its nerve fibers gather posteriorly and leave the eyeball as the *optic nerve.*

This coat becomes insensitive where it lines the ciliary body and iris.

A refractive *lens* lies just behind the pupil and iris.

It is held in position and is influenced to change shape by a suspensory ligament.

This *ciliary zonule* is a system of fibers that radiate to the muscular ciliary body.

The *vitreous body* is a jelly that occupies the large space behind the lens.

Watery *aqueous humor* occupies the space in front of the lens and vitreous body.

The *eyelids* are movable folds of skin that can cover fully the front of the eyeball.

The *lacrimal gland* secretes tears into the *conjunctival sac* (between eyelids and eyeball).

The *tears* are drained away by a duct system at the inner angle of the eye.

B. DETAILED STRUCTURE:

1. Fibrous Tunic.

The outer coat consists of the *sclera* and the modified, transparent *cornea.*

A. SCLERA.

This firm, *external coat* ranges from 0.13 to 1.0 mm. in thickness.

It is expansive and is commonly known as the 'white' of the eye.

On it insert the tendons of the eye muscles.

In the region of the optic nerve the sclera thins into a sieve-like plate.

The outer scleral surface is a thin layer of loose, vascular *episcleral tissue.*

The middle region embraces the main scleral mass; it is the *substantia propria.*

It is composed mostly of densely woven collagenous fibers.

The inner surface is represented by the thin, pigmented *lamina fusca.*

It is transitional into the chorioid (see the suprachorioid layer, beyond).

B. CORNEA.

The front, bulging portion of the eyeball is transparent and nonvascular.

Five layers can be distinguished in this *cornea,* from front to back.

1. The CORNEAL EPITHELIUM is a thin, stratified squamous type.

    It contains only 5 to 6 layers of cells, and is moist and uncornified.

2. The 'ANTERIOR ELASTIC LAYER' (of Bowman) is a prominent basement membrane.

    It is not elastic and is now called the *anterior limiting membrane.*

3. The thick SUBSTANTIA PROPRIA contains about 60 collagenous lamellae.

    These are cemented into a matrix that contains also flattened fibroblasts.

4. The 'POSTERIOR ELASTIC LAYER' (of Descemet) serves as a basement membrane.

    It has atypical elastic qualities; the new name is *posterior limiting membrane.*

5. The ENDOTHELIUM OF THE ANTERIOR CHAMBER is a simple (low cuboidal) epithelium.

    It is not a true endothelium, since it is bathed by aqueous humor.

2. Vascular Tunic.

This coat is primarily *vascular* and *pigmented,* yet one region contains muscle.

It is bound intimately to the retinal coat, but joins the sclera loosely.

Exceptions with firm union are at the cribriform plate and ciliary body.

It has two circular openings: one is the *pupil;* the other, about the optic nerve.

This middle coat comprises, from back to front, the *chorioid, ciliary body* and *iris.*

A. CHORIOID.

This coat extends forward two-thirds of the distance toward the pupil.

The soft, thin membrane is co-extensive with the light perceptive retina.

Four layers can be recognized, from outside inward, as follows:

1. The *suprachorioid layer* is a series of slanting plates that join the sclera.

   Each plate contains branched *pigment cells* and *elastic fibers*.

   Between the plates is a system of clefts, making the *perichorioid space*.

2. The *vascular layer* contains many vessels and stellate *pigment cells*.

3. A *chorio-capillary layer* forms a rather broad-bored network close to the retina.

   It supplies nutriment and oxygen to neighboring portions of the retina.

4. The *basal membrane* (of Bruch) is a double-layered sheet.

   Its outer component is elastic; its inner component is cuticular.

   It serves as a basement membrane to the pigment epithelium of the retina.

   In fact, the cuticular layer is said to be a product of that epithelium.

B. CILIARY BODY.

This division of the vascular coat is a specialized zonary band.

It is interposed between the expansive chorioid and the iris.

It thickens progressively as it nears the iris, and here bears about 70 ridges.

Each ridge is a *ciliary process* that runs in a meridional plane.

The total set makes a wheel-like arrangement named the *ciliary crown*.

These processes anchor the fibers of the suspensory ligament of the lens.

Similar structural layers occur in the ciliary body as in the chorioid.

But a unique and striking feature is the prominent *ciliary muscle*.

This mass of smooth muscle lies within the suprachorioid layer.

Its fibers run meridionally, radially and circularly.

Although a vascular layer exists, there is no specific capillary layer.

Internally the *basal membrane* of the chorioid continues into the ciliary body.

It serves as a basement membrane to the modified retina of this zone.

At least, the cuticular component does; the elastic component splits off

C. IRIS.

The *iris* is a washer-shaped marginal plate, bordering the pupillary opening.

At its attached border, it is continuous with the ciliary body.

Elsewhere it is suspended free in the aqueous space between cornea and lens.

Several layers can be distinguished, from front to back:

1. An indistinct ENDOTHELIUM covers the surface that faces the cornea.

   This is continuous with the 'endothelial lining' of the cornea.

   It is lacking in some regions where crypt-like excavations occur.

2. An ANTERIOR STROMAL LAYER underlies the endothelium.

   It is nonvascular and consists mainly of branched, pigmented cells.

   These *chromatophores* determine the color of the iris.

   The thickness of the layer and its density of pigmentation are factors.

3. The deeper, GENERAL STROMA is a spongy fibro-elastic tissue.

   The fibers are fine, and most of the stromal cells are pigmented.

   Numerous blood vessels characterize this layer.

The posterior surface of the iris is clothed with a continuation of the retina.

   Its pigment layer specializes into dilator and constrictor muscles (p. 311).

D. IRIS ANGLE.

The iris meets the sclero-corneal junction at an acute angle.

   This union subtends a space in front of the iris called the *iris angle*.

Here occurs a spongy meshwork belonging to the scleral and vascular coats.

   Its *spaces of the iris angle* (of Fontana) open off the anterior chamber.

Nearby is the more prominent ring-shaped *scleral venous sinus*.

This canal (of Schlemm) encircles the eyeball at the corneal margin.

It drains by numerous branches into neighboring anterior ciliary veins.

The spaces of Fontana and canal of Schlemm do not communicate directly.

Yet aqueous humor finds ready passage into the canal, and so out into veins.

3. Internal Tunic (or Retina).

This innermost ocular coat lines the tunica vasculosa throughout its extent.

The *retina* arose as a bulge of the brain wall that became a double-walled cup.

The outer layer of the cup is the insensitive *pigment epithelium*.

The inner layer is the *retina proper*, containing several component sublayers.

These sublayers designate regions related to three sets of neurons.

The neurons are linked together into neuron chains.

Most of this soft, delicate membrane, but not all of it, is sensitive to light.

Blind portions are at the optic nerve and on the ciliary body and iris.

Three topographical regions of the retina are recognized descriptively.

These are, from back to front, an *optic-*, a *ciliary-* and an *iridical region*.

A. PARS OPTICA.

This major expanse of the retina extends from the head of the optic nerve to the posterior border of the ciliary body.

Here the truly nervous retina ends in a wavy line, the *ora serrata*.

Except for minor modified regions, the retina consists of ten layers.

All but the first belong to the photosensitive and nervous retina proper.

1. PIGMENT EPITHELIUM.

This single layer of *pigmented cells* is firmly bound to the chorioid layer.

Its cuboidal cells bear numerous pigmented, cytoplasmic processes.

These fringes extend between the rods and cones of the retina proper.

Such interdigitation, however, effects only a loose attachment.

2. RODS AND CONES.

These are the light-sensitive end-portions of the *rod* and *cone cells*.

The cells, known collectively as *visual cells*, are a neuro-epithelium.

They are arranged vertically and parallel, palisade-fashion.

The rods are slender cylinders; cones are shaped like long-necked flasks.

Each is some 60 μ long; rods outnumber cones 130 million to 7 million.

Both possess a slender *outer segment* and a thicker *inner segment*.

The outer segment consists largely of stacked disks, 0.014 μ thick.

An unstable colored substance, *visual purple*, is important in vision.

It occurs, at least chiefly, in the outer segment of rods.

3. EXTERNAL LIMITING MEMBRANE.

This sheet is a sieve-like product of the ends of tall supporting cells, also known as *Müller's fibers* (see beyond).

Through the perforations in this membrane pass the rods and cones.

4. OUTER NUCLEAR LAYER.

The nucleated bodies of the *visual cells* comprise this layer.

Cone nuclei are ovoid, paler and lie just beneath the external limiting membrane.

Rod nuclei are rounder, stain darker and lie at deeper levels.

5. OUTER PLEXIFORM LAYER.

In this region the fiber-like basal portions of the visual cells terminate.

The *rod fiber* ends in a knob; the *cone fiber*, in a branched expansion.

Here *synapses* are made chiefly with the dendrites of bipolar cells.

These latter neurons lie mostly in the next deeper levels.

6. INNER NUCLEAR LAYER.

Here occur the nuclei and cell bodies of *bipolar cells*, of *horizontal cells* (association neurons) and of *Müller's 'fibers'* (supporting cells).

The bipolar cells are the second links in the neuron chains.

7. INNER PLEXIFORM LAYER.

This layer represents a second *synaptic region* in the neuron chain.

The chief synapses are between axons of bipolar cells and profusely branching dendrites of ganglion cells (mostly belonging to the next deeper level).

8. GANGLION-CELL LAYER.

In this layer are the nuclei and cell bodies of large *ganglion cells*.

The ganglion cells furnish the third links in the neuron chains.

Also there are scattering neuroglial cells.

9. NERVE-FIBER LAYER.

Here the *axons* of ganglion cells course radially toward the optic nerve.

This layer also contains the larger vessels entering from the optic nerve.

10. INTERNAL LIMITING MEMBRANE.

It arises from the expanded ends of *Müller's fibers*.

These 'fibers' are vertically arranged ependymal cells, supporting in nature.

They extend as slender elements between the two limiting membranes.

They bear many recesses which shelter the bodies of the various neurons.

Two regions of the retina are modified in organizational plan.

11. MACULA LUTEA.

An area in the direct optic axis is called the *macula lutea*.

This 'yellow spot' is nearly 2 mm. in diameter and yellowish when fresh.

Progressively toward its center, rods disappear and cones become slender and increasingly abundant.

Also the inner retinal layers spread aside, leaving a saucer-shaped pit.

The central, thin region in the macula is the *fovea centralis*, 0.5 mm. wide.

Its sole visual cells are slender cones, resembling rods in shape.

Their fibers slant obliquely from the fovea in peripheral directions.

That is, they pass toward the displaced bipolar and ganglion cells.

These last-named neurons are located more marginally about the pit.

The fovea is the region of clearest vision and greatest visual acuity.

The close packing of slender cones favors the resolution of details.

The absence of other neurons and vessels favors an unobstructed image.

12. PERIPHERAL RETINA.

Near the ora serrata, nervous elements decrease; supporting elements increase.

Rods especially become sparser and disappear, leaving vacant spaces and cones.

Ganglion-cell and nerve-fiber layers cease; the two nuclear layers blend.

(A somewhat similar loss of layers occurs next to the optic nerve.)

B. PARS CILIARIS.

The *ciliary body* bears a continuation of the retina on its internal surface.

Both here and on the iris the retina is wholly insensitive to light.

This blind expanse is sometimes called the *pars caeca*.

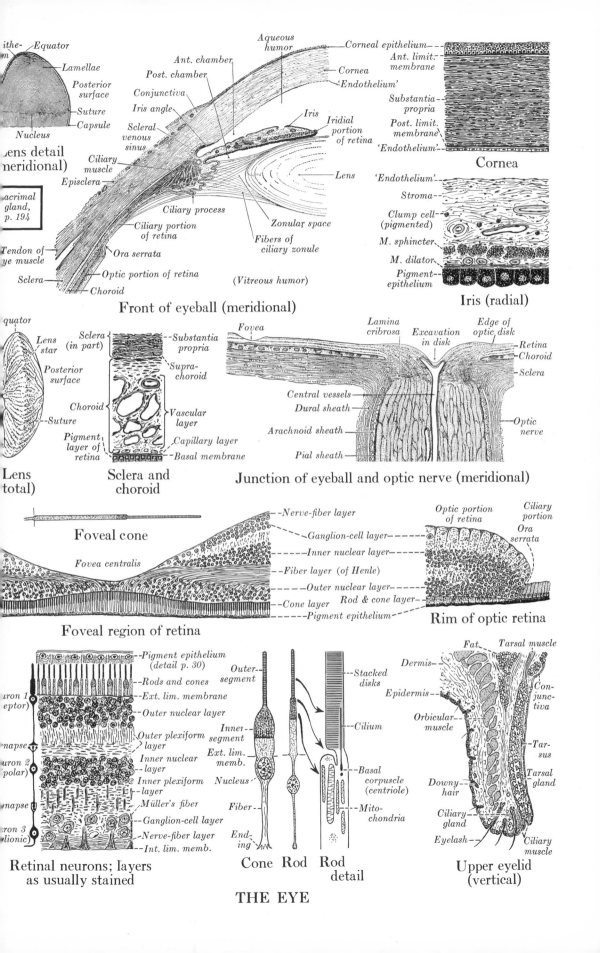

ithe-m — Equator
— Lamellae
Posterior surface
— Suture
— Capsule
Nucleus

Lens detail (meridional)

Lacrimal gland, p. 194

Tendon of eye muscle
Sclera
— Choroid

Aqueous humor
Ant. chamber
Post. chamber
Conjunctiva
Iris angle
Scleral venous sinus
Ciliary muscle
Episclera
Ciliary process
Ciliary portion of retina
Ora serrata
Optic portion of retina

Iris
Iridial portion of retina
Lens
Zonular space
Fibers of ciliary zonule
(Vitreous humor)

Front of eyeball (meridional)

Corneal epithelium
Ant. limit. membrane
Cornea
'Endothelium'
Substantia propria
Post. limit. membrane
'Endothelium'

Cornea

'Endothelium'
Stroma
Clump cell (pigmented)
M. sphincter
M. dilator
Pigment-epithelium

Iris (radial)

Equator
Lens star
Posterior surface
Suture

Lens (total)

Sclera (in part)
Substantia propria
Supra-choroid
Choroid
Vascular layer
Pigment layer of retina
Capillary layer
Basal membrane

Sclera and choroid

Fovea
Lamina cribrosa
Excavation in disk
Edge of optic disk
Retina
Choroid
Sclera
Central vessels
Dural sheath
Arachnoid sheath
Pial sheath
Optic nerve

Junction of eyeball and optic nerve (meridional)

Foveal cone

Fovea centralis

Foveal region of retina

Nerve-fiber layer
Ganglion-cell layer
Inner nuclear layer
Fiber layer (of Henle)
Outer nuclear layer
Cone layer
Pigment epithelium

Optic portion of retina
Ciliary portion
Ora serrata
Rod & cone layer

Rim of optic retina

Pigment epithelium (detail p. 30)
Rods and cones
Ext. lim. membrane
Outer nuclear layer
Outer plexiform layer
Inner nuclear layer
Inner plexiform layer
Müller's fiber
Ganglion-cell layer
Nerve-fiber layer
Int. lim. memb.

Neuron 1 (ceptor)
Synapse
Neuron 2 (bipolar)
Synapse
Neuron 3 (glionic)

Retinal neurons; layers as usually stained

Outer segment
Inner segment
Ext. lim. memb.
Nucleus
Fiber
Ending

Cone Rod

Stacked disks
Cilium
Basal corpuscle (centriole)
Mito-chondria

Rod detail

Fat
Tarsal muscle
Dermis
Epidermis
Orbicular muscle
Downy hair
Ciliary gland
Eyelash
Conjunctiva
Tarsus
Tarsal gland
Ciliary muscle

Upper eyelid (vertical)

THE EYE

The *pigment epithelium* is represented by tall cells, with extreme pigmentation.

Only at the tips of the ciliary processes are the cells shorter and paler.

The so-called *ciliary epithelium* corresponds to the nervous layers of the retina.

It is a single layer of clear, tall, columnar cells; they face the vitreous.

C. PARS IRIDICA.

The continuation of the pigment layer onto the iris becomes modified further.

Most of its cells are *myo-epithelial*, spindle-shaped and radially oriented.

The cell body is epithelial in character and moderately pigmented.

Each end of the cell tapers into an unpigmented fiber-process.

This fiber-like process is myoid both structurally and functionally.

The fibrillated portion of the cell body, as well as the cell processes, lie next to the iridial stroma.

These modified cells constitute the *dilator muscle* of the pupil.

In the stroma of the iris, near its free border, lies a second muscle-mass.

It is the *sphincter muscle* of the pupil.

It is a detached derivative of the primitive pigment layer.

The muscle fibers are typical, except for their ectodermal origin.

They are arranged in a flat ring that encircles the free border.

The continuation of the retina proper also shows modification.

Its tall cells, clear in the pars ciliaris, become heavily pigmented.

Nuclei and cell boundaries are both obscured.

4. Optic Nerve.

Both the embryonic optic cup and stalk are drawn out from the brain wall.

Hence the optic 'nerve' is a central tract, and not a true peripheral nerve.

The *meninges* (dura; pia-arachnoid) of the brain cover the optic nerve also.

At the eyeball the *subdural space* and *subarachnoid space* end.

Here also the sheaths merge into the sclera of the eyeball.

Continuations of the *pia mater* extend into the substance of the optic nerve.

Inside the nerve they subdivide the fiber-content into bundles of nerve fibers.

At the eyeball, this framework thickens by additions chiefly from the sclera.

The result is a sieve-like membrane, continuous with the sclera.

It is the *lamina cribrosa*, through which bundles of nerve fibers pass.

The *optic-nerve fibers* are axons of the ganglion cells of the retina.

At first, these fibers course radially in the nerve-fiber layer of the retina.

Near the posterior pole of the eyeball they turn 90° and enter the optic nerve.

The fibers enter at the circular nerve head, known as the *optic papilla*.

This is a bulging disk that bears a central depression or excavations.

The papilla is insensitive to light; it is the 'blind spot' on the retina.

Once in the nerve, the fibers continue without interruption to the brain.

Just brainward of the lamina cribrosa the naked axons acquire myelin sheaths.

Consequently the nerve doubles its diameter here rather abruptly.

Glial cells and fibers (but not neurolemma sheaths) embed the nerve fibers.

The nerve fibers in each optic nerve total one million.

This is more than three times the number in all other cranial nerves.

A *central artery* and *vein* enter the optic nerve more than midway toward the eyeball.

They proceed to the eyeball in a central strand of supporting tissue.

In the retina they spread fan-wise in the nerve-fiber layer.

Turning toward the chorioid, they extend through the inner nuclear layer.

(The only other vascular supply is fluid escaping from chorioidal vessels.)

5. Refracting Media.

Behind the *cornea*, which is the strongest refracting agent, are four other media.

They are: *crystalline lens; ciliary zonule; vitreous body; aqueous humor.*

These fill the interior of the eyeball and co-operate in image formation.

A. CRYSTALLINE LENS.

The *lens* is a transparent, plastic, biconvex disk situated just behind the iris.

Its posterior surface is more convex than the anterior surface.

The two surfaces meet at the rounded-off edge, or *equator.*

A homogeneous, elastic *capsule* encloses the entire lens.

A single-layered *lens epithelium* of varying height provides an anterior surface.

All the rest of the lens consists of a fibrous *lens substance.*

The component *lens fibers* are altered cells in the form of elongate bands.

Lens fibers are united by a structureless cementing substance.

New fibers are added throughout life from the epithelium at the *equator.*

Daughter cells elongate and become transparent; their nuclei no longer show.

Hence all but the central lens substance is arranged in concentric *lamellae.*

Also the cortical layers are softer than the older, central *lens nucleus.*

Fibers added about the fetal nucleus do not extend from pole to pole.

Their ends abut along *lens sutures* which radiate from the two poles.

These lines make branching *lens stars.*

The lens hardens with age, thereby losing its power of accommodation.

B. CILIARY ZONULE.

The lens is held in position by a system of fibers known as the *ciliary zonule.*

This radially arranged set of fibers serves the lens as a suspensory ligament.

It extends from the capsule at the lens border to the ciliary body.

The component *zonular fibers* are fine, homogeneous, inelastic elements.

Some attach in front of the actual lens equator; others, behind it.

Hence there is a space, bounded by these two sheets and the lens border.

This region is named the *zonular spaces.*

Images of near objects are brought to focus when the lens becomes more convex.

This accommodation is produced by the *ciliary muscle* and *zonular fibers.*

When the eye is at rest, the zonular fibers and lens are under tension.

This is because elastic sheets in the chorioid pull on the ciliary body.

The resulting pull of fibers on the lens capsule stretches the lens.

Accommodation occurs when the muscles of the ciliary body contract.

The ciliary body then moves forward and also bulges toward the lens.

These shifts release tension on the zonular fibers and lens capsule.

The elastic capsule then relaxes and takes a more spherical shape.

The plastic lens substance remolds and conforms to this new contour.

C. VITREOUS BODY.

This transparent, semisolid jelly fills the large space behind the lens and zonule.

In addition to its refractive role, it supports the lightly attached retina.

A *hyaloid canal* runs through it from the head of the optic nerve to the lens.

This was the course taken by the fetal hyaloid artery to the lens.

After fixation the jelly appears fibrillar and a *vitreous membrane* can be seen.

This is merely a condensed peripheral boundary, and not a definite membrane.

D. AQUEOUS HUMOR.

The *ocular chamber* is the space between the cornea and vitreous body.

It is incompletely divided by the iris into two parts.

The *anterior chamber* lies between the cornea, iris and front of the lens.

The *posterior chamber* is a small ring-shaped space, triangular in section.

It is bounded by the iris, ciliary body and vitreous body.

The chamber contains *aqueous humor*, which is a clear, lymph-like fluid.

6. Accessory Organs.

A. EYELIDS.

These are movable folds of skin, protecting the eye and shutting out light.

The thin skin of the outer surface of the lid is modified on the inner surface.

Here it becomes a transparent mucous membrane named the *conjunctiva*.

The epithelium is stratified columnar, and mostly but 2 to 3 cells thick.

Some of the superficial columnar cells specialize into goblet cells.

This membrane also continues, by reflection, over the front of the eyeball.

The number of epithelial layers increases and the surface cells flatten.

It has been described previously where it covers the cornea (p. 307).

The shape of the lid is maintained by an internal fibrous plate, the *tarsus*.

To its proximal border attaches the involuntary *tarsal muscle* (of Müller).

Embedded in the plate are numerous sebaceous *tarsal glands* (of Meibom).

Each gland has an axial excretory duct, into which open many alveoli.

The ducts discharge on the free margin of the lid and lubricate it.

A thin sheet of muscle, the *orbicularis*, acts to close the eyelids.

The upper lid is raised by the *levator muscle*.

Eyelashes, or *cilia*, are coarse hairs, with large sebaceous glands (of Zeis).

Between them are large, spiraling (not coiling) sweat glands (of Moll).

B. LACRIMAL GLAND.

This gland grows out from the upper lateral margin of the conjunctival sac.

There is a superior and inferior gland-mass, imperfectly separated.

Actually a group of individual units is drained by about ten ducts.

Each unit is a compound, tubulo-alveolar *serous gland*.

The *alveoli* have tall cells, whose height varies with their functional state.

Resembling the parotid gland, they have narrower cells and a wider lumen.

Their cytoplasm contains large, pale secretion granules and fat droplets.

The cells are provided with *secretory capillaries*.

Between the cells and basement membrane are stellate, myoid *basket cells*.

Lymphoid and other cells tend to collect in the stroma of the gland.

The secretion supplies the clear, salty *tears* that flush the conjunctival sac.

The tears flow to the inner angle of the eye and are collected by a *lacrimal canaliculus* in each eyelid.

Carried to the *lacrimal sac* and *naso-lacrimal duct*, they reach the nasal cavity.

C. OCULAR MUSCLES; FIBROUS SHEATHS.

Six voluntary *ocular muscles* (four recti; two obliques) insert on the sclera.

Only one movement (direct lateral) is produced by a single muscle.

All other movements result from the combined effort of at least two muscles.

Fibrous *sheaths* invest the muscles and continue into the *bulbar fascia*.

The latter is a fibrous cup ('Tenon's capsule') in which the eyeball sits.

It is attached loosely to the sclera by collagenous fibers.

C. REGENERATIVE ABILITY:

The *corneal epithelium* heals its wounds by cell migation and subsequent mitosis.

The *substantia propria* restores losses by producing ordinary, opaque scar tissue.

The *sclera* acts like any fibrous capsule in the formation of new repair-tissue.
The *chorioid* replaces destroyed areas by differentiating fibrous scar-tissue.
 It is not as well vascularized as before, but may contain many pigment cells.
The *iris* is notable in not repairing traumatic injuries inflicted on it.
 There is perhaps a suppressive influence exerted in some way (by aqueous humor?).
  At least, tissue from the iris can grow when cultivated in artificial media.
The *lens epithelium* will recover a locally denuded area.
 At the equator this restored epithelium can even lay down new lens fibers.
The *retina* heals local injuries by glial proliferation and replacement.
 After interruption of the optic nerve, the retina persists remarkably well.
  Only some of the ganglion cells perish within the ensuing weeks.
  Possibly this is owing to the loss of blood supply rather than to direct trauma.

D. DIAGNOSTIC FEATURES:

A meridional section through the eyeball is unmistakable, even to the naked eye.
Sections through *local regions* would include one, at least, of the following parts:
 Cornea; iris; lens; ciliary body; pars optica and overlying coats; optic nerve.
 Each of these is distinctive, especially if some neighboring region is included.
Sections through *accessory organs* would probably include the eyelid or lacrimal gland.
 Each is unique, although the *lacrimal gland* must be distinguished from the parotid.
  Positively the alveoli have a wider lumen; negatively they lack secretory-type ducts.

E. FUNCTIONAL CORRELATIONS:

Mechanical support and protection are furnished by the fibrous external coat.
 The vitreous body and aqueous humor maintain a pressure within the eyeball cavity.
 This keeps the coats from separating and the eyeball from collapsing.
Vascularity is chiefly maintained by the middle, or vascular, coat.
 Its vessels do not actually enter the internal, or retinal, coat.
 The retina does, however, benefit from seepage out of the vascular coat.
  It also has an individual supply through vessels of the optic nerve.
 Aqueous humor originates in the ciliary body as a 'secretion.'
 It finds an outlet into the veins of the vascular coat.
Light regulation is accomplished through the automatic action of the iris.
 Unique dilator and sphincter muscles control the size of the pupil.
 In this way the intensity of admitted light is regulated.
Image formation is accomplished jointly by the cornea, aqueous, lens and vitreous.
 The variable component that permits changes in focus is the lens.
 The lens changes shape (accommodates) in maintaining sharp focus in near vision.
  The manner of operation is the reverse of what might be expected (p. 312).
Optical isolation of rods and cones is aided by processes of the pigment epithelium.
 The pigmented cells also prevent confusing back-reflection of light rays.
Sensory reception is a function of the visual rods and cones.
 The image is brought to focus at the level of their outer members.
 Bright-light vision (keen vision) is a function of the relatively insensitive cones.
  In the fovea alone is high resolution and color discrimination obtained.
   The retinal modifications here are adapted to these ends (p. 310).
 Dim-light vision is a function of the extremely sensitive rods.
  Yet the resolution of detail is poor, and color discrimination is lacking.
 The different capabilities of the rods and cones correlate in part with their synaptic
  relations to neurons of the second and third order.

The rods connect with the bipolar cells in groups, and respond in groups.
The cones link with bipolars and ganglion cells by individual synapses.
Especially is this true in the fovea, where independent responses are desirable.

iv. The Ear

The 'organ of hearing' is really a compound organ with different functions.
It is receptive to sound waves, which is the basis of the *auditory sense*.
It also responds to the effects of gravity and to movements of the head.
These trigger the sensations known as *static* and *kinetic*.
The organ consists of three related parts, mostly lying within the temporal bone.
These parts are distinct in origin, structure and function.

A. STRUCTURAL PLAN:

One portion is the *external ear*, which shows three subordinate divisions.
The *auricle* is a shallow appendage situated on the lateral surface of the head.
The *external acoustic meatus* is a short tube, leading inward to the ear drum.
The vibratory *tympanic membrane*, or ear drum, closes the deep end of the meatus.
A second component is the *middle ear*, which is a membranous chamber largely within bone.
The main *tympanic cavity* connects with the naso-pharynx by an *auditory tube*.
In an opposite direction leads off an auxiliary chamber, the *tympanic antrum*.
The latter communicates with many irregular spaces called *mastoid cells*.
A chain of three *ear bones* crosses the tympanic cavity.
The set connects the ear drum with the internal ear.
A third part, or *internal ear*, is the receptive apparatus—also contained within bone.
It is extremely irregular in shape and, for this reason, is called the *labyrinth*.
Two different component parts have the same general configuration.
The *bony labyrinth* is an external shell of bone that encases the whole.
The *membranous labyrinth* is a fibrous, epithelium-lined, internal compartment.
As the actual sensory mechanism it consists of interconnecting sacs and ducts.
These are suspended in fluid and are filled with fluid.
The *utricle* and *saccule* are small sacs contained within a bony *vestibule*.
Three *semicircular ducts* are surrounded by bony *semicircular canals*.
The snail-like *cochlear duct* is encased within a bony cochlea of similar shape.

B. DETAILED STRUCTURE:

1. External Ear.

A. AURICLE.

This is shaped and supported by an internal plate of *elastic cartilage*.
It is covered on all exposed surfaces by typical, thin *skin*.
Six *intrinsic muscles*, all vestigial, extend between portions of the cartilage.
Three *extrinsic muscles* pass from the skull to the cartilage.
They are rudimentary, and usually are inactive.

B. EXTERNAL ACOUSTIC MEATUS.

The outer one-half of the tube is supported by *elastic cartilage*.
The remainder is a tunnel through the temporal bone.
A continuation of auricular *skin* lines the inch-long, slightly tortuous tube.
In the *cartilaginous portion* there are fine hairs and large sebaceous glands.
Coiled, tubular *ceruminous glands* are a characteristic feature.

They are modified sweat glands, of the apocrine type, with a large lumen.

The specialized gland cells contain coarse brown pigment granules.

Their discharged yellowish secretion mixes in the external meatus with sebaceous secretion and desquamated cells.

Drying of this mixture produces a thick waxy product, the *cerumen*.

In the *bony portion* the skin is very thin.

Hairs and glands occur only along the upper wall.

c. TYMPANIC MEMBRANE.

The *ear drum*, set at a strong slant, closes the external meatus at its deep end.

It serves as a common partition between the meatus and tympanic cavity.

The membrane is about 0.1 mm. thick and consists of four sheet-like layers.

The *outer surface* is very thin skin, continuous with that of the meatus.

Next deeper is a radiate fibrous layer and then a circular fibrous layer.

In an upper, triangular *flaccid region* these two layers are lacking.

The *inner surface* is a mucous membrane, with a low cuboidal epithelium.

It is a part of the lining of the tympanic cavity.

2. Middle Ear.

The *tympanic cavity* is a flattened cleft contained within the temporal bone.

It is an air-space, traversed by the ear bones, their ligaments and a nerve.

A *mucous membrane* lines its walls and wraps about the ear bones and other contents.

The *epithelium* is simple; in most regions it is low cuboidal and nonciliated.

The medial wall bears the *vestibular window* (oval) and the *cochlear window* (round).

The first is an opening into the vestibule, closed by the base of the *stapes*.

The second is closed by the fibrous, mucosa-covered *secondary tympanic membrane*.

Three movable *auditory ossicles* extend, like a chain, across the tympanic cavity.

The *malleus*, or hammer, is firmly attached to the ear drum.

The *stapes*, or stirrup, is fixed (by its basal plate) into the vestibular window.

It is in direct contact with the perilymph fluid of the internal ear.

The *incus*, or anvil, has a middle position and articulates with the other two.

The *tympanic antrum* (and mastoid cells) is lined with a thin mucous membrane.

This membrane is continuous with that of the tympanic cavity.

The *auditory* (or *Eustachian*) *tube* has a bony and a cartilaginous portion.

Both portions are lined with a *mucous membrane* whose epithelium varies in type.

Near the pharynx it is pseudostratified and ciliated.

Nearer the tympanic cavity it is simple columnar and ciliated.

Some *lymph nodules* occur in the lamina propria.

The submucosa contains mixed *sero-mucous glands*.

The *cartilaginous wall*, nearer the pharynx, supports two-thirds of the tube.

Its *cartilage* (elastic proximally) is a plate, J-shaped in transverse section.

The major limb of the plate supports the medial wall.

The bony wall, nearer the tympanic cavity, surrounds one-third of the tube.

Its mucous membrane is continuous with that of the tympanic cavity.

3. Internal Ear.

This portion of the auditory mechanism is also enclosed within the temporal bone.

But, unlike the tympanic cavity, it contains a system of sensory tubes and sacs.

The greatest length of this apparatus is about 0.8 in.

Externally there is the *osseous labyrinth*—a set of bony canals and chambers.

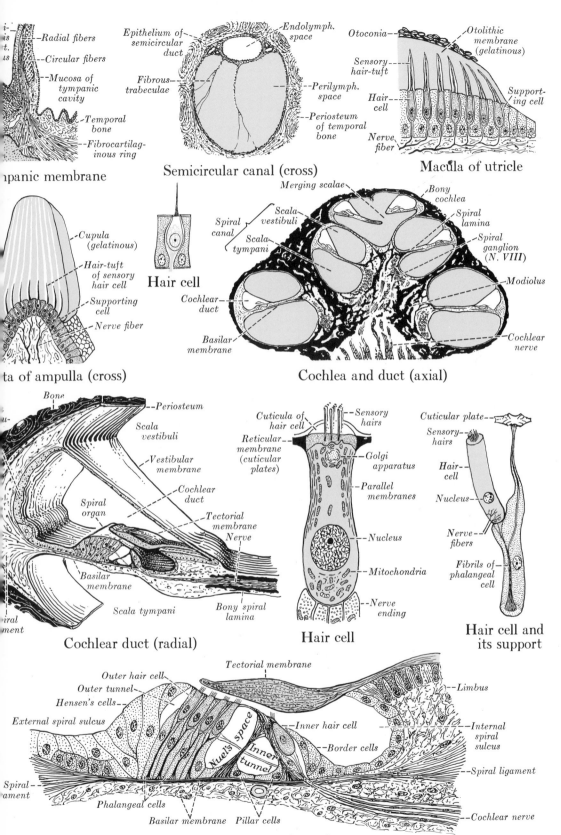

Radial fibers
Circular fibers
Mucosa of tympanic cavity
Temporal bone
Fibrocartilaginous ring

Tympanic membrane

Epithelium of semicircular duct
Endolymph. space
Fibrous trabeculae
Perilymph. space
Periosteum of temporal bone

Semicircular canal (cross)

Otoconia
Otolithic membrane (gelatinous)
Sensory hair-tuft
Hair cell
Supporting cell
Nerve fiber

Macula of utricle

Cupula (gelatinous)
Hair-tuft of sensory hair cell
Supporting cell
Nerve fiber

ta of ampulla (cross)

Hair cell

Merging scalae
Bony cochlea
Spiral lamina
Scala vestibuli
Spiral canal
Scala tympani
Spiral ganglion (N. VIII)
Cochlear duct
Modiolus
Basilar membrane
Cochlear nerve

Cochlea and duct (axial)

Bone
Periosteum
Scala vestibuli
Vestibular membrane
Cochlear duct
Spiral organ
Tectorial membrane
Nerve
Basilar membrane
Scala tympani
Bony spiral lamina

Cochlear duct (radial)

Cuticula of hair cell
Sensory hairs
Reticular membrane (cuticular plates)
Golgi apparatus
Parallel membranes
Nucleus
Mitochondria
Nerve ending

Hair cell

Cuticular plate
Sensory hairs
Hair cell
Nucleus
Nerve fibers
Fibrils of phalangeal cell

Hair cell and its support

Outer hair cell
Tectorial membrane
Outer tunnel
Hensen's cells
Limbus
External spiral sulcus
Inner hair cell
Internal spiral sulcus
Nuel's space
Inner tunnel
Border cells
Spiral ligament
Spiral ligament
Phalangeal cells
Basilar membrane
Pillar cells
Cochlear nerve

Spiral organ (radial)

THE EAR

They are named the *semicircular canals, vestibule* and *cochlea.*

Their lining is periosteum whose free surface is mesenchymal epithelium (p. 26).

They contain a watery fluid, named the *perilymph.*

Internally there is a much slenderer *membranous labyrinth.*

It comprises a series of continuous, closed tubes and chambers.

Their general arrangement and shape follow the bony labyrinth that contains them.

They have a fibrous exterior and an epithelial lining.

Such passages are anchored to the periosteum of the bony labyrinth.

They are surrounded, except for attached regions, by the fluid *perilymph.*

They are filled with a similar, but wholly separate, fluid *endolymph.*

The membranous labyrinth has two divisions, different structurally and functionally.

One deals with the *static* and *kinetic senses;* the other, with *hearing.*

The *static* and *kinetic senses* are served by five major constituent parts.

   (1–3) Three *semicircular ducts* are set in planes at right angles to each other.

   Each bears a swollen *ampulla* at one end.

   (4) Both ends unite with the ellipsoidal *utricle.*

   (5) The utricle communicates with a spheroidal *saccule* by a slender duct.

   From this tube the slender *endolymphatic duct* extends through the bone.

   The duct ends in a dilatation, the *endolymphatic sac*, located just outside the dura mater.

Both the utricle and saccule occupy a middle chamber in the osseous labyrinth.

This *vestibule* lies between the semicircular canals and the cochlea.

The *auditory sense* is served by a tube, coiled spirally like a snail shell.

This compactly coiled tube is named the *cochlear duct.*

Near its base it communicates with the saccule by the slender *ductus reuniens.*

Its tip ends blindly at the apex of the coil.

The lining *epithelium* of the membranous labyrinth is largely simple squamous.

Certain local areas are specialized as sensory *neuro-epithelia.*

There are six of these areas, innervated by branches of the acoustic nerve.

They occur in the utricle, saccule, semicircular ducts and cochlear duct.

A. MACULAE.

Both the utricle and saccule bear a thickened, sensory area, the *macula.*

The macula of the utricle is oval; that of the saccule is heart-shaped.

Their columnar epithelium has two kinds of cells—sensory and supporting.

The sensory *hair cells* are shaped like short flasks with a rounded base.

They do not reach to the basement membrane.

Their nuclei lie in an upper row.

Each free surface bears a cuticular plate and a tuft of *sensory hairs.*

The hairs are nonmotile cilia that project centrally from the cell top.

They are held together by a cementing substance.

The *supporting cells* are slender elements whose nuclei lie at a deep level.

The thinner, upper portion ends at the free surface in a cuticular plate.

The surface of the macula is covered with a gelatinous *otolithic membrane.*

The hair tufts project into slender recesses in this substance.

The recesses, like the general lumen, are filled with watery *endolymph.*

Toward the upper surface of the membrane occur particles named *otoconia.*

These are minute crystals, densely packed.

They are composed of calcium carbonate and a protein substance.

B. CRISTAE.

Each ampulla of the three semicircular ducts bears a *crista.*

This is an elongate crest oriented transversely to the long axis of the duct.

A crista has much the same structure as a macula.

Supporting cells, hair cells and *hair tufts* are similar in both.

Over the crest is a striated, gelatinous mass called the *cupola*.

Into it project the ciliary tufts of the hair cells.

It is comparable to the otolithic membrane, but it lacks otoconia.

c. Osseous Cochlea.

The total mechanism for the organ of hearing is rather complicated.

For this reason the bony *cochlea* requires some preliminary attention.

It resembles a snail shell, with a broad base and narrow apex.

A spiraling, bony case makes about 2½ turns around a central pillar.

This axial pillar is the *modiolus;* it is made of spongy bone.

A bony shelf projects from the modiolus into the cavity of the shell.

This flange, resembling the thread of a screw, is the *spiral lamina.*

From its free border a fibrous *basilar membrane* continues to the outer wall.

Together they divide the *spiral canal* of the cochlea into two compartments.

Above the lamina-partition is the perilymphatic space named the *scala vestibuli.*

One end communicates with the perilymphatic space of the vestibule.

At the other (apical) end it joins the tip of a similar, parallel scala.

This second passage is the *scala tympani*, located beneath the lamina.

Both scalae are lined by a simple layer of mesenchymal epithelium.

Beneath the lamina is the perilymphatic space named the *scala tympani.*

Its fibrous lining, at the beginning of its basal turn, helps close the cochlear window in the bony tympanic wall.

Closure is made by the thin secondary *tympanic membrane.*

Its components are periosteal tissue of the scala and the mucosal lining of the tympanic cavity of the middle ear.

Hence the membrane separates perilymph from the air of the tympanic cavity.

Nearby is the opening into the *perilymphatic duct.*

This canal extends through bone to the subarachnoid space about the brain.

d. Cochlear Duct.

The *duct* is a membranous tube, much smaller than the bony cochlea containing it.

One end is blind; the other end communicates with the saccule.

The latter connection is made by the slender *ductus reuniens.*

Externally there is fibrous tissue; internally, a lining of epithelium.

The duct is something of a right triangle in transverse section.

The more acute angle points toward the modiolus.

The leg opposite this angle attaches to the bony shell of the cochlea.

The base rests on the spiral lamina and its membranous extension.

The hypotenuse is the vestibular membrane, bounded only by fluids.

The *upper surface*, or roof, of the duct is the slanting *vestibular membrane.*

This thin membrane (of Reissner) separates the perilymph of the scala vestibuli from the endolymph of the cochlear duct.

The membrane contains a middle layer of nonvascular connective tissue.

One surface is bounded by mesenchymal epithelium of the scala vestibuli.

The other free surface is bounded by squamous epithelium of the duct.

The *lateral surface* blends with thickened periosteum of the bony cochlea.

This thickening, more extensive than the duct, is the *spiral ligament.*

Its more internal part contains many capillary vessels.

Loops even invade the thick pseudostratified epithelium of the duct.

(This is the only good example of such epithelial invasion in mammals.)

The thickened epithelium and subjacent connective tissue comprise a unit.

The combination is a vascular complex named the *stria vascularis*.

It apparently is the source of endolymph.

The *basal surface*, or floor, of the duct is an epithelium that varies in height.

Part of it is greatly elevated and specialized for sensory reception.

This is the *spiral organ* (of Corti), the receptor for hearing.

The epithelium in general rests upon the periosteum of the spiral lamina, and upon its fibrous continuation to the outer cochlear wall.

The fibrous component of the floor of the duct is, in part, specialized.

Medially the periosteum is thick where it approaches the spiral organ.

This thick *limbus* serves for the attachment of the tectorial membrane.

Laterally, beneath the spiral organ and beyond it to the spiral ligament, stretches a specialized fibrous layer, known as the *basilar membrane*.

The membrane varies in width progressively along the duct.

It is widest at the extreme apical end of the cochlear duct.

It is narrowest at the beginning of the basal turn of the duct.

The basilar membrane consists of three layers.

Facing the spiral organ, the border layer is thin.

It is a homogeneous ground substance.

Facing the scala tympani, the border layer is thicker.

It is a delicate fibrous tissue.

The intermediate stratum is the most important component.

Its main feature is a set of 25,000 *basilar fibers*, strung like harp strings.

They are fine threads, or auditory strings, of a special chemical nature.

The fibers are embedded in a small amount of homogeneous ground substance.

The *spiral organ* has a number of special components.

These will be described in order, from the periphery toward the modiolus.

1. PERIPHERAL CELLS.

Just axiad of the stria vascularis is a groove, the *external spiral sulcus*.

Its floor consists of cuboidal *cells of Claudius*.

Within the border of the spiral organ itself the cells gain height steadily.

They make several rows of supporting elements, named the *cells of Hensen*.

2. OUTER HAIR CELLS.

These outermost sensory cells occur in rows of three to five cells.

Their total number is about 20,000.

They are short prisms that do not extend halfway to the basilar membrane.

The free surface bears a cuticular plate and many sensory hairs.

A space between the nearest hair- and Hensen cells is the *outer tunnel*.

3. OUTER PHALANGEAL CELLS.

These are tall supporting cells (of Deiters), one for each hair cell.

The round base of a hair cell sits in the cupped side of its phalangeal cell.

Above this level the phalangeal cell narrows to a slender stalk.

At the surface it expands, ending in a flat cuticular plate.

4. OUTER PILLAR CELLS.

Each has a broad base and an expanded top or 'head.'

The head bears a convexity on its medial side (see beyond).

Superficially there is a cuticular plate.

Nuel's space lies between these pillars and the nearest of the outer hair cells and phalangeal cells.

5. INNER PILLAR CELLS.

An inner cell resembles an outer pillar cell but its head bears a concavity.

The convexity and concavity of each outer and inner cell-pair fit together.

The arrangement resembles a ball and socket joint.

From this union the two cell columns diverge greatly basalward.

The result is a gable-shaped open space, the *inner tunnel* (of Corti).

6. INNER PHALANGEAL CELLS.

There is a single row of these cells, narrowing greatly toward the surface.

Each forms a small cuticular plate.

7. INNER HAIR CELLS.

There is a single row of cells, similar to the outer hair cells.

Their total number is about 3,500.

The rounded cell base is supported by pillar, phalangeal and border cells.

8. BORDER CELLS.

Inward of the inner hair cells is a single row of columnar *border cells*.

They form a cuticular plate at the surface.

All supporting cells in the floor of the cochlear duct form cuticular plates.

As a whole, these plates constitute the *lamina reticularis*.

In surface view it comprises a mosaic, with regularly arranged 'holes.'

Each gap contains the head of a hair cell (bearing its cuticular plate).

9. TECTORIAL MEMBRANE.

The thick periosteum over the spiral lamina makes an elevated *limbus*.

It is covered by simple columnar epithelium.

These cells are capped by a prominent cuticular membrane.

Continuous with this cuticular membrane is the imposing *tectorial membrane*.

It projects outward peripherally, hanging free over the spiral organ.

It is thickest midway and tapers toward its attached and free ends.

Between the limbus, tectorial membrane and spiral organ is the prominent *internal sulcus*.

The *tectorial membrane* is an epithelial derivative, cuticular in nature.

It is a delicate, flexible, fibrillar, gelatinous substance.

When fresh, it fills about one-fourth of the spiral duct.

Fixation brings shrinkage and distortion.

The lower surface rests upon the tips of hairs from the hair cells.

E. VESSELS AND NERVES.

The arteries and veins pursue different courses.

Arterial blood is distributed through three branches.

One branch supplies part of the saccule, utricle and semicircular ducts

A second branch supplies the remainder of the saccule, utricle and ducts.

It also supplies one-third of the basal turn of the cochlea.

A third branch supplies the modiolus and bony spiral lamina.

It also passes to the outer wall of both scalae and to the stria vascularis of the spiral duct.

Veins likewise have three lines of drainage.

Some come from the semicircular ducts and part of the utricle.

Others come from the saccule, stria, spiral lamina and utricle.

Still others come from the bony spiral lamina and its spiral ganglion.

There are no vessels in the vestibular membrane.

The same statement is true for most of the basilar membrane.

Probably endolymph from the stria vascularis nourishes the spiral organ.

All vascular arrangements give protection against sounds from pulsation.

Lymphatics are lacking; the perilymphatic spaces collect and remove excess fluid.

The *auditory nerve* has a vestibular and a cochlear division.

Its ganglion cells are bipolar, with a peripheral and central process.

Peripheral processes are functional dendrons; central processes are axons.

The peripheral fibers, after a short course, lose their sheaths and branch.

The *vestibular nerve* supplies the maculae and cristae.

Its *vestibular ganglion* lies at the outer end of the internal meatus.

The dendrons end by forming baskets about the hair cells.

The *cochlear nerve* courses in the modiolus and supplies the spiral organ.

Its *spiral ganglion* lies in the thick base of the bony spiral lamina.

Bundles of *nerve fibers* pass outward in the spiral lamina.

Some fibers are distributed to the inner hair cells.

Each fiber ends about one, or at most two, cells.

More fibers cross the tunnel and Nuel's space to reach the outer hair cells.

Each fiber supplies only a single hair cell of these rows.

All fibers terminate by arborizing about the hair cells.

C. REGENERATIVE ABILITY:

The *external ear* heals as skin (p. 189) and cartilage (p. 69) do elsewhere.

The ear drum will heal perfectly after surgical incision or septic perforation.

Only in unusual circumstances does scar tissue develop.

The *middle ear* promptly resurfaces defects made in its mucosa.

The *internal ear* will repair injuries inflicted on its nonsensory membranous labyrinth.

Unlike taste buds, whose innervation is similarly related to secondary sense cells, the spiral organ does not degenerate following destruction of its nerve.

D. DIAGNOSTIC FEATURES:

The *auricle* is characterized by thin skin on both surfaces.

Internally, elastic cartilage occurs and skeletal muscle may be included.

The *external meatus* (outer half) retains the cartilage but has only one cutaneous surface.

Large sebaceous glands and prominent, coiled ceruminous glands are diagnostic aids.

The *middle ear* presents a variety of appearances, depending on the plane of section.

The *tympanic cavity* has a thin mucous membrane, with simple epithelium, applied to bone.

Its cavity may include cuts through one or more small ear bones.

Such bones are covered with reflected mucous membrane.

The *tympanic membrane* is a very thin partition between two cavities.

It has thin skin on one surface and low cuboidal epithelium on the other.

The mucosal side may attach or adjoin a slice of bone (the malleus).

The *auditory tube* is characteristic in its course outside the skull.

Its wall contains mixed glands and a cartilage, hook-shaped in transverse section.

The *internal ear* is unique for its small, epithelium-lined passages.

Each lies in a far greater space, except where attachment occurs to surrounding bone.

Specific identifications of parts are often difficult in a single, random section.

Only the *cochlea* is easy to identify by itself.

If cut in a radial plane, its modiolus and arrangement of chambers are unmistakable.

The *spiral organ* is specifically diagnostic even when cut in an unusual plane.

Sections cut tangentially or horizontally to the coils tax interpretative ingenuity, however, on the first encounter.

E. FUNCTIONAL CORRELATIONS:

The *auricle* evolved as a sound-collecting appendage.

It is far more important in mammals whose auricle is deeply cupped and movable.

Cerumen protects the skin of the external acoustic meatus from drying.

Its bitter taste is said to repel insects and other intruders.

The *ear drum* is a vibratory membrane, set in motion by sound waves.

The chain of *ear bones* acts like a bent lever in transmitting vibrations.

They convert the movements of the drum into intensified thrusts.

The foot plate of the stapes, set in the vestibular window, acts like a piston.

It transmits vibrations directly to the perilymph.

The incompressible perilymph, thus 'pushed in,' is enclosed within a bony capsule.

It compensates by 'pushing out' the secondary tympanic membrane.

The *auditory tube* permits pressures in the tympanic cavity and outside air to equalize.

This takes place when the tube opens during swallowing.

The open communication, however, presents a potential avenue of infection.

The *utricle* informs concerning the *position of the head* in space.

This static function depends on a shifting in the position of the otolithic membrane.

Gravitational pull acts on the otoconia, and the hair tufts are moved.

The stimulus thus transmitted initiates compensatory postural reflexes.

The utricle also informs concerning *linear acceleration*, either positive or negative.

Evidence on the saccule is conflicting but tends to discredit vestibular function.

It seems to be associated with the cochlea by receiving slow *vibrational stimuli*.

The *semicircular ducts* inform concerning any *rotational movements* involving the head.

Any degree of rotation of the head leads to stimulation of the cristae.

Displacement of the endolymph against the cupola disturbs the hairs of hair cells.

The ensuing information is a part of the kinetic and proprioceptive senses.

The responses lead to compensatory movements of the eyes, head and limbs.

Each crista is stimulated by movements occurring in the plane of its canal.

The *spiral organ* (and specifically the hair cells) is the receptor for *sound*.

Perilymph vibrates at the same frequencies as those of the air-borne sound waves.

Pressure changes in the scala vestibuli are transmitted across the vestibular membrane.

Induced pulsations in the endolymph displace the basilar membrane correspondingly.

These sympathetic vibrations affect the relation of sensory hairs to the tectorial membrane, which rests directly upon them.

Such bending (or stretching?) of hairs is the basis of an effective stimulus.

(A minority views a trembling tectorial membrane as the stimulating agency.)

Pitch is correlated with the variable width of the basilar membrane.

This membrane is a narrow ribbon (high tones) in the basal cochlear turn.

It grades into its greatest width (lowest tones) at the apical end.

There is evidence pointing to a difference in function among the hair cells.

The outer hair cells are more effective in responding to feeble stimuli.

The inner hair cells are more effective in discriminating sound accurately.

Index

Entries are under nouns, rather than under adjectives or other qualifiers. An exception is where eponyms are involved.

323

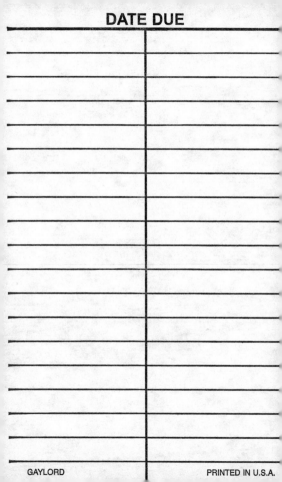